A Veterinary Journal

A Veterinary Journal

By

Kate McKelvie

Blackie & Co
Publishers Ltd

A BLACKIE & CO PUBLISHERS PAPERBACK

First published in 2002

A CIP catalogue record for this title is
available from the British Library

ISBN 1 903138 28 0

Blackie & Co Publishers Ltd
107-111 Fleet Street
LONDON EC4A 2AB

Acknowledgements

There would be no Veterinary Journal without the inspiration of my friends, colleagues and clients who make Clayfern Surgery what it is. I am very grateful for their friendship and custom over the last ten years.

Thanks also to Marguerite who kindly looked critically at the initial manuscript and suggested that it was in fact, readable.
A special mention to Julie, without whom operating days and out-of-hours work would be so much duller. Thanks also to her son, Rod, who produced the illustrations.

Lastly, but most importantly, there would be no Veterinary Journal without the constant support and encouragement from Jay. As always, 'the wind beneath my wings'.

Thursday 1st January

New Year's Day and I am on duty. Unlike most folk nearby, I have a surprisingly clear head. Drinking too much is not possible on duty as you might have to work or even drive. Leaving Jay in bed, the dogs and I set out on the first walk of the New Year. We stop at the farm to collect Jonno, Sheila and Colin's dog, before taking the track up the hill behind the cottage. It is a dry, cold day without much wind (unusual for these parts) and the track is coated in ice. One or two yellow flowers are to be seen in the gorse hedge, a touch of colour in an otherwise muted world. The 'pop' of guns echoes in the distance. Most shooting parties will take place tomorrow, but some enthusiasts have started early. Almost on cue, a brightly coloured pheasant erupts from the undergrowth and flies laboriously over the fence, descending into the field below. Pheasants always live on the edge - they are always *just* making it over obstructions or *just* taking off before a dog grabs them. On the roads, they are notorious for playing 'chicken' - 'Will I go? No, I won't; Yes, I will!' straight into the path of a car. Probably as many are killed on the roads as are shot.

Although it is nearly full daylight, an owl hoots in the woods, advertising his territory to interested parties and a buzzard mews overhead, gliding effortlessly, looking for breakfast. He seems a creature of habit - we have seen him several times recently. As the track wends up through the woods, a dusting of snow covers the ground - we have passed the snow line. From here onwards, the world is white. Emerging on the far side of the hill, the dogs take off, hot in pursuit of a winter hare; except for Jonno who remains by my side. Chained night and day in a filthy farmyard until rescued by Sheila when he was 5 months old, he has missed out on the normal puppy's exposure to the sights and sounds of a household which make them well-adjusted pets. He does not behave like the others, only watches them with bemused disbelief. However, he seems to enjoy our expeditions and is always thrilled when we appear to collect him.

We work our way past the deer pen with its small herd of red deer. There are green patches in the snow where they have been lying, but they have got up as we draw closer and are watching us with a mixture of suspicion and anticipation. We occasionally bring old fruit and veg for a treat, but they are out of luck today. They follow our progress down the side of the pen, heading back to the house. There is a patient to be seen in half an hour, an ongoing case being treated on a daily basis. So far, a good start to the year.

This is an account of a year in my life - My name is Kate McKelvie and I am a single-handed vet based in the small village of Clayfern on the border of the Scottish highlands. There is a surgery in Clayfern which is open for consultations mornings and evenings; much of the rest of my time is spent in the surgery attached to my home - a cottage situated on Fern Farm, four miles from Clayfern. I live with my partner Jay and our two dogs Kippen and Fintry. Unusually for a vet in a rural area, I deal solely with small animals, that is - dogs, cats, rabbits and other pets. Also unusually enough, there is enough work to make a living, although not perhaps as generous a one as can be achieved in larger city practices. Jay and I moved from such a practice several years ago in an attempt to avoid the rat race. Certainly the financial rewards were good in the city, but it involved working hard from morning till night and much of the hard-earned cash was spent getting away from it all. Here the pace of life is slower (usually!) and work is generally a pleasure, with time to see to patients properly and chat sociably with their owners. There is also usually time during the day to go for walks in the surrounding countryside. We are truly spoilt for choice, with hills and woods behind the cottage and rolling fields descending gently to the River Clay in front of us. The farm scene is always changing, wildlife abounds and the passing seasons mean there is always something of interest to be seen or heard.

Of course, there is one major disadvantage to being a single-handed vet - you are almost always 'on call' and cannot stray more than half an hour from home. When I am out and about, the answering machine gives my pager number for use in the event of an emergency. This little contraption travels with me at all times and has to be practically surgically removed from my waistband if I am off duty. This only occurs when the surgery can afford to pay for a locum to cover for me. At present, I have one half day off per week and one weekend per month, plus the occasional evening off if there is something special to do. I also carry a mobile phone to respond to calls coming through on the pager. Thus equipped to communicate with the outside world, I am free to roam the countryside on our doorstep. The dogs are used to the sudden increase in pace required if an emergency call summons me back to the surgery and can always be relied upon to rise to the occasion. Today we have been uninterrupted and leisurely descend into the valley, refreshed, relaxed and ready for action.

Sunday 4th January

High winds and snow, snow and snow! Unfortunately, this has meant power cuts and more power cuts. At home, we have been without electricity for two days and the blizzards are hampering repairs. Fortunately, Clayfern has had only short spells without power so routine work has carried on as usual at the surgery there. We had an emergency call the night the power went out. Jay stood in the road waving a hurricane lamp to guide the way and I examined the patient using the lamp and strong torches. The old cat had lung cancer, spread from a malignant mammary lump. No treatment possible, only a peaceful putting to sleep.

This morning our road is blocked and we are completely cut off from the outside world. It is rather exciting apart from the worries of maintaining emergency cover for our patients. Luckily, it is a quiet time of year for the surgery and the telephone is still working so at least we can give advice. The whole county has virtually ground to a halt. The power of the weather is impressive and means we cannot venture out for long. Snow flies horizontally, cutting visibility to mere yards and pebble-dashing exposed skin. Snowdrifts form at the back door making even the trip to the woodshed a major expedition. Thank goodness for our woodburning stove. At least the living room is warm. Its hot plate will heat homemade soups and stews; baked potatoes do nicely in the embers and bread toasted over the burning logs smells and tastes delicious. The rest of the house is truly arctic and each night we scuttle to beds warmed with hot-water bottles and many extra blankets. Outside the wind howls unceasingly and doors and windows rattle wildly. Both of our mothers have been visiting over New Year and are now stranded. We have effectively reverted to the lifestyle of a bygone era. Deprived of our modern appliances, domestic tasks take up much of the day - brushing the floor takes much longer than hoovering and handwashing clothes is no fun at all. The remainder is spent playing games or reading by fire-light and candle-light. Many a battle has been fought over the Monopoly board and I will have to work hard to pay off the rent due to my mother; she always manages to acquire all the plum properties. The blizzards will have to die down before the roads can be cleared and power restored.

Monday 5th January

The wind and snow have finally ceased and our world is silent - insulated in a cocoon of snow. There is no need to watch for traffic as we walk the dogs along the road, as a 6 foot snowdrift blocks our progress only 200 yards from the cottage. No chance of getting to Clayfern this morning. Gillian, my nurse, lives in Clayfern and can explain the situation to the few customers braving the elements - luckily there is nothing urgent and they can all return this evening. With luck, by then, the road will be passable. Our neighbouring farmer has the bucket on his tractor and is clearing the road from his farm to ours. Colin is clearing to the next farm and so on to the village.

While waiting to be rescued, I load up the sledge with a cargo of old apples and carrots and slowly begin the exhausting haul up the field behind the cottage to the bottom of the deer pen. The large hay bale they got on Saturday is nearly all gone and the deer receive the fruit and veg enthusiastically. It all has to be bowled in different directions to prevent the more dominant members of the herd bagging the lot. Once the sledge is empty, I collapse into it gratefully and am borne homeward at breathtaking speed. At last the road is passable and we pile into the old grey estate car to stock up with provisions. Clayfern has been cut off as well and the High

Street is congested with delivery vans. So far the choices are limited and rationing is in force - only two loaves per family.

It seems strange to see electric lights and appliances working as normal - we still have no power at Fern. After an uneventful evening surgery, I enjoy the luxury of washing my hair in the surgery sink with lovely hot water on tap. It makes a change not to smell of woodsmoke. I feel like a time traveller tonight, leaving electric lights and heating in Clayfern for candles and woodburner at home and take back fish suppers for a welcome surprise.

At 8 pm, without warning, the lights suddenly come on and electrical sounds recommence. We all rush for the things we normally take for granted - long, leisurely baths, television programmes and a good wash for our smokey clothes.

Thursday 8th January

We have had several days of beautiful weather - bright sunshine, light winds and sparkling snow. Work has been undemanding and we have taken full advantage of a winter break on our doorstep. In the afternoons, Jay and I and assorted friends have set off up the track to the far side of the hill where we have enjoyed our own winter sports on the snow covered slopes. We have skied and sledged until our limbs are on fire, then towed each other behind the old estate car in a heavy, bobsleigh-like contraption rigged up by Jay and Colin. We have achieved speeds of up to 30 mph which has been exhilarating. Afterwards,we traipsed homewards for apres ski cups of steaming hot chocolate with cream - and a little brandy.

This morning I receive a call from an elderly couple living in an isolated cottage cut off from the main road. Their old dog has been failing for some time and the extreme weather has finally pushed him over the edge. Their car cannot make it down the track, so I borrow Jay's old estate, collect nurse Julie and attempt to get through to our patient. Thank goodness for the ancient, battered estate which heroically rises up, over or even through the snowdrifts blocking the way. The sad deed is done as the poorly old dog lies collapsed in his basket. I don't think he even noticed we were there. His owners are philosophical, but will miss him badly. Julie returns with me to the farm surgery where we have some operations today - nothing too taxing, just some routine neuterings and a cat for a teeth scale and polish. Much of our operative load is routine work such as this - it is surprising how much there is to do in such a small community. I worry occasionally that we might run out of animals to operate on, but so far (touch wood!) this hasn't happened. Most of our clients are seen initially at the Clayfern surgery, but all the operations are carried out at the farm surgery. This seems like a strange arrangement, but it works well in practice. Cats can be brought up from Clayfern in my car, while the dogs are brought directly by their owners.

After our work is over, I take Julie home. It is becoming even colder and her little car refused to start this morning. She is off to beg her mechanic friend to take a look. We stitched his dog's foot after surgery one night before Christmas, so she should have some bargaining power.

The wind has freshened now, the wind chill factor putting our ambient temperature at approximately -16°C. I call in at the local garage to book my car's service and find both boss and mechanic in the office - they had to stop work when their spanners began sticking to their fingers in the intense cold.

On the drive back to Fern, I hear the local radio station recite its litany of blocked roads, closed schools and cancelled events. The snow report is excellent - if anyone can get through to the ski centres!

There is time for a short walk before evening surgery, so I don my thermals and head down to the river. The sight that greets us is truly impressive - the river is tidal here and great sheets of ice have formed between the high and low tide levels, piled on top of each other to form massive platforms. Ice floes are slowly moving down river, creaking and groaning as they go. This looks more like the Arctic than Scotland. A soft pink light illuminates the scene as

6

the sun gradually sets behind the hills. Once the sun has gone, the cold bites with renewed vigour. It is not the weather to dawdle in, so we briskly head for home - even the dogs seem glad to be back in front of the fire.

Driving home after evening surgery, I am treated to another arctic phenomenon - across the river, ghostly sheets of green and silver dance and shimmer in the clear northern sky - the Northern Lights, or *aurora borealis*. The spectacle continues during the five minute drive by the river but is already fading before I can alert Jay. Within minutes, the sky is still again. We cannot resist looking outside every so often during the evening, but unfortunately, there is no action replay.

Thursday 14th January

After such an invigorating start to the year, the snow has turned to rain and high winds are sweeping the country, leaving considerable damage in their wake. At the weekend, an old beech tree blocked our road for several hours requiring much cutting, dragging and lifting before the way was cleared. A helpful workman chainsawed the branches into manageable logs and, after much to-ing and fro-ing in the muddy field, our woodshed is now full to the rafters. The wood will be better if left until next year, but we may be tempted before then.

Another product which matures with time is the contents of the farm muck heap. After the cattle are turned out in spring, the barn is cleared out and a steaming muck heap grows by its side. This has now degraded into excellent fertiliser and is now being spread on the field behind us. The smell has also matured, our sinuses have never been so clear. We are at pains to point out to clients that the odour emanates from *outside* the surgery.

Driving to Clayfern for morning surgery, flocks of fieldfares and redwings flutter from bush to bush. They are winter visitors from Scandinavia, so this weather is presumably nicer for them than it would be at home. Our buzzard sits on his usual fence post; he is there most mornings. Today he waits for the car to pass before returning to his meal - a rabbit killed on the road. Buzzards are lazy birds and soon realise that it is easier to wait for road kills than to hunt for themselves. A client who is a farmer mentioned that he has even seen them following the plough, waiting for worms to be unearthed. An earthworm cannot be more than an appetiser to such a big bird.

By Abbeygate Farm, the resident ducks and geese have forsaken the millpond and are dabbling in the middle of the flooded road. Round the next bend, a tractor trundles along bearing winter feed to stock. Rushing to work is often not possible due to such hazards. Luckily, I arrive just in time to meet an emergency case - two panic-stricken owners carrying an unhappy-looking dog. Muffie, an elderly collie, was very sick this morning, then tottered around wildly as if drunk. Clearly both Mr and Mrs Collins think that *'the end has come'* and are deeply distressed. They have had Muffie since she was 6 weeks old - she is now fifteen. Muffie herself is also in a state - covered in saliva and badly imbalanced, falling repeatedly to one side. On closer examination, her eyes flicker rhythmically from side to side (a symptom known as nystagmus). These symptoms make a partial diagnosis easy. Something is affecting the balance centre in Muffie's brain; as well as feeling unbalanced, Muffie will be feeling nauseous (just as we do when we feel seasick). This scenario is not uncommon in older dogs. Unfortunately, the brain is totally encased in bone and not easy to examine so we usually cannot tell *what* is affecting the balance centre - it could be infection, inflammation, tumour, traumatic damage or even vascular accident, better known as a stroke. In the absence of extra diagnostic signs such as fever or infected ear canals, it is impossible to tell. Radiographs are seldom of any use diagnostically; more specialised imaging techniques such as CAT or MRI scans would be used in human cases. These techniques are only now becoming available in veterinary medicine, but there are very few centres offering this facility. The procedure is very expensive and in most cases surgery is not an option so most patients like Muffie are treated medically. All we can do is treat the symptoms with anti-inflammatory and anti-sickness drugs and see what happens. Many do recover and it seems likely that these incidents are similar to strokes. Some are left with a permanent head tilt which looks rather weird but seldom bothers the patient. I explain all this to the Collins and beg them to relax a little. Not only does poor Muffie feel literally sick as a dog and is unable to walk properly, but she is also picking up on her owners'distress and is badly frightened. Although not totally out of the woods, Mr and Mrs Collins and Muffie eventually leave the surgery considerably happier than when they arrived.

Walking the dogs later in the day, the results of the gales are evident in the woods - trees uprooted like skittles, leaning on each other at crazy angles. In the wind, branches touching neighbouring trees emit bloodcurdling wails and shrieks. A heart-rending, low pitched creak, almost a groan, draws my attention to a strange sight. Two trees - a sycamore and a Scots pine - have grown together and their trunks are joined for several feet like woody Siamese twins. Sap from the damaged bark has seeped down their trunks. I feel quite sorry for them. What a shame one hadn't blown over and freed them from their agonising existence.

Thursday 21st January

At last the sun has come back today - a mere half an hour's worth flooding the back garden, but a good omen of times to come. Living as we do at the bottom of a large hill, the sun does not clear the horizon between the end of November and the end of January. We have to climb the hill or go down to the river to get a welcome boost of sunlight. Drying household and surgery washing becomes a chore during this time with much of it draped in front of the woodburner most of the time. The fire stays alight continuously from early autumn till late spring except when we have a locum! Keeping it going is easy with a little experience, but it is like one of the mysteries of the universe to our regular locum, Linda. Her record so far has been four days - then she resorts to twentyfour-hour central heating, a hot-water bottle and a duvet!

Apart from the return of the sun, today has been rather dismal. Last week, I removed a small growth from Bonnie the collie's neck. The lab report came through today - a very malignant tumour. Bonnie might be lucky, or deadly cells may already be multiplying elsewhere in her body - none are detectable to us, but this is no guarantee that she will survive. Bonnie's poor owners are now doomed to a tense future, ever watchful for signs that the cancer has returned. Sometimes, just when owners and vet think that we have 'got away with it', more symptoms appear. Jay and I went through this with our old cat and know what a miserable time it is. It is so hard to handle the uncertainty.

Buzby MacTavish was a similar case. He was a bad-tempered, middle-aged collie brought to the surgery with a lame hind-leg. It was necessary to examine him under sedative and take an X-ray to confirm the diagnosis - a ruptured cruciate ligament in his stifle (knee) joint. This ligament keeps the two bones in the joint correctly aligned; when it ruptures (breaks), the bones can be moved relative to one another, giving what we call a 'drawer forward'sign, unmistakable in Buzby's leg. The damaged ligament needs to be repaired, using a graft fashioned from surrounding connective tissue. And so, Buzby received an initial anaesthetic injection which allowed me to pass a tube directly into his windpipe - this tube is known as an endotracheal tube. It was then connected to the anaesthetic machine which administers anaesthetic gas to the patient - a routine procedure repeated several times a day during an operating session. But in this patient, we saw something unexpected when his mouth was opened to insert the tube (Buzby's temperament was such that no one ever attempted to open his mouth when he was conscious!) A sinister ulcerated lump lay attached to the gumline - obscured by his hairy lips when he was awake. It is not generally possible to tell what type of growth is present just by looking, although certain guidelines can sometimes give vets a rough idea. If the growth is round or oval, painless, slow growing and distinct from surrounding tissue, then it is likely to be benign. If it is rapidly growing, tender, ulcerated and growing into nearby tissue, then the chances are that it is malignant. Buzby's lump had features of both. We fixed the dog's leg then removed the lump and sent it to the lab for histopathology: the discipline in which tissue is examined under the microscope. It is important to get an accurate diagnosis of the type of growth as this influences treatment and outlook. The results appeared several days later - 'malignant melanoma; evidence of lymphatic spread; prognosis very guarded'. Not good news. Unlike in humans, malignant melanoma of the skin in cats and dogs is relatively uncommon and usually follows a benign course. Not so in the mouth, where they are usually highly malignant and carry a poor outlook. They spread via the blood and lymphatic circulation to organs such as the liver or lungs. Although the primary tumour can be managed by surgery or even radiotherapy, invariably the patient dies within six months from secondaries. Chemotherapy is not effective for this type of tumour in dogs.

As luck would have it, Buzby's knee surgery healed exceptionally well and for three months, he lived a normal life. During this period of respite, both vet and owner hope that we have got lucky, or even that a mistake has been made, but inevitably, the cancer begins to bite. Buzby began to have trouble swallowing and developed a soft cough. The lymph nodes by his throat were the size of tennis balls and, through the stethoscope, his chest sounded harsh. He was put on a high dose of corticosteroids which had an initial near-magical effect - his glands reduced in size and he seemed to feel well and full of life. However, the outcome was inevitable, we were just buying him a few extra weeks. Owners will generally know when the time has come and so it was with Buzby's. He deteriorated rapidly over two days, stopped eating and became restless and miserable, panting continually. We put him to sleep on his settee in his kitchen - the first and last time I was able to do anything to him without a muzzle.

Monday 25th January

Our young nephew Tom and his parents are staying for a few days. After hearing the tales of our fun in the snow earlier this month, he is desperate to go sledging, but Clayfern and surrounds so far remain untouched by the forecasted snow showers. In an extravagant mood, I have persuaded Linda to work today, so we are all going to find the snow in Glen Shee - one of the main Scottish ski centres; only an hour and a half from our doorstep. As the road is rather tortuous, we encourage our visitors to take travel sickness tablets before setting off. Soon we are travelling through flurries of snow and the countryside is blanketed in white. Tom is impressed to see Christmas trees in their natural habitat - we suspect he thought they came from the supermarket. Eventually, the ski tows and chair lifts of the ski centre hove into view and we enter the car park in near blizzard conditions. The family piles out, grabbing assorted sledges from the boot. Over the years, Jay and I have built up a collection - there are the two wooden sledges; one tall and elegant, the other low and sporty; the utilitarian red plastic variety and the *piece de resistance* - the 'mini sledge' spotted on a trip to Norway. It resembles a large plastic shovel blade with a short handle. The idea is to sit on the blade with the handle between the legs. The legs are then lifted off the ground and away you go. It is reminiscent of the tin trays we used as children - very fast with no steering whatsoever. The cautious Tom descends sedately on the big wooden sledge while the adults hurtle downhill on the 'Norwegian Shovel'. Eventually everyone is soaked, glowing and exhausted. A quiet evening in front of the fire would be sensible, but tonight is an important date in the Scottish calendar - Burns Night, in honour of our national poet - and we are going to a Burns supper and *ceilidh*. The supper consists of haggis, neeps and tatties (swedes and potatoes to *Sassenachs*), giving plenty of scope for teasing the rather gullible Tom. In time, he will learn the truth about haggis, but for now, he will no doubt spend the last few days of his holiday searching the hills in vain for a glimpse of the elusive shaggy creature doomed to run round hills forever in the same direction - due to the haggis's legs being shorter on one side than the other!

The *ceilidh* is a real success. The many jigs and dances are not hard to follow and the frantic regrouping of the dancers after tricky manoeuvres adds to the general hilarity of the occasion. Tom is completely overawed with the elephantine stomping and exuberant hooching of his strange Scottish relatives.

As we come up the cottage path, a fox screams in the woods - it is time for them to seek mates for the breeding season and the bloodcurdling shrieks are common at this time of year. We tell Tom that he is privileged to hear such a sound - the rarely heard mating call of the local Clayfern haggis. We may have pushed our luck too far: the exhausted little boy flashes us a withering glance before heading indoors and straight for his warm bed.

Tuesday 26th January

Lucky Tom - still in bed as Jay and I drag ourselves up for work. The 'Norwegian shovel' is hard on the stomach muscles and we both feel we have had gone several rounds in a boxing ring. We also have bruised toes from indiscriminate stomping at the *ceilidh* and another day off to recover would be nice.

Julie and I have a stressful morning to get through - we have to spay a friend's dog. The friend is ultra nervous about the operation and the tension has been building up for days. 'She will be okay?' she asks anxiously, 'She's very special to me.' The atmosphere is tense as the operation commences. There is an old veterinary adage that if anything is not to go smoothly, it will be with an animal belonging either to a friend, neighbour or a doctor. We like to think that we are professional enough not to let outside influences affect us and the procedure proceeds as planned. Once the surgery is finished and the bitch is recovering in her kennel, we heave a mutual sigh of relief. 'There was only one sign that you were nervous,' Julie says, 'You kept tying extra knots on the ligatures.' 'We would be nervous wrecks after too many more of these,' I comment. A statement such as that is all it takes to set us off on our tension-relieving pursuit of inventing amusing imaginary scenes. As we clean and tidy the ops room, we visualise a rest home for stressed-out vets - one inmate sits continually tying knots; another bends and straightens like a yo-yo, peering under a chair - checking an imaginary post-op. patient in a kennel. Meanwhile, a clapped-out veterinary nurse repeatedly grabs eating utensils from other residents, cleans them then puts them in the microwave in polythene bags (parodying the procedure for dealing with dirty surgical instruments). This makes us sound completely mad, but I like to think that it is such daft imaginings that help to keep us sane.

The rest of the day passes uneventfully and I find time in the afternoon to visit my aunt in the local old folks' home. On the way in, Matron asks me about the resident cat who has had a 'funny turn'. She explains: 'She was sitting on the desk when she suddenly began to hyperventilate; her mouth was open and she began to salivate.' Two nurses nearby stop chatting and listen intently 'She was fine when I saw her ten minutes ago,' one exclaims in horrified tones. Much hilarity ensues when it is pointed out that we are talking about the cat - not my aunt! As often occurs when the vet calls, Lacey is nowhere to be seen. It sounds as if her turn may have been an asthma attack. When I was training to be a vet, it was thought that cats don't get asthma. It is now known that they do. I recall a story told by a speaker at a veterinary conference. His client - an attractive young lady - complained that her cat was ruining her love life. Everytime she had a big date, the cat had an acute asthma attack. The date was invariably cancelled and instead the evening was spent at the local veterinary clinic. It transpired that the cat sat on the dressing table as she got ready for her date and it was obviously reacting to one of the sprays or perfumes used in the beautifying process.

I suggest to Matron that if Lacey has another 'do', she makes a note of anything nearby which might cause a reaction. I will check the cat when I next see her.

As I leave, thick clouds of cavorting rooks are coming in from the surrounding fields to roost in the nearby trees. Their raucous calls are as evocative a winter sound as that of the geese cackling by the river's edge.

Sunday 8th February

A friend visited this weekend. She arrived on Friday evening - rather later than anticipated after an unscheduled detour round Glasgow! After one visit, Clayfern is easy to get to, but the route can seem complicated for the first time. Sue's trip from the north-west of England involved travelling on no less than nine motorways and several more dual carriageways before a trip across country on rural minor roads.

We enjoy having visitors. It is generally easier for them to come to us than vice versa, as a casual weekend visiting friends (so simple for *ordinary* people) involves the expense of engaging a locum and a fair degree of forward planning - the downside of being a single-handed practitioner. We are lucky to live in a scenic area and our slightly eccentric lifestyle holds novelty value for our guests. In the evenings, they become used to my brief absences to answer phone calls and longer absences to attend to emergency cases. The more intrepid quite enjoy meeting in-patients recovering from any dramatic intervention.

As luck would have it this Saturday, Gillian was ill, so Jay and Sue were enlisted to help during morning surgery. It was an uneventful surgery until our final patient - a duck named Donald (apt if not blindingly original!). Donald had survived a brief encounter with a dog, but his white plumage was covered in blood. The wound on his wing was superficial and easy to mend, but the fresh blood dripping from his rear end caused me more concern. Poor Donald had sustained considerable damage to his nether region and a further half hour was spent piecing the torn sections together so that, hopefully, outflow was not obstructed. Luckily, domestic wildfowl and hens, having relatively insensitive skin, seem to bear stitching with fortitude and Donald was no exception. This episode made Sue's visit - a small ceramic duck we found in a local gift shop will remind her of this weekend and no doubt the tale of Donald and his injuries will go down well in her city office!

16

Tuesday 10th February

I am sitting on my rock at the top of the hill watching the sun go down. There is a misty haze over the hills on the opposite side of the river and the sky is turquoise, hightlighted with purple-grey streaks of cloud. A pheasant chirrs in the wood behind and the dogs rummage diligently in the undergrowth. At last I begin to unwind after an exceptionally busy day. Tuesdays are our operating day for one of the local animal charities and are always busy. The charity believes in neutering all animals *before* they go to homes and they have recently been inundated with unwanted litters of pups. Perhaps their policy will help to reduce the numbers of unwanted animals in the future. Three of today's youngsters spent their first twelve weeks shut in a cupboard and need much tender loving care to bring them out of their shells. We handle them very gently as they are still nervous and are rewarded by wagging tails. As nurse Julie observes, the anaesthetic hits the waggy tails last and wears off there first.

As well as our quota of routine operations, we have had an extra case today - a little terrier first seen three days ago with gastro-enteritis. We treated her at the time and an appointment was made for Saturday. When she didn't show on Saturday, we assumed that all was well. Unfortunately, poor Cassie has continued to vomit all weekend and is now quite seriously ill and very miserable. Occasionally, owners do not turn up for check-ups and we assume that the patient must be fully recovered. We are at a loss to explain why they stay away when the animal is still ill. Perhaps the possible expense worries the owners, but it always costs more to regain lost ground than to treat early in an illness.

Anyway, Cassie has been admitted for intensive treatment and investigation. Earlier today, she was connected to a drip to replace the fluids she had lost, then an X-ray was taken. This showed a suspicious amount of gas in her intestines which suggests a foreign body, so an exploratory operation is next on the diagnostic trail. No foreign body is to be found, but the entire gut is very inflamed and the local lymph nodes massively swollen. We take biopsies (samples of abnormal tissues for microscopic analysis),

17

blood and faeces samples which go to our local diagnostic laboratory. Meanwhile, Cassie will continue on intensive care until we get some results. She is given antibiotics, a painkiller, vitamins and an anti-vomiting drug and will be kept on the drip to provide fluid and rest her gut. If the vomiting eases off, she will be offered small quantities of a special recovery diet - this is a palatable food, easily digestible and containing more energy than similar quantities of ordinary dog food.

Although every vet is slightly disappointed that exploratory surgery does not yield immediate answers, it is quite surprising how many patients will pick up after the surgery. It may be simply that the anaesthetic gives valuable respite from the pain; it has even been explained that the surgical incision corresponds to acupuncture points thus effecting a recovery. Whatever the reason, any improvement is always gratefully received and we fervently hope for such a response from Cassie.

So, today has been very long. My colleague Linda has been booked to do evening surgery as I am due to attend a veterinary meeting in Edinburgh tonight. These meetings are important for keeping up to date, but tonight I am playing truant. The vet school will send on the notes and I have heard the lecturer before. Little Cassie is settled in a warm kennel, more comfortable than before but still in need of regular care and attention over the night to come.

The dogs have been patient all day and have thoroughly enjoyed their late outing. It is lovely that it is still light at 5.30 pm. The long, dark nights of winter are finally over. As I sit winding down, the sky darkens gradually and the lights of the farm twinkle in the distance. While I walk past the deer pen on the way home, Honky the stag (so called because he is white) stands his ground and stares at us, protective of his hinds and hopeful for a few carrots or apples. 'None today, I'm afraid' - and I head down the hillside, looking forward to a glass of wine in front of the blazing woodburner.

Wednesday 11th February

It is a peculiar fact of veterinary life that totally non-infectious conditions will sometimes appear in 'runs'. Often with no logical reason - just a whim of fate. Thus we have 'broken toe' week and 'heart failure' week when several cases will come in one after another. This week is evidently 'bird bottom' week. Having had Donald on Saturday, I have just treated 'Treacle', a bantam with a decidedly raw rear - the result of an encounter with barbed wire. Luckily, judicious applications of antiseptic cream are all that should be necessary. I am looking forward to ringing my friend Sue tonight and mentioning that a bird's bottom reminded me of her.

I feel rather jaded today after our hectic day yesterday. Although I was spared the trip to Edinburgh, little Cassie required a fair bit of attention over the evening. It is very useful living next door to the surgery, especially when a patient is hospitalised. Some require virtually constant supervision; others only need a friendly face from time to time. I regularly spent time with Cassie last night, talking to her, offering food and taking her for short walks in the garden to relieve herself. She is a strange, nervous dog who does not seem to appreciate company like most others do. Usually even the most stand-offish animals warm to our friendly overtures after being hospitalised for a day or so. However, some have short memories in this respect. Recently I was called to Clayfern one evening to rescue a young cat holed up under a car after being hit by another vehicle. Her injuries were not severe - some shock, superficial skin wounds and a fractured pelvis. Luckily, the broken bones had not been displaced from their proper position so, after the initial painkillers and antibiotics, strict rest was the only treatment required. She remained in a kennel in the surgery for two weeks while we waited in vain for an owner to claim her. During this time, we all spent hours stroking her, playing with her and keeping her amused. Much to the dogs' disgust, she sat on my knee in the house each evening. Eventually, a new home was found for Friday (so called as she appeared on a Friday) and we looked forward to a touching reunion when she returned to have her stitches removed. No chance. Friday rebuffed my delighted greeting with an imperious 'Do I know you?'

stare before returning to her absorbing task of an all-over groom. So much for gratitude.

Wednesday is usually my morning off but a novelty is in store today. A pet nutrition company have invited several vets to take part in a Telesymposium - a unique event - for me at least. Over 350 vets are to be connected by phone to experts in the USA. The experts will each deliver short presentations then take questions. The connection is made to the branch surgery to avoid tying up the main phone line. Gillian has been grooming this morning and an excitable terrier is barking and rattling the kennel door. I wonder what the collective sounds of background noises from 350 surgeries will do for the experts' presentations, but modern technology has the situation well under control. The speakers come over in splendid accoustic isolation - only the baleful howling of a post-op. patient in the background during a question gives any clues that it is a veterinary audience. On the way home, a quick trip to the Post Office. The postmaster asks if my phone bill has come. I experience a tremor - does he know something I don't? The nutrition company should be paying for the hour long transatlantic call. Luckily, the question is only to confirm what he already suspects. He has not had the usual billing day rush and now reckons that BT are sending their bills in staged lots. Strange coincidence though - life is full of them.

Friday 13th February

Friday 13th! Not the most auspicious day for our ops list this morning. The local charity has inherited two Rottweiler dogs from a family break-up and our job today is to castrate them. Rottweilers can be charming pets, but some can be difficult and I have had a few narrow escapes with them in my city practice, where I suspect they were often bred for the characteristics which cause us problems. These incidents have made me a little twitchy around the breed. This is a serious disadvantage. There is an old saying amongst doggy people that fear travels along the lead. This is very true - animals are incredibly sensitive to emotions. They are like little radios tuning into the waves emanating from people nearby. Waves of nervousness or irritation will always adversely affect the animal's behaviour, so it is important to be relaxed and confident when working as a vet. It is also important to relax owners as a nervous owner will upset their pet. All vets will have had the experience of a dreadful consulting session when nothing seems to go right and the patients are all downright awkward. This usually happens when the vet is anxious or uptight, perhaps rushing to make up lost time. Part of a good vet's job is to put both owner and patient at their ease by exuding warmth and confidence. After years of practice, it is possible to control your demeanour, but this can be hard work sometimes! So we take it very carefully with the Rotties. Neither dog makes a fuss when given a sedative injection - a good omen. This calms both patients - and vet - and the day goes smoothly. Vets do have an ability to read animals' behaviour borne of many years of observation and I find this instinct seldom lets me down. I rarely get bitten these days - if I do, it is usually because I have been careless and pressed on against my better judgement.

As well as 'bird bottom' week, we are also having a 'rat' week and our next task is to remove a tumour from Roland the rat's back. This has grown rapidly from pea to hazelnut size. Nowadays we have very effective anaesthetics for small creatures. Roland is injected with a combination of anaesthetic drugs, then is given a reversing agent to bring him round when the operation is finished. Before the surgery, he is given a small quantity of fluid under the skin to prevent dehydration. During and after the surgery, he is kept on a heated pad - heat loss can easily kill these small patients - and soon after recovery, he is offered food to keep his energy levels up. He recovers well and goes home with a happy owner.

Unfortunately, our next rat is not so fortunate. He is rushed in as an emergency but has broken his back and we can do nothing but painlessly put him to sleep, leaving his young owner heartbroken. Rats make lovely pets as they are intelligent and gentle, seldom being known to bite. It is one of life's paradoxes that we spend so much time treating these little rodents while elsewhere great efforts are made to destroy them. The old factory in Clayfern is being demolished this week and the resident rats are on the move - into the nearby houses. During surgery tonight, I see a little Yorkie who might have eaten some rat poison left in a garage. Checking the name of the product on my chart, I confirm that it is a relative of Warfarin, an anti-coagulant. These drugs work by increasing blood vessel fragility and reducing the blood's ability to clot. The victims literally bleed to death. It appears unlikely that our patient could have eaten enough to cause a problem and she seems well so far, but I give her an injection of vitamin K1 as a precaution. This helps the blood's ability to clot. We will check her again tomorrow to be on the safe side. Rat poison is usually incorporated in grain but seems to be irresistible to dogs and cats and poisoning scares are not uncommon. The cat belonging to the local school actually retrieved several sachets of poison and deposited them on the doorstep. It certainly made a change from the more usual dead bird or mouse.

Saturday 14th February

A run-of-the-mill surgery until our last patient, Cassie, our poorly terrier. Although very helpful in ruling out certain complaints, her lab tests have not come up with a definite diagnosis. However, she seemed improved over Tuesday and Wednesday and went home on Thursday morning. Yesterday, she started to be sick again and we appear to be back at square one. I re-admit her for yet more treatment and investigation. Many vets tend to feel almost guilty when cases such as Cassie cannot be resolved quickly - this is quite illogical when one considers how lengthy investigations can be in human medicine. Of course, humans do not have to pay for their treatment which is another factor to consider with our patients. We advise all our clients to take out pet insurance, but the response is depressingly low. We sometimes have to tread the difficult path of treating our patients effectively while trying to stick to a budget.

I am a little preoccupied with money (or the lack of it) today. There is a large drug bill and a VAT return to pay at the end of the month and cash is going to be tight. Cassie's owners and one or two others are going to be paying by instalments. Theoretically, clients are meant to pay at the time of treatment, but this does not always happen and cash flow is a perennial problem. It is depressing to be working hard yet still struggling to make ends meet. Cassie is settled in her kennel with the radio for company, so I do what I always do when feeling a little down - set off on a long walk with all three dogs. Up the track we go and into the woods, where I come upon a bleached skull lying in the leaf litter. I am presently reading a novel about a forensic pathologist and become absorbed in analysing my find. It is too large for a rabbit or hare; too light for a sheep. The eye sockets face sideways - therefore not a predator. Herbivore teeth – so it's most probably a deer, one of the roe deer that roam the surrounding countryside. A young deer by the look of it - the teeth are scarcely worn and the skull sutures - the joins between the bones of the skull - are still easily apparent. Pleased with my analysis, I wedge the skull between two branches for future collection - probably when young nephews and nieces come to stay. A holiday here is very popular with our young relatives, partly due to expeditions in the countryside to find squirrel dreys and badger setts, collect old birds' eggs, feathers and assorted skeletal remains! The last is less popular with parents, but it is fun to see a love of wildlife being kindled in the kids and the pride with which their prizes are borne off to be displayed in their city classrooms. The surgery is also an enthralling place for children. The animals are a great attraction of course, but there is also the thrill of rides on the hydraulic ops table - pumped up to the 'top floor' then descending rapidly to the 'basement', whirling round through 360 degrees then unceremoniously 'ejected' when full tilt is applied. Much fun can also be had when our small visitors are connected to ECG monitors or pulse oximeters (a device for measuring the amount of oxygen in the blood), or listen to their own heart directly through the humble stethoscope. Yes, veterinary surgeries are exciting places, especially when you are under ten.

As usual, my walk has made my worries fade and I feel lucky to live and work in such a wonderful place.

Friday 20th February

This has not really been the best of weeks. On Monday, we admitted Amy Cox for investigation. Amy is an old friend, a thirteen-year-old collie who has kept us busy over the years with various complaints, all of which Amy has thrown off with ease. Now she has an unpleasant discharge from one nostril. Antibiotics have not helped, so more needs to be done. Further investigation can involve X-ray, blood sample, nasal swab and possibly flushing the affected nostril with saline and collecting the dirty fluid for microscopic analysis. The hope is that she might have a foreign body lodged in her nose, or perhaps a bacterial or fungal infection which can be treated. Unfortunately, the X-ray revealed the grim diagnosis - an aggressive tumour was destroying Amy's delicate nasal bones; the outlook was grave. Neither surgery nor chemo - nor even radiotherapy - would be of use, so old Amy was put to sleep while still under the anaesthetic. At least I could reassure Mrs Cox that Amy's last moments were pleasant. She loved coming to the surgery and regarded us all as her best friends. As I injected the anaesthetic, her last conscious action was to wag her tail and lick the side of my face. Poor Mrs Cox has lost her constant companion and her last link with her dead husband. At her age, she will not get another dog and my heart aches for her every time she returns to an empty house. Two friends have gone out of my life and I will miss them both.

On Tuesday, I put Nelson Young to sleep. The old one-eyed cat had suffered from dodgy kidneys for so long that it was almost a shock to realise that this time he would not recover. Special food and regular injections had prolonged his life for years but this time was different. Some cats with progressive kidney failure have acute episodes from time to time but can rally with intensive treatment. Nelson was beyond such attempts now. His breath smelt like ammonia cleanser from the toxins in his blood stream (normally cleared by the kidneys) and ulcers lined his mouth. Time to call a halt. We as vets are so fortunate to be able to put our patients to sleep when the outlook is hopeless. They die painlessly and with dignity in their owner's arms.

The rest of the week has continued in much the same vein.

Another old dog put to sleep on Thursday; a last pat and a biscuit as he went - the crumbs still in his mouth after he'd gone. Typical Labrador - last thoughts of food!

Surgeries have also been rather *difficult* this week. My usual opening gambit of 'How is he/she today?' has been greeted more frequently than usual with 'Well he's not any better' delivered in suitably funereal tones. This is a truly depressing sentence and can signal the need for more extensive tests or investigations which may or may not end happily; sometimes it only means persisting with treatment until we hear the magic words 'He's been fine today.' On bad days, it is all too easy to develop a pessimistic attitude, waiting for the next problem to occur and I feel I am sinking fast. Luckily, one or two brighter moments have saved the week. Tuppence the cat came in for routine vaccination and worming. This time last year, she had a hyperactive thyroid gland, was half her present weight and on the verge of heart failure. Hyperthyroidism is a fairly common condition in older cats and can be treated medically with tablets, surgically by removal of the affected glands or even by injection of radioactive iodine which localises in the gland and destroys the abnormal tissue. We operated on Tuppence a year ago and it has been a resounding success. Hard on her heels comes Poppy, an elderly Boxer dog. She had major surgery last June to remove an ulcerated mammary tumour. By the time these tumours have ulcerated, it is likely that they will have spread elsewhere and the surgery was undertaken more to buy her time than to cure her. Yet here she is eight months later, still going strong. Cases like Tuppence and Poppy help to remind us that things do occasionally go well.

Saturday 21 February

Will this week never end? An emergency call at 7 am. starts the day 'Cat collapsed and frothing from the mouth' - doesn't sound good. It only takes fifteen minutes to get here but the cat is dead on arrival. This is a worry - a year ago, there was a spate of deliberate poisonings in this cat's neighbourhood. Tests at the lab detected a toxic chemical used on farms - it was no accident that the victims managed to eat some. No culprit was ever found. Nothing obvious shows up on *post-mortem* today and our client does not want further tests performed. She will mention the tragedy to her friend, the local policeman. Hopefully, his presence will scare off anyone with malicious intent. It is frustrating not to have a definite diagnosis, but I can understand my client not wanting to spend more money when the cat is already dead.

My first task in Clayfern is to put yet another old cat to sleep. Two dead cats already and the day is still young. Fighting off feelings of impending doom, I lose myself in the reassuring routine of examining sore ears, emptying blocked anal glands and other mundane tasks. Not very glamorous perhaps, but the backbone of the job. An elderly vet once told me that a vet will ease more animal pain and suffering by effectively diagnosing and treating ear mites and impacted anal glands than by performing the most sophisticated surgery. What a wise man he was.

Our last patient scotches any hopes of a prompt finish and escape up the hill. Horace the cat has been gradually losing condition and is now completely off his food. A miserable, scraggy creature stands hunched on the table, visibly tensing when I gently palpate his abdomen. My fingers close on a large, knobbly mass which should not be there. His owner and I discuss the next move. We could take X-rays and blood samples to gain more information first, but the owners opt for immediate exploratory surgery. Poor Horace is so miserable that he raises no objection to the insertion of a canula into his vein; the anaesthetic seems like a blessed relief. Opening into his abdomen, the diagnosis is immediately clear - his liver is a mass of tumour tissue; there is scarcely any normal tissue to be seen. We will not be bringing him round to face pain again.

I suppose it was inevitable that this week should also see the end of Cassie. She has been in the surgery all week while we attempt to cure her unexplained vomiting. She has had exploratory surgery, endoscopy, radiography, biopsies, several blood samples and a faeces sample, none of which has given us a diagnosis. She has had intravenous fluids, nasogastric feeding (feeding through a tube threaded through her nostril directly into her stomach) and every imaginable combination of drugs, all to no avail. After much discussion, her owners have decided to call it a day. It has been particularly sad in Cassie's case that we have not been able to comfort her. Apparently, she spent the first two years of her life shut in a shed before being rescued by her present owner. In the time she has been with us, she has scarcely shown any emotion - 'Lights on but no one home' as my nurse suggested. She was put to sleep in her owner's arms, the only person she showed any response to. What a sad episode and what a sad, wasted little life.

It was to prevent pups from growing up like Cassie that led us to start puppy classes at the surgery. Although Cassie was an extreme case, it is known that the way in which pups and kittens are treated in the first months of life has a profound effect on how they behave as adults. The chances are that any dog or cat scared of say, children, has not been exposed to them during this golden period. At the puppy classes which are run by Gillian, the pups meet other dogs and their owners and the owners are encouraged to expose the pups to as many novel experiences as possible - children, cats, traffic, cars and so on, are all grist to the mill. They must also accustom the pups to having their teeth cleaned and their ears, feet and other parts examined. If the pups get used to this as babies, it is accepted as normal when they get older and makes life much easier for all concerned. Gillian also teaches some basic obedience. The 'pupils' have a wonderful time thundering around the waiting room and learn to associate the surgery (and nurse and vet) with pleasant times. I like to think that our former pupils enjoy coming to see us and are well equipped for their adult life.

Monday 23rd February

I start today feeling somewhat battered after all the miserable occurances last week. Veterinary life has its ups and downs; it is depressing when all the downs come at once.

The weather lifts my spirits this morning - it is

unseasonably mild and all at once there are signs that spring is not far away. The first primroses and crocuses are out at the side of the track as we go on our morning walk. The trees are budding and the daffodils grow inches every day. The farmers are busy drilling and ploughing their fields and the countryside has a patchwork appearance; the green of the winter barley contrasting with the chocolate brown of the plough.

It is like the calm after the storm today: only two cats to castrate - or 'dress' as the locals say. This greatly amuses my English friend: when a client asks for their cat to be dressed, she is sorely tempted to ask 'what as?' I have also been asked to *castigate* tom cats or even *canonise* them! Females have come to be *splayed* (ouch!), *sprayed* (certainly - what colour?) and even *to have a spade fitted!* One tomcat today is called 'Mackerel'. In the past, I have neutered a Kipper and a Smokie, but this is definitely my first Mackerel.

Once the cats are done, a less inviting task remains. Gillian needs my help with a dog grooming. Fred McAinsh is a hefty spaniel who never stands still. He is not one of our veterinary clients, but has evidently been barred from other grooming establishments for his unruliness. His owner is so impressed that 'this is the only place that he likes to come.' If only she knew why! For some obscure reason, Fred is totally and deeply in love with me. From the moment the door opens, his hot lust-filled eyes seek me out and a dismal two hours are spent repelling his energetic advances while Gillian does her stuff. This obsession is totally directed at me; Gillian holds no attraction whatsoever. Unable to decide whether this is a compliment or an insult, I steel myself for the onslaught, but a different, calmer Fred walks placidly into the room. I feel almost rejected, no longer attractive even to Fred. Gillian has the explanation - since we last saw Fred, his prostate gland has been causing problems and his vet has carried out the treatment of choice - castration!

Friday 6th March

After the wonderful day yesterday, snow and gusting winds takes us by surprise today. During the morning walk, I feel like a character in one of those little snow domes as snow swirls around us in wild circles. I expect a peaceful morning surgery but it is incredibly busy - each customer had thought that no one else would venture out in such bad weather!

We had a 'lump removal' day on Monday and the patients are coming in for their interim check-ups. Polly the Boxer had an ulcerated nodule removed from her paw. Histopathology tells us that this was a *benign cutaneous histiocytoma* - a peculiar little growth that can look sinister with its rapid growth and raw, ulcerated surface. If the sample had been sent to a human pathology lab, it would set alarm bells ringing as it looks malignant. However the veterinary pathologists know that it is virtually always benign in dogs. This a good example of why one should not extrapolate from humans to animals and vice versa. There are quirky differences between species and what goes for one does not necessarily go for another. Some drugs can be used in different species but this cannot be taken for granted. For example, Penicillin, a lifesaver in many species, will kill guinea pigs; a highly effective human anti-arthritic drug has caused several fatalities in dogs. It is vital to be aware of such important variations. Nowadays, vets use human drugs rather less than before, as we have to abide by a system of prescribing known as *The Cascade*. If a suitable veterinary drug is available for a particular condition, then that rather than its human counterpart must be used. Only when no suitable veterinary product exists can we dip into the human armoury. This can be very irritating for both vet and client because veterinary drugs are invariably more expensive than their human counterparts. Doing the right thing is not always the easy option.

Next after Polly was the elderly Nuisance. His growth was a *haemangioperiocytoma*. This tumour can infiltrate (invade surrounding tissues) locally and can recur. It always seems to appear on an extremity where spare skin is in short supply and it is hard to remove with a good margin of safety. This growth was a recurrence close to where Nuisance last had surgery over a year ago. If at worst we have to remove a growth every year or so, then we can live with that.

Last of our 'lump run' is Glen, a Border collie. He had a painless, tomato-sized swelling on his chest which his owner thought had appeared quite rapidly, although it may be that the growth was present for a time before it was noticed. It did not look or feel worrying, but I have learned from bitter experience that in most cases, it is not possible to diagnose a growth just by examination and with the possible history of rapid growth, the decision was made to operate. On parting the skin during the surgery, a shiny white oval of fatty tissue came into view and peeled easily away from the surrounding tissue - *a lipoma* - a benign growth composed of fat. An easy operation and a happy outlook. The wound has begun to heal well so Glen is unlikely to have any further problems.

Monday 9th March

At last, a bright, sunny day after a snowy, windy weekend. Morning surgery is busy as is usual for a Monday, but as a welcome change, there are no routine ops scheduled for today. Our Clayfern clients frequently behave as if they are each a part of a single being; hence the surgery's rollercoaster progression - some days so busy that we can hardly survive without another vet; other days so quiet that we wonder if we can survive at all. Either everyone comes in all at once or they stay away en masse. As busy periods invariably follow quiet spells, I enjoy the peace while I can. The weekend was fairly brisk with assorted emergency calls - two stitch ups, one fitting dog and a cat with a dislocated hip - so I do not feel guilty about taking it easy now. The dogs are ecstatic at the thought of a second morning walk and we head up the track in the sunshine. Water is running down one side of the track under the ice, looking like large, squirming tadpoles which Fintry spots and pounces on, puzzled at finding no prey.

There is some heat in the sun today and the heady,

coconut-vanilla aroma of the gorse is in the air. My poor old Kippen is feeling his age today - his arthritic legs are troubling him as he shambles slowly behind us. For his benefit, we cut through the woods. Here it is soft underfoot and the path is almost level so he can potter at his own speed, investigating the many smells *en route*. The wood is a mixture of pine and broad-leaved trees and is magical in the frost. Hawthorn and alder are first to bud, adding a green tinge to the background. The sun dapples through the branches and cobwebs stretch like delicate fibre-optic strands - Jay would laugh at veterinary terminology encroaching even when I am relaxing. My family smile when I *bandage* presents for Christmas,or work out our holiday shopping at *two slices of bread twice daily for two days!*

There is more noise in the woods now that better weather is here - wood pigeons flap away in a panic as we approach and flocks of tits and finches flit from tree to tree. A buzzard screams overhead - perhaps we are scaring away his prey. His cry is almost like a cat - *'mee...ooohh; meee..oohh'* - but high pitched and strident. All three dogs are ranging far and wide, investigating burrows and following intriguing scents. Even a mere human can smell the acrid scent of fox and it is driving the dogs wild. I relax sitting on an old tree trunk but the peace is short-lived as young Fintry thunders down the hill scrunching loudly through the leaves. Seconds later Kippen and Jonno reappear and we set off back to civilisation.

Although there are no patients to be seen or operated on, there is still work to be done; booster reminders and bills to be sent out, bills to be paid and leaflets to be printed on a variety of topics designed to inform and educate our clients; the flea control leaflet and the one discussing home dental care are in particularly short supply. The rest of the day passes quickly in a mountain of paperwork and suddenly it is time for evening surgery. I am hoping for a sharp getaway as there is a veterinary meeting in Stramar tonight, but, as usual, Murphy's Law is in operation - the last patient comes through the door thirty seconds before closing time - and, as usual, I set off late. Any hopes of a quick journey are scotched almost immediately by getting behind a brand new BMW crawling along the road. It seems unfair that such a fast car should be driven so far below its potential - if the driver doesn't want to go any faster, perhaps they would like to swap theirs for my slower estate car! The meeting has started when I arrive and a sea of youthful faces turn as the door opens. It must be a sign of age - the vets are looking younger! Vets are expected to spend a minimum of thirty five hours per year on what is officially called continuing professional development (CPD). Most of us enjoy such lectures and seminars and find them interesting. Much is revision, but veterinary knowledge is increasing at an incredible rate - doubling every ten years according to one source - and it can be quite a challenge to keep up. A lot of what I learnt at university over twenty years ago is out of date as new treatments and techniques are constantly appearing. There is also an increasing degree of specialisation within the profession. It is now possible to study for extra qualifications in such disciplines as cardiology, orthopaedics, dermatology, ophthalmology, neurology. Such specialists will accept referrals from other vets. As they see many cases in their field, their expertise increases and they can afford to invest in expensive equipment desirable for their speciality. Such equipment can run to many thousands of pounds and is beyond the scope of most GPs. When I was a newly qualified vet, CT and MRI scanners, air-turbine driven dental equipment, laser therapy, blood transfusions and kidney transplants were in the realms of fantasy for veterinary use, yet we have them now. I wonder what will be in store in the next twenty years.

Tuesday 10th March

One of life's strange coincidences again this month: Diabetes mellitus is not a particularly common condition - in a small practice like this, we might see two or three cases per year; but, guess what? Two came in last week. Excess drinking and urinating are cardinal signs of the disease and these two patients presented with exactly those symptoms. Finn, a fourteen-year-old cat, had been drinking increasing quantities of water and had taken to wetting in the dog's bed. The drinking had largely escaped his owner's notice, but constantly changing the dog's bed was beginning to irritate her. My request for a urine sample was easily granted and a blood sample confirmed the diagnosis. Diabetes mellitus is caused by a shortage of a substance known as insulin. When food is digested, the glucose produced is taken into the blood stream to provide fuel for every cell in the body. Insulin is required to allow the glucose to pass from the blood into the cells - if it is not present, blood glucose levels remain high, triggering the kidneys to pass out the excess. This increased urination in turn causes excess thirst. As the glucose is unavailable for fuel, body fat is broken down in an attempt to provide the energy that the body needs. The animal loses weight and feels unwell as a result of the toxic by-products of fat breakdown. The main treatment for diabetes in animals is to provide the missing insulin in the form of regular injections, usually once or twice a day. It is important to get the dose of insulin correct - too little and the damage to body organs continues; too much and the blood glucose levels drop so low that there is insufficient to power the brain - a condition known as hypoglycaemia. Hypoglycaemia initially causes confusion and dopiness, progressing eventually to fits, loss of consciousness and death.

Both Finn and the other patient, Guinevere, also a cat, have been started on daily insulin injections - first administered by me and then by their owners as they have become confident with the procedure. Owners are initially terrified of having to give injections, but after being introduced gradually to the daily routine, most manage very well. The patients are fed and injected at the same time each day. Improvement in symptoms indicates that treatment is having the desired effect and urine test strips checked at home help to monitor the effects of treatment, but serial blood samples taken every couple of hours throughout the day give a more complete picture of how controlled the disease is. This is why both cats are in today. The plan is to feed and inject as normal and take blood every two hours to determine the blood glucose levels over the day. Ideally, the sampling period should extend over a full twenty four hours, but practically, both vet and patient are flagging before then - we routinely manage fourteen hours, but will continue overnight if the results after this time are not easily interpreted. So at eight this morning, we had an influx of diabetic cats, complete with everything necessary to see them through the day - bowls, food, vials of insulin, toys and favourite blankets.

After an initial flurry of activity settling both patients in, we take our first samples. Both cats are then fed and injected with insulin. We carry on with the other operations of the day, falling into the familiar routine every two hours - Guinivere out first then Finn. We have a small piece of equipment known as a glucometer which makes today's procedure possible. Used by human diabetics, this instrument is designed to measure blood glucose from a mere spot of blood. Humans prick their finger to collect this; we use a small hypodermic needle to quickly nick a small blood vessel in the ear flap. This yields enough blood for the test and usually the patients don't object. Unfortunately, Finn has sensitive ears, well frayed at the edges as a result of many cat fights - and he gets harder to handle each time. We start to dread the clock creeping round to the end of another two hours. Guinevere was a terror in her youth, but has fortunately mellowed with age and seems almost to be enjoying the day. She is usually alone while her owners are at work so perhaps today's company is a novelty. Julie and I have added extra interest by each backing a cat. Julie bets that Finn's glucose levels will drop lower than Guinevere's. I am backing Guinevere. In between blood samples, we spay two bitches, castrate two cats and clean a terrier's teeth, so the day passes quickly. Guinevere and I win the bet so Julie will buy the doughnuts next operating day.

Jay helps me with the evening samples until the cats are picked up after 10 pm. We now have a graph of how each cat's blood glucose levels vary over the day which I have used to decide what changes must be made to the daily regime. It has been a long day and we all have some battle scars from when Finn decided that blood-letting should be for everyone, but it has also been satisfying to be able to fine tune the treatment to best effect.

Wednesday 11th March

Today really is a busman's holiday. I am spending my precious morning off completing a job first started seven weeks ago when I visited Mrs Adams, one of my favourite clients. Her old cat, Lacey, suffers from chronic respiratory problems and occasionally needs a course of treatment. While I examined Lacey, Mrs Adams mentioned that Lacey's brother Cagney had lost weight. Cagney is a super cat, friendly and cheerful with above average intelligence. Happy to be the centre of attention, he is no trouble to examine. He certainly looked thinner; 'He's eating very well - in fact I can't fill him,' observed his anxious owner. An extremely fast heart rate and palpably enlarged thyroid glands clinched the likely diagnosis; Cagney was hyperthyroid. Overactive thyroid glands speed up the cat's metabolism, resulting in the symptoms observed - most commonly - weight loss, ravenous appetite and increased heart rate. Although affected cats initially seem very well, they will eventually progress to heart failure if left untreated. Next day, Julie and I took a blood sample from Cagney to confirm the diagnosis and two days later, Mrs Adams and I got together to discuss treatment options. We covered the three possibilities: medical treatment with tablets to be given up to three times daily; surgery to remove the abnormal tissue - generally successful, but with potential risks; and radioactive iodine therapy. This last treatment is frequently used in humans - radioactive iodine is given by a simple injection, localises in the thyroid glands and knocks out the abnormal tissue. The treatment is very simple and risk free, but complications arise from the potential risks to people and animals in contact with the treated cat who is now effectively radioactive. Stringent health regulations dictate that the cat has to be kept in isolation for a month - handled as little as possible, with all waste being disposed of in accordance with strict guidelines. Few centres in Britain can offer this treatment and Glasgow is one of them. As Mrs Adams is almost blind, tablet-giving is out of the question. She does not like the idea of surgery and since she has recently received a modest inheritance, she decides to opt for treatment at Glasgow. Although old, Cagney is a happy-go-lucky chap and we don't think that the change of scene will be too traumatic for him. After consultation with the vets at Glasgow vet school, all is arranged and six weeks ago, Mrs Adams and I delivered Cagney for his treatment. All has gone well. Mrs Adams has phoned me regularly with progress reports about Cagney's settling-in period, his injection then his month in isolation. Now his sentence is up: he has put weight on and is fit to go home.

Mrs Adams is a delightful lady with interesting tales to tell and the journey to Glasgow passes quickly. During our last trip to

Glasgow, we stopped for lunch at a scenic pub. Mrs Adams surprised me by ordering Chicken korma - her first curry at the age of ninety three. Today, Mrs Adams is game to try more. There are plenty of Indian restaurants in Glasgow, many fondly remembered from my student days. But although very pleasant, pub curries often bear little resemblance to the real thing and I have a twinge of anxiety as we enter my favourite curry house. I needn't have worried - popadoms, chutney, chicken tikka masala, pilau rice and a naan on the side - all are enthusiastically demolished. Thus fortified, we set off to collect Cagney. He looks heavier already and his latest blood results show that the treatment has worked. After her exciting morning, Mrs Adams sleeps throughout the return journey while Cagney wails unhappily in the background. Safely delivered back home, Cagney inspects his surroundings - and his sister - carefully, to reassure himself that nothing has changed in his absence. As I rush out of the door, late for evening surgery, Mrs Adams' parting words ring out ominously: 'Doesn't he look heavy beside his sister. Come to think of it, she seems to have lost weight recently.'

Thursday 12th March

Despite a cold, snowy start, morning surgery is busy and we also have quite a full ops list. Before too long, the routine procedures are finished and we turn our attention to our inpatient, Yoyo. He came in as an emergency case at 10 pm last night. Arriving home late, Yoyo's owner found the fifteen-year-old poodle holding his left hind leg awkwardly and obviously feeling miserable and sore. He was settled in a comfortable kennel overnight, having been given a mild sedative and a painkilling injection. Today, we gently administer an anaesthetic and examination of the unconscious animal suggests a dislocated hip; an X-ray confirms the diagnosis. After some manipulation, the hip pops back into place without much trouble. I am relieved that the job is not too hard, but caution is still necessary. Sometimes the easier it is to replace the hip, the easier it is for it to redislocate. Yoyo will need to be restricted in a cage to allow the hip to settle down. Every cloud has a silver lining and this is the case for Yoyo. For over a year, I have been trying to persuade

Mrs Henderson to allow us to sort out his disgusting mouth, but she has been too anxious about the anaesthetic to give permission, despite my assurances that the risks are small. Although old, Yoyo checks out well medically. We have had to anaesthetise him for the dislocated hip so we take the opportunity to give him a thorough makeover - full dental, matts trimmed from coat, nails clipped and ears cleaned. When Yoyo comes round, he is a different dog, standing on all four legs, wagging his tail happily - a satisfying case.

Friday 13th March

Friday 13th - unlucky for some and especially for poor Yoyo. Linda discharged him during evening surgery, heavily stressing the importance of keeping him restricted. Yoyo was so named due to his incessant bouncing up and down, so proper restraint was vital and we lent his owner a cage for the purpose. A very sheepish Mrs Henderson returned fifteen minutes later - she left Yoyo in the car while collecting some groceries; on her return, he was on the floor, miserable and shivery - the hip dislocated again. So this morning is a re-run of yesterday's procedure. Fortunately, all goes well and, as if we'd flicked a switch, Yoyo is once again transformed to his cheerful, tail-wagging self. When Mrs Henderson collects him, she vows that he will stay in his kennel or firmly clutched in her arms until we check him again on Monday.

Time for a quick walk up the hill in the sunshine. Sitting on my favourite vantage point, I see the first bumblebee of the year and enjoy the sound of the skylarks high in the blue sky. Something suddenly catches my eye - a rusty piece of metal protruding from a tussock. This turns out to be a rather magnificent old horseshoe - at least nine inches long. I can imagine a large Clydesdale steadily plodding across the fields, dragging a heavy wooden plough. The horseshoe now has pride of place at the surgery door - open ends upwards to keep the luck in.

Saturday 14th March

Saturday surgeries seem more relaxed than those on weekdays, probably as there is no ops list or evening surgery to deal with. However they are often very busy and today is no exception. It is a typical surgery this morning, lots of variety but thankfully no unhappy situations or nasty surprises. First in is Tammy McTavish for routine weighing. Tammy is a rotund little cairn terrier who is a frequent visitor. Two years ago, this little fat barrel rolled into the surgery, coughing badly and wetting wherever she stood. Her owner brought up the rear, armed with a box of tissues to mop up the damage. Tammy demonstrates well the value of slimming - after one kilogram loss, her cough disappeared; after losing two kilos, the indiscriminate wetting stopped and her attempts to jump onto the settee were finally successful. In all she lost a third of her body weight and became a new dog. Unfortunately, her owner died, things slipped and we are now back where we started. Happily re-homed with a neighbour, a coughing, weeing Tammy is again on a diet and early results are promising. The cough is fading and she only wets if excited. A good start.

Next is Guinevere, our diabetic cat, doing well on her new insulin regime; then Chatsworth, a twelve-year-old Labrador with arthritis. I dispense anti-inflammatory drugs and make an appointment to see him in a week, telling his owner to restrict him to gentle exercise. Like our Kippen, Chatsworth loves to chase his ball but the extra strain on his old legs make the arthritis worse. If owners are observant, they can predict when more medication is required - perhaps after a longer walk, or a play with a friend or a soaking in rain or river. Hopefully, better weather is on the way and our arthritic patients will soon have some relief.

Two booster vaccinations follow, then a stitch-removal for a cat spayed last week. Just Ricky Marsh to go. Ricky is a Scottie with more than his share of problems. Although only six, he suffers from bad skin, bad legs and colitis. This can make management tricky as treatment for one condition can worsen another. Luck is with us today as Ricky has improved since last time. A different diet and more frequent, smaller walks, dips in water and topical antiseptics applied directly to the affected areas of skin all seem to be helping, although inevitably we will need drugs when one or other condition flares up. Just as in humans, simple lifestyle changes can often reap large benefits.

We have a late arrival - a shot ferret. The ferret was being used to flush rabbits from a burrow and was accidently winged. Only one small hole is visible on her flank but no shot can be felt below it. The ideal approach would be to take X-rays to locate the shot. If it is in the abdomen, the ferret will probably die unless it is removed. The ferret is a little tender by her backbone and I suspect that the shot is lodged there. She does not seem particularly distressed and the owner does not want to spend much money so we have to compromise. I dispense antibiotics for the next few days and insist that the surgery is contacted if the ferret becomes ill. The embedded shot will not cause any problems through lead poisoning where it is - a popular fallacy; only ingested lead will produce symptoms of poisoning. As many ferret owners would not seek veterinary advice at all, the pragmatic approach adopted in this case is better than nothing.

Finished at last. Gillian and I exit at speed, both with the same thought - what a great day for a walk with the dogs. In a week that has seen its share of snow and ice, spring seems to be winning today. In the woods, small young nettles are appearing through the undergrowth and I know that soon the woods will be off limits until late autumn - these innocent baby nettles will shortly turn into three foot triffids with a savage sting. Birds are singing their hearts out in courtship rituals and overhead a rook labours to carry a large twig back for nest construction. We pause at the top of the hill for the first sunbathe of the year, listening lazily to the skylark's sweet song before heading homeward to embark on the weekly shopping expedition. It comes as a surprise to some customers that even vets need to perform such mundane tasks – that is, if the pager does not summon us home *post haste*. All vets in practice have an ear perpetually pricked for the sounds of bleeping pagers or trilling phones. When this happens at veterinary meetings, it is quite comical to see everyone else reaching automatically for their own communicators. Even pelican crossings or ringing tills can have similar effects. My shopping trip is undisturbed and I arrive home with happy thoughts of a relaxing meal and an evening spent vegetating in front of the television. While unpacking the shopping, such dreams are rudely shattered; a frantic banging at the door announces alternative plans for the evening. Jude, a young German Shepherd dog has been hit by a car and her owner has rushed straight here in a panic. *'This looks serious'*, I think as we stretcher her into the surgery and I automatically fall into emergency routine. Thank goodness Jay is not working today and is able to help. We need to deal with life-threatening conditions first, broken legs and skin tears can wait till later. A quick examination shows Jude to be deep in shock - a situation where the circulation is in imminent danger of irreversible collapse. The body's initial response to severe trauma is to shut down the blood circulation to the extremities, concentrating on supplying vital areas such as brain and kidneys. This initially helpful response can be fatal if it continues for too long. Jude's gums are white as a sheet and her ears and feet are frigid. Her heart is indistinct, very fast and weak and her breathing is laboured. This is going to be touch and go. Fast action is necessary. We wrap her in blankets and position an oxygen mask by her face, then insert an intravenous catheter, inject anti-shock drugs and rapidly run in blood volume expander (the nearest substitute for blood that we have). She is very frightened and struggles at first until weakness overcomes her and she flops back on the table. Her owner, Cath, helps by trying to keep her calm. Once everything is connected or administered, I try to examine Jude further. This is not easy as she is a big dog. All of us think privately that we are going to lose her. I have met Jude's owner before and like her very much. First appearances were deceptive, as she is a fully-fledged punk, but a kinder, more committed pet owner is hard to find. We got to know each other quite well while treating Jude's mother Jenny. Jenny died and I want so much to save Jude for her.

We are now stuck in suspended animation, drugs running in and oxygen hissing while we wait for any change. Cath has to collect her toddler from a neighbour, so bids a semi-conscious Jude a tearful goodbye. We have been working on Jude for over an hour. Jay remains in the surgery while I monitor our patient, checking and re-checking colour, temperature, heart etc. I try to connect a pulse oximeter to her lip. The device measures the oxygen concentration in a peripheral blood vessel - no reading - poor peripheral circulation. Yet another bag of fluid is heated and attached to the drip. Feeling her ears again - 'Are they slightly warmer - or is it just wishful thinking?' I agonise. Jay agrees her feet are also slightly better. Her colour is still awful but is there the merest hint of pink? Ten minutes later, there is no doubt that things are improving and we get a reading on the pulse ox. – 95 per cent - not bad at all. Twenty minutes later, her ears and feet are warm and her gums are pale pink. Her breathing is less laboured though still far from right. After a further 20 minutes we remove the plastic clips running oxygen into her nostrils and observe her closely for ten minutes - no deterioration. At 8.40 pm we transfer her into a warm kennel. At last she appears stable and we risk going into the house for supper. Jude gets checked every fifteen minutes initially, graduating to every half hour. She remains warm and her colour is improved, but her heart and breathing are still fast and I detect occasional irregularities in her heart rhythm. The drip is closed off at 11 pm. She accepts a drink of water. I finally go to bed at midnight, setting the alarm for 2 am.

Sunday 15th March

2 am. - Jude remains stable and accepts a drink of water.

7 am. - Stable but restless. I suspect she is in pain and top up her painkillers. There is some 'clonking' on examining the left side of her pelvis but I cannot feel anything conclusive. There are no sharp boney edges on rectal examination. The patient accepts three dessertspoons of recovery diet. This food is high in energy - for decades it was thought that ill or injured patients use up less calories while lying immobile. We now know that the body's metabolic rate increases in those circumstances so a calory dense, easily digestible diet is important to aid recovery. During the day, Jude is checked every hour or so. She remains stable and at 2.30 pm polishes off a plateful of recovery diet.

4 pm - her owner visits.This provokes quite a response; she stands for the first time - and wags her tail. The situation is much improved on yesterday, but I warn Cath that we are not out of the woods yet. The cardiac irregularities seem to be reducing but we must be cautious - like any other organ, heart muscle can be damaged in an accident and this can be potentially fatal. Strict rest is vital. We will probably need X-rays to investigate Jude's pelvis, but a general anaesthetic is rather risky just now.

The evening wears on, punctuated by regular trips to the surgery to monitor our patient. I am happy with her progress until the pre-bedtime check at midnight - Jude's heart rate has accelerated and sounds irregular. Connecting her to the ECG monitor, I count twenty PVCs (premature ventricular complexes) per minute. This indicates heart muscle damage. Electrical impulses cause the heart to contract in an orderly manner; the impulses pass through the heart in waves causing first the auricles then the ventricles to contract. These 'waves' show up on the ECG as a characteristic form. In heart disease, there is often a change in the shape of the ECG wave which can tell which part of the heart is affected. In Jude's case, the ventricles are contracting more frequently than the auricles - this sounds chaotic through the stethoscope. She does not appear distressed and her circulation is holding up, but her breathing is rather rapid. I decide against giving any medication until we can seek an opinion from a veterinary cardiologist. I set the alarm for 3 am. just in case there is any deterioration.

Monday 16th March

7am. - an early start to check Jude and clean out her kennel. All our inpatients are bedded on veterinary fleece, an excellent material which allows fluids to drain onto the underlying newspaper leaving the patient warm and dry. It is quite a performance persuading her first to leave the kennel and then to return after cleaning. Her heart is still irregular and fast, but she seems cheerful and even gives a small tail wag before eating some breakfast. After morning surgery, Gillian and I return to carry out her ECG examination. The dog is connected by several leads to an ingenious device which transmits the ECG waves through the telephone lines to a heart expert. He will examine the trace and send recommendations for treatment. Jude is not the calmest of dogs but Gillian does a sterling job of restraining her while the examination is in progress. Later in the day, the results appear. As we suspected, the irregularities are due to cardiac contusion (bruising) which typically 'ripens' after 24–48 hours. He recommends a drug which we collect from the local chemist - it is a human drug, there being no licensed veterinary drug for this condition. As Jude is becoming increasingly difficult to handle and her owner is very sensible, we decide to send her home with a collapsible kennel to ensure complete rest. As with Yoyo, the poodle with the dislocated hip, it is not possible to explain to animal patients the importance of staying still. Cath will keep in close touch with the surgery and I will check Jude in a few days.

How marvellous it is to have an empty surgery overnight. It is very satisfying to deal so closely with in-patients - but it is also very tiring and it will be lovely to have an unbroken night's sleep (phone permitting, of course).

Tuesday 17th March

First patient this morning is a pheasant found lying at the side of the road. It is a male, a magnificent bird with vibrant red, blue and green highlights to his chestnut plumage. Although beautiful, pheasants have no road sense and seem to revel in playing 'chicken'. The local highways are littered with pheasants who have woefully misjudged their last minute dash. Luckily, this one is only stunned and has been lucky enough to be rescued by a kindly lady who happens to keep chickens. He will be recuperating in a warm shed with plenty of grain.

Today we are putting on our dentist's hat (or rather mask and gloves!) as we have two dogs and a cat in need of dental attention. Like human doctors, vets try to practise preventative medicine, and dentistry is an area where a little bit of effort from the owners at an early stage can prevent major problems later in life. We encourage our owners to start cleaning their pups' and kittens' teeth from the start so the animals accept regular brushing as part of life. Raw vegetables and tough pieces of meat also help to keep teeth clean. In addition, there is now a multitude of treats specially designed for this purpose. One biscuit is engineered so that the fibres lie in one direction and act as a squeegee on the teeth. These were first marketed with a demonstration kit consisting of a screwdriver, a bottle of Tippex and the biscuit. The screwdriver was coated in Tippex, allowed to dry then pushed into a normal biscuit - this biscuit would shatter almost immediately, leaving the Tippex layer intact. The test biscuit does not shatter until the screwdriver almost reaches the far side and lo, the Tippex is mostly removed. Veterinary staff and clients have had many a good laugh over this performance, but it does prove its point and in practice, the biscuits are a useful aid. Most dogs and cats over three years old have already started on the vicious cycle of tartar deposition, receding gums and bacterial invasion of the gap between tooth and gum, so home dental care really does make sense. It slows the progression of the cycle (known as periodontal disease), reduces bad breath and makes the pet feel better.

One patient today is an old spaniel who has obviously never been told to brush. Her foul breath pervades the entire surgery and very few of her teeth are saveable - her gums are oozing with pus and her teeth have been loosened to such an extent by periodontal disease that they are easy to remove. As we work in her mouth, the smell makes us feel sick, but at least the job is done quickly. Usually, dog and cat teeth are much more difficult to remove than human teeth. The roots need to be painstakingly separated from their socket using sharp tools known as *elevators*. Some teeth have three roots and it is occasionally necessary to split the tooth in half to aid removal. In the past, this was done with a hacksaw, but nowadays most vets have dental drills for the purpose. If the teeth are coated with tartar but are otherwise healthy, only a thorough scale and polish is required. We use an ultrasonic scaler and polisher for this. Ultrasonic waves from the scaler tip dislodge tartar from the tooth surface. The device produces a mist of water droplets contaminated with bacteria – which is why we wear masks and goggles when working.

Within an hour, our old dog is sitting up looking extremely bright. She has had painkillers and will be on soft foods for a day or so, but it is not unusual for such patients to polish off a dish of dry food within a day of surgery - obviously healthy gums are less tender than disgusting teeth. When many old animals slow up, their owners assume this is due to ageing. After a thorough dental procedure, it is amazing how many have a new lease of life. It is not age but the effects of having a painful, infected mouth which slows them down.

Our other canine dental patient today is Gill, a middle-aged standard poodle. Her owners, Mavis and Fred, are frequent visitors to the surgery with their three 'girls' and we have become friends. The 'girls' are kept in immaculate order despite enjoying the usual doggy antics. As usual, Gill required only a quick scale and polish and was collected shortly after lunch. During evening surgery, the following epistle appears on the reception desk -

Dear Auntie Kate,
I am writing this letter, or sorry, my Dad is typing it for me as my paws are too big for the keyboard. I wish to thank you for cleaning my teeth as I have now got minty fresh breath and this improves my chances of getting a boyfriend (some chance my Dad says).

HOWEVER, my Dad is not happy because you have made a hole in my trousers. I have told him not to bother about it, but he keeps going on about the price of Wranglers and having said that, my knee is now poking out of the hole and is itchy. My Mum and Dad have put Vaseline on it, but I keep licking it off
...WILL THIS AFFECT MY TEETH?

I don't want to end up with ANOTHER hole in my breeks.

Anyway, the purpose of this letter is to tell you that my Dad is not happy about the hole in my breeks. He is going on about court cases, damages, compensation etc whatever all that means.

MAYBE I could suggest that I would settle for a couple of

TITBITS. This would also help from licking the Vaseline as they taste better. Don't worry about what my Dad says, I can take care of him. Have an excellent holiday, take care and let me know about your travels when you return.
Your ever loving patient and puppy,
Gill.
P.S. Could you make sure Mum and Dad have enough dog food for us before you go.
P.P.S. If you see any really unusual doggy treats on your travels, please feel free to bring samples home.

This makes an amusing end to the day and my few days' holiday is feeling pleasantly close. I will do my best to find a suitable gastronomic gift for Gill *et al.*

Saturday 21st March

We have been on holiday for a short break and are steeling ourselves for a return to work this morning. It is a blissfully mild day and the valley seems to be suddenly wakening up. Most fields are now green and tractors are much in evidence - ploughing, seeding, fertilising; sometimes working late into the night guided by their powerful headlights. This looks quite spooky from a distance - disembodied lights moving slowly across the fields. We are sitting with a coffee by the back door listening to the morning sounds. The farm cockerel has been crowing since first light and ought to be hoarse by now. Like the crashing of a car's gears, a pheasant is chirr-chirring in the field and for the first time this year, we hear the falsetto giggle of the green woodpecker. Elsewhere in the wood, greater spotted woodpeckers are drumming loudly on their chosen trees. The wood now appears variegated, the coconut-mat colour of winter trees mottled with the lime green of budding larch and deeper shades of evergreen pines. After the inactivity of winter, suddenly so much is going on. A large dog fox trots purposefully up the field, probably heading home to newly dug holes amongst the trees. Much of the wonder of living here is in the changing seasons. Half-forgotten sights, sounds and smells come round each year like old friends, stimulating anticipation of the following season's delights. Now we look forward to long days spent outside - gardening, playing tennis, taking trips to the seaside and holding social barbecues lasting late into the evening. And in autumn, we anticipate brisk walks in chill weather, warm woolly clothes, winter sports and comforting stews and soups on dark evenings spent in front of the fire.

It would be pleasant to spend the day in peaceful contemplation of nature, but there is work to do. First, morning surgery in Clayfern, then a major operation on a dog seen yesterday by Linda. Moss the collie was rushed to the surgery after collapsing suddenly. He was a fit, active working sheepdog until a mere fifteen minutes previously. On arrival at the surgery, he was deep in shock - pale and cold and unable to stand unaided. His owners were mystified, but Linda soon had her suspicions as to a diagnosis. After stabilising the dog on intravenous fluids and oxygen, she continued with a thorough examination. Moss's abdomen appeared enlarged and tender and an X-ray confirmed the presence of a large mass at the front end of the abdomen. This was most likely to be a liver or spleen problem. Next, Linda inserted a small catheter into the abdomen under local anaesthetic and was able to collect free blood, confirming her suspicion that Moss was bleeding intra-abdominally. A biochemistry screen showed no evidence of liver damage or malfunction. The most likely diagnosis at this stage was a ruptured splenic tumour. The scenario was fairly typical - sudden collapse of a previously healthy animal with no history of trauma, showing signs of severe shock. Sometimes the dog may recover on its own from such an incident, but invariably a fatal bleed will occur if no treatment is given.

After an hour of intensive treatment, Moss had improved. As long as he remains stable, the next step is scheduled for today. He has been checked regularly throughout the night and is in much better shape than he was. The plan for today is to open into Moss's abdomen and if the diagnosis is correct, remove his spleen. Fortunately, it is possible to survive without a spleen. Although off duty, Linda volunteers her help which is gratefully accepted and, with Gillian monitoring the anaesthetised dog, we begin our exploratory surgery. Linda's diagnosis is confirmed within minutes. Large, fist-sized clots of blood are seen through the abdominal incision, free blood glistens round the organs and a massive spleen is soon in view. One end contains a ruptured tumour - like a squashed tomato - which oozes ominously as we manipulate the spleen towards the surgical site. Our next task is to tie off all the blood vessels leading to and from the massive organ before removing it completely. We must be careful because the spleen shares a blood supply with the pancreas and stomach and it is vital not to damage their supply. We start at opposite ends with the tedious process of dissecting out, then tying off, all vessels leading solely to the spleen. Finally the job is done and the damaged organ is lifted free of the abdomen - a good two pounds in weight and floppy like a dead fish. A sample of the growth will be sent to the lab for identification. After checking the other organs for tumour spread, we flush the abdomen with saline then close the large wound. At last, Moss is installed in a warm, recovery kennel. He is still not out of the woods - he has to recover from the anaesthetic and surgery and regain his strength, but at least he is safely over the first hurdle. Once the tumour type is known, we will have an idea whether it is likely to have spread elsewhere.

After such major surgery, the operating room resembles a slaughter house - even a little blood goes a long way and there has been plenty around today. The tumour behaved like a soft jelly, spontaneously falling apart with even minimal handling - the dog is really very lucky to be alive after the initial bleed. There is a good feeling of camaraderie amongst the surgical team as we begin to clear up the mess. Although cautious, we all feel fairly elated; the anaesthetic and surgery have gone smoothly and Moss is coming round according to plan. Finally, we adjourn to the house for richly deserved coffee and doughnuts and that golden time after a job well done when we can relax and swap reminiscences of similar cases. Like fishermen comparing their 'catches', I'm sure a certain amount of exaggeration creeps into the discussion!

I am in and out of the surgery like a yoyo over the next few hours checking and comforting our patient. Overnight, he accepts some recovery diet and a drink. He stays with us until Sunday night when he is discharged with instructions for strict rest and a collapsible kennel with which to enforce this. He has a lot of blood loss to make up and is weak - like an anaemic person. I'm sure he will be only too happy to spend the next few days being waited on hand and foot - sounds wonderful to me!

<u>Monday 23rd March</u>

There is a distinct seasonal feel to this morning's surgery. Several cats require worming - no doubt after increased hunting activities - and three itching dogs need looking at. The spring increase in pollens and seeds often brings misery to dogs with allergic skin disease. In the lucky ones, symptoms may only appear for a short period, others suffer through all the warmer weather. Successful treatment cannot be guaranteed unfortunately and we have to impress on owners that our realistic aim is to control, not cure, the condition. Fleas and other parasites also increase with the warmer weather and we all stress the importance of routine parasite control. It is unusual not to see at least one animal with fleas during a consulting session.

One of our diabetic cats - Finn - comes in for a routine blood sample. He has been doing well; his drinking is much reduced and today his blood glucose is within normal levels. With the better weather, he spends more time outside and I have a fleeting worry that his increased activity might reduce his glucose levels, possibly leading to a hypoglycaemic episode. However, his owner assures me that he is in fact a very successful hunter, so we reckon that the prey he catches will boost his glucose levels enough to compensate for the effects of greater exercise!

Moss's owner telephones with a progress report. He is still weak but seems cheerful and is eating well. He is taken regularly into the garden to 'do his duty' but is always glad to return to the kennel. So far so good.

At the farm surgery, we are expecting Jude - our traffic

accident - for a check up. Her owner has kept me informed about her progress. In general, she has been improving well but her appetite is not good. My first impression is that her breathing is heavier than I would expect after a week's convalescence. Her heart sounds much improved with no trace of irregularity, but her breathing sounds are a little muffled, so I suggest taking an X-ray just to rule out the possibility of a diaphragmatic hernia. This can occur after trauma - the diaphragm tears and allows abdominal organs to herniate into the chest cavity. This herniation can happen immediately post-accident, or at a later date. Our X-ray shows an intact diaphragm but there is definitely increased density in the middle of the lung field reflecting the severity of the damage to Jude's lungs. Nothing surgical can be done. Hopefully continued rest will bring about more improvement; but there is a risk that Jude's breathing may never be 100 per cent. Cath can gradually reduce the heart tablets now and I will check her again in a few days.

I am relieved that we do not have to operate on Jude: diaphragmatic hernia repair is high risk surgery. Two years ago, a distraught owner appeared at the surgery with her Labrador who had been 'run over' by a landrover - the driver actually felt the tyres going over the dog. Expecting a moribund patient, we were amazed to see a virtually unscathed youngster bounding from the car up the path to the surgery in search of the usual biscuit. Everything checked out okay - apart from a few superficial grazes, the dog seemed to have got off scot free. The accident happened on a gravel drive so we assumed that the gravel had given under the dog, cushioning her from more serious injury. All was well for nearly a week until the dog jumped a low fence and suddenly developed severe breathing difficulties. The strain of the jump had pushed abdominal organs through an area of diaphragm damaged during the previous week's accident. Luckily, the hernia was successfully repaired and she made a complete recovery.

After a weekend spent looking after Moss, the prospect of a long walk is extremely appealing. The weather has been dry for several days, so a walk through the fields to the river is possible. Although the crops are growing, we can still walk through the fields if we stick to the tractor tracks, but in wet conditions, the tracks are too muddy and we have not ventured down for weeks. A large flock of geese congregate at the edge of the field, watching warily as three dogs and I troop down the tram lines in Indian file. A pair of swans have taken up residence in the oil-seed rape field over the fence. One was missing for a while and, watching them from the surgery, Julie and I did wonder initially if one was injured, but they regularly fly off for a while before returning to their patch. Younger swans do occasionally have 'trial runs' at pairing before eventually nest-building and rearing young. It is possible that this is what is happening here. During our day's comings and going, all of us locals keep an eye on the pair, curious as to what they will do next.

The sky is full with the sound of singing skylarks, mere dots in the distance and a bird scarer discharges its four shots on the next farm. This is supposed to scare the birds away from the growing crops but our geese are made of sterner stuff - a quick glance then back to grazing again. At this time of year, the skies are frequently full of ragged skeins of geese, temporarily scared off their preferred feeding grounds either by bird scarers or, occasionally, irate farmers with shotguns. Approaching the river bank, the blackthorn bushes are a shock of snowy blossom - in a few months, they will be heavy with sloes. What a pity no one here likes gin.

The results of the high spring tides are spread on the rocky shore - half an oar, a life belt, plastic washing baskets from the potato picking upriver and the usual selection of plastic containers and old buckets. It is amazing what gets washed up and beachcombing is always interesting. In the surgery's early days, the sandbags used to hold patients in position for X-rays were made from old tyre inner tubes which we had collected from the plentiful supply down here. Within moments of reaching the shore, Kippen has found yet another football to add to his collection. This will be faithfully carried home and played with relentlessly until usurped by a 'newer' model. Unfortunately, Fintry has found a sheep's leg and is carrying it around with great pride, watched by an envious Jonno. The unlucky sheep fall in upstream and wash up on the tide. This one had obviously been in the water for a while and provides an interesting lesson in anatomy - bare bones are held together with the last vestiges of tissue. Luckily, Kippen loses his grip on his ball, providing enough of a diversion for me to grab the leg and lob it back into the river out of reach. I don't mind balls in the garden, but draw the line at skeletons! Fintry's Achilles heel is that she *always* wants what the other dogs have and the chance of grabbing Kippen's ball was too tempting to ignore.

We walk along the shore to a small, stone-built building, one of several along the river bank. These are old fishing lodges, a relic of the days when salmon fishing was a major local industry. Each lodge has a large open fireplace and cot-like beds where the fishermen waited for the tide. Heavy fishing with ever more efficient methods has reduced the salmon numbers drastically and fishing is now strictly regulated, leaving the lodges disused and falling into disrepair. What once was one of the main industries in Clayfern is now no more than an occasional sideline: no one earns their living from the salmon any more. An old map in our hall conjures up an impression of life a century ago: every lodge has a name - Jock's Hole, Camcase, Dominie's Scalp to name but a few. The sandbanks visible at low tide are also named - Wonder Bank, Peeswit Bank and the ominous sounding 'Sure as Death' Bank. Seals and wildfowl can be seen on the banks at low tide and the sandy expanses look benign, but they are hazards to passing vessels. Warning buoys indicate the safe passages but even experienced skippers have been known to run aground. Looking over the black river at night, it is strangely comforting to see the green hypnotic winking of our nearest buoy.

A trip to the river is always full of interest, even down to the amazing variety of rocks on the foreshore. There are spotted, wavy and knobbly ones, all shapes and colours. I pick up an attractive piece of blood-red jasper to add to the collection filling a large bowl on our kitchen window. Looking up, the opposite bank of the river is completely obscured by a battleship-grey curtain of rain. This may be our last trip to the river for another few days if that comes our way. Time to head home. I wish I could paint the scene before me - the green of the sprouting barley, the mauve-brown of the plough stretching to the farm buildings where white blossom and yellow gorse and daffodils stand out from the faded pink of corrugated roofs. A truly pastoral scene.

Thursday 26th March

A welcome phone call from Jude's owner this morning - Cath is thrilled at how much better the dog is. Today, she pinched the cat's food and chased a rabbit. Progress is definitely being made!

Today will be a day of phone calls. First, Moss's results are faxed to the surgery. Unfortunately, the diagnosis is a splenic haemangiosarcoma - a nasty malignant tumour which has a high risk of spreading to other organs. As cancer medicine advances so rapidly, I consult a recent textbook to find current thinking on treatment options and am amazed to find chemotherapy mentioned in connection with this type of tumour. I need more information, so decide to discuss the case with a cancer expert based at one of the veterinary colleges. We are very lucky to be able to speak directly to international experts at the forefront of their subject, but getting connected often requires much patience and tenacity. The day goes something like this:

11 am. First call - specialist is giving a lecture –
        try 12.30 pm
12.30 pm - involved with emergency - try in half an hour.
1.00 pm - still involved with emergency - will call me back.

I am now condemmed to remaining close to the phone for an unknown period. Unfortunately, I have certain other things to do including a visit and, hopefully, a short dog walk. Indecisive, I busy myself with paperwork until 2.30 pm, hoping that my quarry might go to lunch then call on her return but no luck. Trying to second guess prospective callers is a difficult business and it is amazing how many will actually ring during the one half an hour in twenty four in which the phone is not manned directly. I decide to go on the visit and dash home afterwards. I half expect a message on the answering machine effectively putting us back to square one, but no calls are recorded. The afternoon wears on, as I ignore the dogs' increasingly pointed hints about walks - it will soon be time to leave for evening surgery - please ring before then or I'll have to go through the same procedure tomorrow.

AT LAST! Our expert rings at 4.15 pm and makes up for the delay by being exceptionally helpful and informative. Chemotherapy is possible for this case, but the results are generally poor. The treatment is expensive, requires repeated stays at the surgery and can cause unpleasant side-effects. At best, it might increase the average survival time from three to six months. I don't expect Moss's owners to opt for treatment, but relay the information so that they can decide for themselves. During evening surgery, they phone back with their decision - not to attempt chemotherapy. It is difficult to imagine that the rapidly recovering Moss may only have a few months to live; at least it will be a good few months as his owners resolve to thoroughly spoil him in the time he has left.

Tuesday 31st March

Four nights ago, I paid an emergency visit to old Bert, a mongrel belonging to Jenny, a favourite client. While Jenny was away on business, Bert was staying with Jenny's parents, but was having increasing difficulty with his legs and breathing. Really, he was deteriorating badly and was 'just done' as Jenny's mum aptly put it. As Jenny was due home the following day, I gave the old dog some treatment so that he could be put to sleep with his owner present. By the next day however, Bert had staged an amazing recovery and tripped round the surgery, wagging his tail and investigating corners. Both Bert and Jenny had a stay of execution, but the improvement was sadly and inevitably short-lived; this morning we put the old lad to sleep after he took a turn for the worse. Occasionally, this happens - treatment produces an unexpectedly good short-term response in a gravely ill patient - we call it the *swansong syndrome*. It can be an extra precious few days for a devoted owner, but it is also very hard on the emotions.

Today has produced two pending cases; ones which might blow up into major problems. The first is Jeff, a spaniel with a persistent nosebleed. Not only has his nose been bleeding since last night, but on examination he also has pinpoint haemorrhages on his gums and small bruises under his skin. This rings warning bells - either a blood clotting disorder or possible poisoning with rat poison. The latter is a distinct possibility as the property next door has been laying bait. Investigation finds that the poison used is related to Warfarin, a drug which prevents blood from clotting as it should; the rodents die from internal bleeding. So far, Jeff is cheerful and does not appear to have lost too much blood but things may deteriorate. A blood sample is taken before Jeff is given a mild sedative and an injection of vitamin K to aid clotting. His nose is packed with absorbent wadding and he goes home to be kept under close observation. His owners will call with progress reports later in the day by which time the blood tests should be through.

On my way to visit one of Edith McNaughton's dogs, in my mind, I run through possible scenarios for Jeff. If the bleeding continues, he might require anaesthetising to allow us to pack his nose further; if blood loss *still* persists, he might even need a transfusion. One or two specialist centres hold stocks of blood but this is not feasible for small surgeries such as this. The blood only remains usable for a short time after collection. In most practices, blood transfusions involve blood taken from a donor animal (Fintry or Kippen) and immediately injected into the patient. Although rough and ready, this procedure can save lives in emergency situations - blood grouping in animals is such that one transfusion without previous cross-matching is unlikely to cause a problem.

Back to the present - Meeny McNaughton. Edith called after hours last night, worried about Meeny. At the surgery, we are all familiar with Edith's 'emergencies' - after our mercy dashes, three happy, healthy-looking dachshunds usually hurl themselves at the visitor. Then follows a search to find a problem to correspond to Edith's worries. You could say that she cries 'Wolf!' I always visit anyway to allay her fears - and in case there really is a problem. Last night, the visit was definitely justified: Meeny was certainly not herself. She was reluctant to move and even snapped at the other two when they came to investigate. Her back was arched and tense and her hind legs seemed weak. Matching a diagnosis to these symptoms is not taxing in a dachshund. The breed are prone to slipped discs.

Symptoms vary from minor lack of limb control through to complete paralysis. In mild cases such as Meeny's, strict rest may allow the problem to abate, but more severe symptoms - or worsening of mild cases - often require surgery. Meeny has been confined to her kennel since last night. Today she is still depressed but thankfully the symptoms are no worse. I suspect I will be visiting I hope, almost daily until, we see some improvement. Edith adores her dogs and could do with the moral support.

Jeff's lab results are on the fax machine when I get home - his platelet count is reduced quite considerably but as yet there is no anaemia. As if on cue, his owner telephones minutes later. Reasonable news - the nose bleed has decreased but is still seeping a little blood occasionally and Jeff is resting quietly in front of the fire. Most of my evening is spent trawling through textbooks for up-to-date information on causes of platelet disorders. I had forgotten how complicated the clotting mechanism is. At the end of the night, my knowledge of bleeding disorders has received a transfusion of its own.

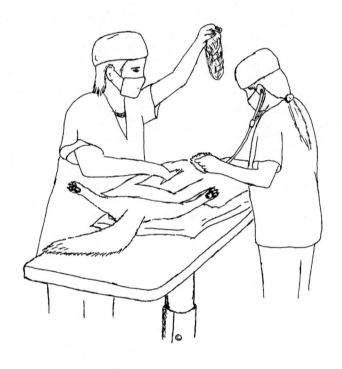

Thursday 2nd April

We waken early this morning to sun streaming through the windows and set off on a longer than usual morning walk towards the river. Daffodils line both sides of the road and birds sing in the hedgerows. We seem to have a 'plague' of yellowhammers this year - they are everywhere, bright yellow heads standing out like beacons. From a distance, you could be forgiven for thinking that a flock of budgies had escaped. As we walk down the side of the field, our two swans fly overhead, preparing for a landing in the oil-seed rape. Although 'Mute', when flying, the swans' wings generate a loud whirr or whistle, almost like the hum of a generator which can be heard over a considerable distance. Perhaps they commute in every day? We will watch to see if they go away at dusk. I hope that farmer Colin lets them stay - its probably best not to mention that each swan can eat up to four kilograms of vegetation per day! Having had swans in the surgery, I know with certainty that they will at least be fertilising the field.

Dogs walked, it's back to business. On the way to Clayfern, the first lambs are gambolling in the fields near the village. If the weather continues like this, it should be a successful lambing season.

Morning surgery is fairly quiet so Gillian and I brighten the waiting room by pinning the entries from a recent children's painting competition on the notice boards. February was 'Pet Smile' month and the competition was to *Draw a Healthy Smile*. The nationwide winner is to be used as a logo for next year's 'Pet Smile' month, a worthwhile publicity campaign increasing awareness of pet dental hygiene. Our local primary school set about it enthusiastically, producing an impressive variety of entries. Unfortunately, one class had just been on a trip to a nearby sea-life centre and many of their offerings featured fish of all shapes and sizes; very beautiful but rather missing the point of encouraging pet owners to clean their pets' teeth - apart from a leering shark, showing an impressive array of fangs, in hot pursuit of a pair of legs protruding below the ocean surface. In all, the standard of entries is very high and we have had a hard job picking the winners to send into the national competition.

After an edgy couple of days, our two worrying cases have

settled down a little. Meeny seems happier and less uncomfortable. Edith has recognised the urgency in my warnings and is religiously keeping the little dog in her cage. Often, when patients begin to feel better, they overdo things and land in trouble again. Jeff too is holding his own. The nose bleed has stopped but he still has some bleeding from his gums. He has had daily injections of vitamin K and is now on tablets. We will take a blood sample weekly to monitor his progress. Apparently, some newer rat poisons can cause symptoms for up to one month.

Back at the farm surgery, Julie and I make a start. Our first patient is a Rottweiller for castration. He is a big chap, decked out in a macho leather collar adorned with metal studs. Between us, we heave all fifty two kilograms onto the operating table (*small* animal practice?) and begin his anaesthetic with an intravenous injection. Julie restrains the reclining dog on one side of the table while I inject from the other side. As the anaesthetic takes effect, the bulky body threatens to topple to Julie's side, so Julie adopts her trademark position - being extremely fit, it is no trouble for her to stretch one leg on the table alongside the dog to prevent further listing. Unfortunately, the dog then lists in my direction. With considerably more effort, I stretch my leg along the dog's other side. We are now both stretched out along the table facing the window with the unconscious dog sandwiched between us.
'I hope no one is out there with a camera', I gasp;
'Yeah,' gasps back Julie, 'fun with Rottweillers!'
The dog is tubed without further incident and the operation proceeds smoothly. As I stitch the small wound, we idly wonder whether skin staples rather than stitches might add more to the dog's street cred'.

Friday 3rd April

Julie and I have a treat in store today - a trip to the British Small Animal Veterinary Association Congress in Birmingham. This is the largest veterinary conference in Britain, not bad for a branch of practice which was a minority interest less than fifty years ago. The event runs for four days, attracting veterinary workers from all over the world. A choice of up to eight lectures run simultaneously from 8.30 am. to 6.30 pm. There is also a very large commercial exhibition; a showcase for new equipment and drugs. In past years, we have endured the seven-hour drive down the country, but this year we are flying down just for one day. This involves a 4.30 am. start to reach the airport for the early flight to Birmingham. What a morning! Gale force winds and horizontal rain lash the car as we travel along empty roads. Reports of fallen trees and flooded roads are broadcast by the local radio station. This is weather of truly epic proportions! The only signs of life are the welcoming lights of lambing sheds on local farms. The hill farmers here do not begin lambing until April to avoid the worst of the weather. At least these lambs are indoors: this weather will be a disaster for any outside. We suspect the flight might be cancelled, but it takes off on schedule and we have a relatively pleasant, though bumpy, ride to Birmingham where it is mild and sunny.

The decision as to which lecture to attend often depends on which cases are freshest in one's memory. With Moss and Jeff in mind, I attend a talk on blood disorders and blood-loss anaemia. How things have moved on since I was a student. Much of the talk is of blood transfusions - not only whole blood, but concentrated red cells, plasma and other blood products. The American speaker comes from a university which runs a blood collection service similar to our blood transfusion service. Fully equipped vehicles travel to different areas to collect blood from healthy 'volunteers'. I wonder how the 'volunteers' actually volunteer. Blood typing is carried out and the blood stored in a bank for emergency use. This is a far cry from the usual situation here, but one or two specialist centres are beginning to type and store blood and I'm sure this will be common practice in several years time. The rate at which veterinary medicine advances is quite mind-boggling. Often some new piece of equipment or technique will appear for the first time in an isolated paper - in a year or two, no article is complete without it. Typical examples are ultrasound imaging and pulse oximeters - never heard of in my student days but now commonplace.

In the commercial exhibition, we stare enthralled at state-of-the-art equipment like kids in a candy-store, before setting to work. Over the last few weeks, we have produced a list of queries regarding certain drugs and pieces of equipment. We begin with a visit to the manufacturer of our pulse oximeter. It has been behaving erratically occasionally. The salesman laughs when we say that we often cannnot tell if it is us or the machine that isn't right. This is evidently a common statement with some devices. The strange behaviour probably means that the machine's probe requires replacing, costing at least four times more than I expected. Being state-of-the-art isn't cheap. Chastened, we continue on our trip round the stands. Julie has strict instructions from Jay to handcuff me if I display a dangerous interest in anything expensive: it is easy to get carried away when faced with so many goodies. However, there is one purchase that I have planned for today. Computers have been trickling into veterinary life for many years and the trickle is becoming a flood. Many practices are fully computerised, with patient records called onto monitors in consulting rooms and all pricing, invoicing and ordering stock done electronically. Our computer use at present is confined to printing invoices, educational leaflets and letters, but educational CD-ROMs are becoming common and it is my intention to purchase some material today. Like textbooks, CD-ROMs are produced with information on most aspects of canine and feline medicine and surgery; but unlike textbooks, they are updated every few months. A down payment buys the starter discs and new versions are sent out bi-monthly. This seems a better idea than investing in expensive books which go out of date very quickly. After a demonstration of the product, I sign on the dotted line and leave the stand with my new toy.

During the day, we run into old friends and catch up on all the veterinary gossip. We meet two young vets who saw practice with me in our city surgery. All veterinary students are required to see practice with a number of surgeries during their holidays from university. This involves shadowing the vet for a period of time and occasionally being allowed to examine a patient first, or carry out a procedure under supervision. These two are now qualified vets making names for themselves in their chosen specialties. I slink off feeling as old as Methuselah.

The day passes in a flash and by 10 pm, we are back in

Edinburgh. The drive home makes us realise what horrendous weather we have missed. We have to make several detours to avoid roads blocked by flooding or fallen trees, before finally arriving home at midnight, exhausted but satisfied. Quite a day.

Saturday 4th April

On rising this morning, it is immediately apparent that yesterday's weather was quite something. It has rained steadily for the last twenty four hours and the results are dramatic. The field opposite the house is transformed into a lake crowded with several hundred geese - pink-footed geese - our usual winter visitors. Going up the track with the dogs, the air is filled with two sounds – more cackling geese and the roar of running water. A fast-flowing stream tumbles down each side of the track. We can even hear the roar of the burn at the far end of our field. The road leading east is closed by flooding and the one over the hill is blocked by a mudslide where the banking has collapsed. The fields which have been tended so carefully are now under several inches of water; a drain in one field has caved in, opening a canyon which could swallow a tractor. Perhaps we spoke too soon about Spring.

As usual after heavy rain, our tap water has turned a delicate brown like weak shandy. Our supply comes from a spring rising deep within the hill and is subject to the vagaries of the weather. During dry spells, it is sometimes worryingly sparse. Over dinner with friends in the evening, we compare notes - their water has taken on an interesting opaque appearance. A stream under the house can be heard thundering in the background as we eat. The next-door house was formerly a coaching inn whose basement was deliberately flooded to keep the beer cold. During wet weather, the present occupants rely on pumps to keep the rising water levels at bay.

Monday 6th April

Another day of torrential rain. The geese are having a wonderful time and the dogs have been swimming where they have never swum before. It is great sport for both Kippen and Fintry to run full tilt into the water, scattering spray everywhere. Jonno stands watching by my side, fearing for their sanity. There is possibly method in their madness, as they both receive a 'chittery bite' when they come home. This is a Scottish term denoting a small snack given to relieve the discomfort of a dip in bitter Scottish waters; all too familiar to those of us who spent frozen childhood holidays on the beaches of eastern Scotland.

Although Easter is a week away, today is a public holiday in Clayfern. Confusion over which shops are open and which are shut will now arise at regular intervals over the summer. As each small town in the area has their own local holidays, some businesses will close on local holidays; others will take national holidays. Today the grocer, the Post Office and the butcher are all shut, but luckily the chemist is open. I have a favour to ask of Karen the pharmacist. I have an epileptic patient on phenobarbitone, the drug of choice for this condition. Unfortunately, the fits are still ocurring with unacceptable frequency and it is time to try a new tack. We are going to try potassium bromide, an old-fashioned drug seldom used nowadays in human medicine. Sad to say, many effective human fit suppressants do not work well in our patients, but this one can be helpful. My wholesaler has supplied a jar of powder which needs dividing into dog-sized doses. I ask Karen if she could make up tablets; in this day and age, there is no call for this once necessary skill as all drugs come prepackaged, but amongst my collection of old medical instruments, there is a rather impressive brass pill-making machine complete with different sized moulds and I wonder whether she would like to relive her days at college spent concocting pills and potions from raw materials. However, Karen points out that we lack the necessary bulking agents and other additives. Instead, she offers to weigh out the powder into small envelopes of the correct dose. Practical, but somehow lacking mystique. Karen and her staff have been incredibly helpful to the surgery over the years - perhaps our requests for help with outlandish queries adds some variety to their day. As she works, we enjoy a joke - during times of war earlier this century, potassium bromide was the drug allegedly put in the tea of over -amorous servicemen on active duty. Perhaps we could establish a black market trade in Clayfern for anyone whose partner is a little too frisky!

Friday 10th April

Good Friday - not that it makes much difference in Clayfern: it is business as usual. We feel quite sorry for ourselves, remembering our days in England when today would be the start of a four-day break. However, being on holiday now would be a dubious benefit because the weather is still appalling. Torrential rain has given way to sub-zero temperatures, gale-force winds and flurries of snow. After their near constant presence last week, there is no sign of the geese today. They probably reckon that with weather like this, they might as well go home to the Arctic: I feel a kindred spirit as I rescue the washing - stiff as a board - from the far end of the field.

Although some people are on holiday from work, we have been extremely busy this week, both with consultations and routine operations. This might be expected as Gillian is also on holiday for a few days. It has been exhausting dealing with some busy surgeries single-handed. This is frequently the rule; moderately busy surgeries with a nurse, hectic surgeries without one. During quiet spells, we have our tricks to attract customers. Putting the kettle on is frequently successful, while nurse nipping to the shops often results in the waiting room filling as if by magic. Murphy's Law is definitely alive and kicking.

We have had quite a spate of emergency cases recently. Happily, Jude the traffic accident, Moss the splenic tumour and Jeff the rat-poisoned spaniel are all doing well. Meeny the slipped disc is also improving slowly. This week, Guinevere the diabetic cat has been staying at the surgery while her owners are on holiday. We do not board animals as a rule, but she is on insulin injections twice daily - a bit much for either friends or a cattery to cope with. The family have not had a holiday for five years, so I volunteered in a moment of weakness. She has been no trouble really. She is fed and injected at 7 am. and 7 pm. With visits in between to alleviate boredom and a final check at bedtime, she has taken up a fair bit of time. Thankfully, she is going home tonight.

A lighter moment during evening surgery brightens the day. We have a large, deep display window in Clayfern in which we produce displays on various pet care topics. For Easter, our subject is 'Caring for your rabbit' and to illustrate key points, there are a group of fluffy rabbit toys to one side. As I chat to a client at the reception desk, her toddler son waves at the window and says 'Hello.' 'Are you talking to your little furry friends?' I say cheerfully. The child shoots me a withering stare. *'Actually,'* smiles his Mum, 'He's talking to his sister in the pushchair outside.' This child is now convinced that the vet is a complete idiot.

Sunday 12th April

This has been a pleasant, relaxing weekend with few emergency calls. The sun has come out between snow showers so we have managed some bracing walks in the howling winds. Fintry was exhausted this morning after chasing a hare round the entire perimeter of the field. On her way back, a pheasant flushed from the long grass necessitating another long chase. Pheasants have a tendency to flap along close to the ground for several hundred yards before getting airborne, allowing the dog to think she is in with a chance. One day she almost got lucky and returned with a mouthful of feathers - *that* pheasant will be quicker off the mark next time. Fintry is a funny mixture, the product of a broken home. She was left alone all day and had taken to wrecking the house. No doubt her original owners punished her when they returned. This will only have made things worse. Unless a dog is chastised within half a second of performing an unwanted act, he doesn't make the connection. Video cameras have shown that punishing a house-wrecker after the event only makes them more likely to repeat the behaviour. When Fintry first came here, she was alternately as hard as nails or a submissive wimp. She had no personality whatsoever and reacted stonily to any attempts at play. It has taken over a year for the transformation to occur and we have spent a fortune on new beds to replace the vandalised ones. For the first six months, Kippen's luxuriant beard was gone, nibbled to a stubble by the anxious puppy. The soft old fella had just let her get on with it. Rescued dogs are often not easy, but given time and patience they will often become model pets. Although ostensibly a gun dog, she displays a disturbing tendency to want to murder rabbits, pheasants and other small creatures. As with many bullies, she is also a total coward. When the cattle are in the field next to the garden, she will dash out stiff- legged, hackles raised, barking loudly. As cattle do, they back off a few paces, then advance with curiosity to investigate this strange black porcupine. This is Fintry's cue to bolt for the safety of the kitchen! She has both a soft mouth and a vice-like grip as befit a gun dog. This was illustrated dreadfully one day when I spotted her chasing daddy-long-legs in the garden. Minutes later, she was discovered in front of the fire pulling the legs one by one from one unfortunate creature which had been carried *alive* from the garden.

On the other hand, our lovely Labrador-cross-something else, Kippen, is a gentle soul who would never hurt a fly. He has tended generations of poorly pups and kittens and was once seen lifting his foreleg to allow a spider to crawl past. They make a strange pair but hopefully, we think we see signs that Kippen's gentle ways are beginning to rub off on the young thug.

Monday 13th April

The Surgery From Hell this morning. No nurse, phone ringing constantly, even simple cases come with strings - 'While I'm here, could you just trim his nails, check his ears, provide an entire, unabridged history for the new vet when we move?' I begin to hate with a vengence the creak of the outer door admitting even more customers into the full waiting room. One waiting customer is Hector, with his faithful whippet Lena. Never in a hurry, Hector enjoys a busy surgery, engaging the captive audience in conversation on a variety of topics.

Hector is of aristocratic lineage - his forebears owned large tracts of the Highlands - but he is a simple soul who lives alone with Lena in a bothy in the hills. Various unidentified ailments prevent him from holding down a regular occupation, but he does odd jobs here and there to earn a crust. Trips to the surgery are an important part of his social round and, coincidentally, Lena always manages to produce the symptoms necessary for him to come. We seldom find anything wrong with her, but a thorough examination, a vitamin injection and twenty minutes' chat seems to work wonders. Recently, the frequency of his visits have decreased and, I am told by a mutual friend that he now has a 'Girlfriend'. Calling him in, I wonder if today's visit means that the course of true love is not running smoothly, but for a change, Lena actually has a problem; she has badly ripped a toe on a wire fence. We sedate her and install her in a kennel until surgery is finished. She is a well behaved character and will be no trouble to take to the farm surgery.

On the way home, the sun is shining on the river, which looks positively Mediterranean; only the white horses give the game away, the wind is still bitterly cold. There are some ewes with their lambs in the fields. At least they can shelter from the wind and get some sun today, but there have been losses over the last week. The older lambs are going around in gangs, playing 'tag' and 'king of the castle' on an old bale. I could watch them all day, but Sheila is waiting for me at the farm surgery. In our more irreverent moments, we have referred to Sheila as 'Nail' or 'Straw' as in 'last one in the coffin' or 'last to break the camel's back' as she has the ability to push a comfortably busy day over the edge. Just when we finish our ops list at a civilised time, Sheila will roll up with a car load of feral cats for treatment. Apart from emergencies, we have eased the problem by leaving time for her on two days of the week and training her to come then. It is hard to predict the workload in advance, since much of Sheila's work involves trapping unwanted feral cats and who knows which cats will go in the traps. The inclement weather has kept them away, so today we only have some of Sheila's own feral colony to attend to. Much of her work involves neutering the ferals then returning them to the site they came from. The locals are happy because the colony size remains static and, as long as there is a reliable food source, the cats enjoy a better quality of life. Inevitably, she ends up with some who cannot be returned for various reasons. They live out their lives in luxury on the farm. Many are totally unhandleable and need to be first caught in cat traps then transferred into crush cages before we can deal with them. Crush cages have a movable side so it is possible to squeeze the cat against one side of the cage to administer an anaesthetic injection. Luckily, modern anaesthetic cocktails can be injected into almost any part of the body. In the old days, anaesthetising a feral cat involved packing the cage into a large bin bag, then feeding anaesthetic gas into the bag. Not very pleasant for either cat or handler.

We attend to Lena first. Her toe is badly damaged and we end up amputating the whole digit, she will not miss it and no one will notice its absence once the fur has grown back. Hector will be pleased: he is guaranteed several legitimate visits to the surgery over the next two weeks until Lena is signed off. We finish Sheila's lot by early afternoon; time for a quick walk with the three musketeers (or stooges - whichever seems most apt). We bump into our Postie on the way out. It may be a bank holiday in England, but for our post it is business - and bills - as usual. I look suspiciously at a pair of sinister brown envelopes; 'Ach, dinnae worry,' says Pete, 'Thats jist yir passport and yir census form.' He is a marvellous postie who works far beyond the call of duty. He still delivers our post from our old address along the valley although we moved over six years ago and will gladly drop off boxes of eggs or jam from one neighbour to another along his route. When he retires, he will be sorely missed.

I pause for a moment's contemplation at the stones, while Kippen and Fintry indulge in a spot of formation rolling - not in anything unpleasant, just for the pleasure of it. Happy dogs! Cutting through the woods, I arrive back on the track without Jonno. This is unusual as he seldom strays far from my side. Looking back, I realise my mistake; deep in thought, I have threaded my way through newly growing brambles and wild raspberry canes. Being long-coated, Jonno hates heavy undergrowth, especially the prickly kind and is hovering uncertainly at the top of the hill. Time to climb back up through the creepers and reroute via an easier path.

We are not out for long - duty beckons. We have friends arriving tomorrow and are then 'fully booked' until mid May. It is lovely to see them and fun to go for expeditions to local attractions, but sometimes hard to reconcile with work especially when you work from home. Veterinary work carries on as usual, but paperwork often falls by the wayside when visitors are around. Today, I plan to attack my in-tray, reducing it to manageable levels so that it can be ignored for the next week. Resisting the beguiling blue of river and sky, I spend two hours whittling down the untidy pile.

After evening surgery, Jay and I help our friend Andy catch his sheep and trim its feet - a task requiring regular attention. Being downwind of the gentian violet foot spray, we are both transformed into passable extras for Mel Gibson's *Braveheart*. I'm sure that Andy did it deliberately. Unfortunately, it does not wash off so we will be getting strange looks over the next few days. Our visitors will be thinking that we have really gone native.

Tuesday 14th April

Today promises to be very busy; already full with routine ops, we have picked up two emergencies this morning. The first is Chloe, a ten-year-old Afghan hound. Last night she seemed a little off colour; this morning she is acutely ill - drinking gallons, vomiting and producing a vile discharge from her vulva. This is a condition known as *pyometra* - an infected womb, quite common in elderly bitches. The treatment of choice is to remove the pus-filled womb as toxins from the womb are being absorbed into the bloodstream and are affecting the kidneys, resulting in a very sick animal. Despite her illness, Chloe has never been a co-operative patient. Although she is friendly enough, any interference is invariably met with gnashing of teeth and manic struggling, so we routinely muzzle her before attempting any examination or treatment. Even today when she must feel lousy, the same approach is necessary before we can hoist her onto the table in an undignified tangle of legs. We set up a drip first to help flush the toxins from her system - this will run for most of the day both during and after the op. Then an anaesthetic injection into the canula sends her to sleep. After a minute or two exploring the exposed abdomen (hauling and hoicking as Julie irreverently calls it), the distended uterus appears. The organ is V-shaped, unlike the human uterus which is Y-shaped. Each horn measures about 9 inches and is swollen to around 4 inches diameter. Vile smelling discharge oozes from under her tail as I carefully manipulate the uterus from the abdomen. As long as Chloe can survive the trauma of the surgery, she will be a lot better off without it.

We have now to turn our attention to Muffin, a young spaniel who has been vomiting and is now not wanting to eat. There are many causes of acute vomiting, but sudden onset vomiting in an otherwise bright young animal raises the immediate suspicion of a foreign body. In the last year, we have removed carpet underlay, golf balls, peach stones, teats from babies' bottles and socks from the intestinal tract of several patients. Peach stones and teats are surprisingly common, as are the inevitable swallowed stones. One sock was a heavy-duty winter one which the patient had swallowed in one gulp when pursued by an irate (sockless) owner. The sock filled the entire stomach and was not hard to find during surgery. Unlike some cases, there is no helpful history of an unsuitable object being eaten by today's patient, but Muffin's abdomen is definitely uncomfortable and I can feel a thickened area which shouldn't be there. Opening into Muffin's abdomen, her small intestine is gathered in a clump rather like over-pleated curtains. This signifies a linear foreign body - not good news. The foreign material can cut deeply into the wall of the intestine causing serious damage. Our last case of this was a dog who swallowed an audiotape (Cliff Richard if I recall). Some of the tape protruded out of the dog's rear, but gentle pulling failed to remove the obstruction. Luckily, the owners did not pull too hard - they could have ruptured the gut and their pet would have died swiftly from peritonitis. We had to open the gut in three places to remove the tape. Muffin has clumps of some synthetic fibre along one foot of her intestine. This material will not slide at all and

71

requires five incisions to remove it all. The intestine is badly inflamed and we have to be guarded about Muffin's outlook. Although successfully through the surgery, it will be a few days before we are confident of her survival.

At 4.30 pm, we now have two patients on drips and more ops to finish so Linda receives a frantic phone call. Luckily, she is willing and able to take evening surgery - a real Godsend today.

Our poor visitors arrived in the middle of today's events and have been abandoned in the house with directions to help themselves to tea, coffee whatever. Luckily, they have been here before and are used to fending for themselves until Jay gets home. When Julie and I finally pause for a break, *they* make *us* a cup of tea!

Chloe's owner Alison has been ringing for progress reports during the day and at 7 pm, I suggest that she visits. Chloe is very difficult to manage, even a mere six hours after surgery. She has wet her bed, but any attempts to clean her up are met by snarling and snapping. If she responds well to Alison, she will probably be better at home. Alison is very capable and will call if she has any worries. She will return to the Clayfern surgery tomorrow for a check. Luckily, her owner's arrival entices Chloe to her feet. Her tail wags cheerfully and she heads purposefully, if a little unsteadily, towards the door.

Little Muffin is staying overnight. She is remarkably well and has already managed to eat a small portion of recovery diet. During the evening, I pop in and out regularly to check her. Our visitors are impressed by my appearance after each trip - it is snowing heavily and I am dusted with flakes even after the short distance between surgery and house. This was not what they had in mind when coming for an Easter break. We have been reminiscing to them about previous foreign bodies - always an intriguing topic for non-vets. We are surprised that Fintry has not required surgery yet to retrieve sundry objects - her digestion must be cast iron. Her most bizarre 'snack' was an entire bar of *Vanish* soap. She did not have the good grace to have even a mildly upset stomach. At the time, we joked about coming in to find an empty black skin in front of the fire.

At 11 pm, the pup comes out in the garden for an opportunity to spend a penny. Snow scrunches underfoot, the sky is deep indigo with cream highlights and, on the river, a small fishing boat glides purposefully towards Clayfern. The deep throb of the engine reverberates across the fields as the pup follows up interesting smells. No go with toileting however, so she is returned to her kennel where she promptly squats and floods her clean bed.

Wednesday 15th April

6.45 am: Muffin seems well and manages to perform outside instead of in her kennel. After she enthusiastically polishes off more recovery diet, I remove her partially chewed i/v line - I can see how she got her foreign body. While I unbandage her, she grabs at pieces of bandage and cotton wool and even has a go at the scissors. With her clean and settled, there's time for a walk with the dogs before her owners phone. There is no snow on the ground here, but it lies above a distinct line halfway up our field. The deer are lying in snow under a brilliant blue sky like a scene from Lapland. Their coats are very thick just now - just as well really, it is bitterly cold. Judging by the large number of tracks in the snow, the other residents of the hill have been active overnight.

Once Muffin has been collected, I have the rest of the morning off so can at last spend some time with our friends. We enjoy a pleasant few hours shopping in Stramar and a leisurely lunch before I have to be back on duty. After evening surgery, I need to visit Chloe who is refusing to get into Alison's car. We suspect that this is more recalcitrance than illness as she has had a reasonable day - she has eaten and has visited the garden several times, which is more than some patients manage after major surgery. Pyometra patients may require intravenous fluid the day after surgery and may not eat at all for the first twenty four hours. After a few false starts, Alison fits Chloe's muzzle so that antibiotic can be administered and the i/v canula removed. It has been left in place in case more fluid support is required. All seems well so Alison is left with antibiotic tablets for the next few days. Our next battle will be in ten days when the stitches are due out.

We are all settling down after dinner when an apologetic Andy telephones: he has a lamb with a broken leg, could I take a look? Since lambing is in full swing, we will travel to him. This is a treat for our friends who are enthralled by the lambing shed. Expectant ewes congregate in straw covered courts, while mums and offspring occupy individual pens. My patient is five days old with a broken foreleg. There are plenty of willing helpers to restrain the lamb on a straw bale while I apply Plaster of Paris to the leg. It is an uncomplicated fracture and should heal well in a couple of weeks or so. Mother is suspicious at first when her offspring returns to the pen sporting a smart white stocking, but after much snuffling and nuzzling, she recognises her baby and allows the squirming lamb to return to his favourite spot - the milk bar. Small tail wagging furiously, he butts his mother's udder and attaches limpet-like to a teat, stomping his plastered leg in excitement. There is always a special atmosphere in lambing sheds - the rustle of hooves on straw, bleating of lambs and the answering cries of the ewes and the unique smell of intermingled bedding, manure and wet fleece. Peaceful just now, but no doubt it was the scene of many a drama over the last fortnight. Andy has the characteristic appearance of shepherds at this time of year, unshaven and dead tired. Lambing is a twenty four-hour business - in fact rather more ewes tend to give birth during the night than in daylight hours. Although he has an assistant Andy seldom gets more than four hours undisturbed sleep at a time for the duration of the lambing season. Our occasional overnight callouts seem to pale into insignificance alongside such dedication.

Saturday 18th April

Our friends leave today. Typically, after three days of rain, snow, hail and freezing fog, the day dawns beautifully - warm sun with just the hint of a breeze. I hope they have enjoyed themselves despite being left in the lurch so often. Even breakfast is interrupted this morning when Sheila appears with a sick cat. This is not unusual: with such a large colony of cats, we regularly encounter virtually all infections known to man. Cats are notorious for harbouring many unpleasant bugs. Respiratory viruses can remain latent in the animal, ready to flare when the creature is stressed. These are readily spread to all in-contact cats. Other nasties such as Feline Leukaemia virus and Feline Immunodeficiency virus (a relative of human HIV) can lower the cat's resistance allowing them to suffer excessively from any passing infection. Today's patient is not eating and looks thoroughly miserable; she is snuffly and snotty with small ulcers in her mouth - typical cat flu. We give her antibiotics, vitamins, painkiller and some fluid, administered subcutaneously (under the skin), to correct minor dehydration. Careful nursing from Sheila should do the rest. We'll repeat the treatment tomorrow and every day until she bucks up.

Next to be seen is Moss, the splenic tumour patient and his three companions for their annual booster vaccination. It is nearly a month since he collapsed and required emergency surgery, but he is now looking extremely well. His owners know there is a high probability that the cancer will recur, so in the meantime, he is enjoying special privileges and enjoying life to the full.

Off to Clayfern for morning surgery. Little Muffin - Tuesday's foreign body - gave us a scare yesterday when she seemed quiet and ran a temperature. Thankfully she is back to her usual self today. With an operation such as hers, the risk of post-op infection is an ever-present danger. All vets have a shorthand method of referring to our patients; hence we have Moss the splenic tumour and Muffin the foreign body. Clayfern has a similar system; thus we have Donna the bank, John the Post Office and I'm Kate the vet.

The morning wears on with the usual variety of patients; Tammy McTavish is in to be weighed - another kilogram lost, along with her cough and stiff legs. She has not required any anti-arthritic tablets for three days. Her owner is thrilled and has shown her appreciation by bringing a surprise - an antique veterinary bottle for my collection of old instruments. This is a lovely gesture, although she has done all the hard work, sticking doggedly to the slimming diet and refusing the dog's strenuous attempts to wheedle titbits. Hungry dogs can be very persistent - this works in our favour, as there are few who cannot be won over by a doggy treat from the large jar in the consulting room. Cats unfortunately are too cunning to submit to such blatant bribery.

Our final task today is Bugs - a rabbit with a suspected dental problem. He began by dropping food, slobbering profusely and is now refusing to eat at all. This is a common problem in pet rabbits and is unwittingly caused by caring owners trying to be kind to their pets. Rabbits are designed to eat poor quality roughage such as grass and other herbage. Their teeth grow constantly but are continually ground down at an even rate by such material. Tame rabbits however are often fed a concentrate mix consisting of cereal, dried peas and grass pellets; with only a small amount of hay on the side. Not only do their teeth not get worn down, but the rabbits pick out the cereal and peas in the concentrate mix - which upsets the ratio of calcium to phosphorus entering the body. These two factors cause the cheek teeth to grow too long and at abnormal angles; the edges don't quite meet and sharp spikes develop which lacerate the tongue and gums causing great pain. The treatment is to nibble the spikes away with tooth cutters and file any remaining sharp edges. This is done under general anaesthetic. Rabbit mouths are not particularly roomy but finally the job is done. Poor Bugs - there is a deep groove cut into his tongue which will have been excruciatingly painful. The same procedure will need to be carried out every six to eight weeks from now on. The ideal feeding regime for pet rabbits is to try to mirror the situation in their wild relatives - roughage, roughage and more roughage.

Leaving a recovering Bugs, we depart on our afternoon walk. The hill seems extra steep today, probably because Julie has given me her cold. I am content to sit in contemplation at the 'thinking stones' while the dogs range far and wide. The stones are set in rough grass on a rock outcrop overlooking a valley; large meadows slope to a small stream at the valley bottom; on the far side, smaller fields are surrounded by irregularly patterned woods.

Behind the stones is a small stand of Scots pine, larches and an elderly beech tree. The snowcapped mountains and the river are in the distance. Sitting here drinking in the familiar view, I automatically relax. Like painting by numbers, the colours of the year are gradually filling in: grass sprouts through the dried vegetation, green shoots appear in patches throughout the woods. Several distant fields contain oil-seed rape, unpopular locally for its supposed ill-effects on hay fever sufferers. It smells quite pleasant from a distance, but is cloying close to. The yellow flowers have attracted butterflies, the first of the year. Eventually, we have to go home, an easier trip now that it is all downhill.

An early night seems called for by the nicely maturing cold. Perhaps a long sleep will chase it away. I am fast asleep when the phone rings. Midnight, I notice with a sinking heart, grabbing frantically for the receiver, the last thing I feel like is attending to an emergency. 'Is that the vet?' a gruff voice grunts.
'Yes it is' I answer,
'My bitch is due to whelp in the next day or so' comes the reply, 'What's the problem?'
'I'm just checking that there will be someone on duty.'
Some people have absolutely no consideration.

Sunday 19th April

Waking early this morning, I can barely see the end of the garden as fog shrouds the valley. While we head up the hill in the ghostly mist, the sun is a watery white disc struggling to penetrate the gloom. Uncannily, the stones are clear of the fog which lurks to each side like opaque curtains framing a stage, leaving a clear vista stretching to the bottom of the field. The dogs appear and disappear through the fog curtains like wraiths, while I bask in warm sunshine. Gradually, the fog begins to move, its cold fingers obliterating the sun. Some geese pass unseen overhead, advertising their presence with their usual cacophonous cries; obviously they haven't all gone to Greenland yet. Sunbathing over, we set off down the side of the deer pen. Honky, the white stag, is having trouble with an itchy groin. He repeatedly lifts his hind leg in an agitated manner before finally inclining his head and delicately scratching the offending spot with the tip of his antler. Heart in mouth, I silently gesture to the dogs and divert speedily into the woods - startle him now and he may well disembowel himself!

We arrive home early for the expected client - the whelping bitch from last night. After my rude awakening at midnight, I suggested that we check the bitch this morning and exacted a small measure of revenge by making the appointment as early as possible. (Usually people active at midnight tend to sleep in on a Sunday.) Of course, this involved my getting up early as well.

Our patient, a small spaniel, is unsettled, glancing uneasily at her hind quarters and panting intermittently. The pups can be seen moving in her abdomen and the foetal heartbeats are strong - no need for any veterinary interference as yet. Her owners take her home again with instructions to get in touch if they are worried. All seems in order, but even so, the prospect of an imminent whelping dictates how we should spend the day. It is sensible not to stray far from home, just in case, so we restrict ourselves to a short trip to nearby Drumdurn for lunch and a foray round the local antique shops. The early mist has cleared to leave a beautiful sunny day and as we pass Abbeygate Farm, three cows are in the small corner field with their new calves. They are all standing together by the gate - a typical group of new mothers with their pre-school offspring. In one antique shop in Drumdurn, there is a decorated pottery cat identical to one in Mrs Adam's living room - she has had it for a long time but cannot remember anything of its history. The shop keeper is very knowledgeable and I am looking forward to telling Mrs Adams the full story - her little pot cat was been made by an artist once involved in producing the famous Wemyssware range of pottery and will be worth a considerable amount of money. As we arrive home after a pleasant and relaxing day, a sea haar creeps stealthily up the river and out over the fields. A Curlew's eery cry completes the ghostly scene. The valley closes down around us once more.

At 8.30 pm, the spaniel's owner telephones as requested - she has had five pups and may have more to go. All seems well, so hopefully she will manage on her own. The relaxing effect of the day will evaporate in a flash if we have to perform a Caesarian in the small hours of the night. Off to bed again, with one ear cocked for the phone.

<u>Thursday 23rd April</u>

This has been a pleasant week, not as hectic as we have been over the last fortnight. It is nice to see ongoing cases gradually resolving - Jeff, our rat-poisoned dog has had yet another blood test which shows that his platelet and red cell count are gradually improving. In himself, he is very well and no longer has small haemorrhages on his gums. It is three weeks since he was first brought in with a problem. He will stay on the Vitamin K until the blood tests are back to normal. Hector has been in to morning surgery with Lena who is due to have her stitches removed. 'This dog is costing me a fortune,' proclaims Hector to the crowded waiting room on his way out, causing Gillian and I to exchange amused glances. Since Hector has shown absolutely no inclination to pay so far, this is not strictly true. As usual, he will pay eventually but until then, we are effectively footing Lena's bill.

Muffin, last week's foreign body, is also in for stitch-removal. She seems to be completely back to normal. After much thought, her owner has come up with an explanation of what the foreign material was - it seems that their neighbours had stored an old settee in the garage and have now discovered that some of the stuffing has been hauled out. Why do dogs eat such things? Lightning has struck again at home too - Fintry has eaten yet another bar of soap, lavender scented toilet soap no less. So far, there have been no side effects, not even lavender-scented diarrhoea! She really must have the digestion of an ox.

Talking of oxen, we have been kept busy this evening with the young cattle from the farm. Today, they were due to be turned out from the barn into the field. This usually passes off uneventfully, but this year's bunch are a wild lot. As they stampeded up the track towards the field gate, three calves failed to be diverted into the field and careered off into the woods. After much cursing, tractors are positioned strategically to block the track below the gate, a search party is assembled and sets off up the hill to drive the escapees back into the fold. We spend ninety minutes strung out in a line, advancing through the woods, struggling through dense undergrowth and scrambling over rotten logs and brambles. All to no avail. Marvelling at how three sturdy bullocks can vanish into thin air, we return home for a late supper. Glancing out after our meal, the three fugitives are ambling down the track to talk over the fence with their more co-operative comrades in the field. Fast action is necessary: I clamber up our field and along the top of the hill to make my way round onto the track above the cattle. Meanwhile, Jay drives slowly to below the gate and positions the car across the track. We cannot believe it when we meet with no cattle in between. Cattle are not generally known for stealth and cunning, but these three seem to be exceptions. At the least, they must have stood in total silence while I passed by - not typical cow behaviour at all. There is much hilarity at the thought of guerrilla cows adorned with camouflage leaves and charcoaled faces, melting quietly into the undergrowth. By now, darkness is falling so we head wearily homeward yet again.

We have no sooner collapsed onto the comfortable settee when the surgery bell rings. We do not encourage unannounced customers, especially at this time of night and I leap off the settee, grumbling mightily. An apologetic teenage girl stands on the doorstep clutching something wrapped in a woolly cardigan - a young rabbit who unwisely tried to cross the road as she drove homewards. The steep banking near Clayfern abounds with baby rabbits at this time of year and many come to grief. Rooks and buzzards regularly patrol the area - easy pickings. This little bunny is not dead, but cannot stand without falling to one side. There are no external injuries and his vital signs are good - the car has probably just dealt him a glancing blow. While the Good Samaritan holds the patient, I hastily grab some dried grass from the verge and make a cosy den in a kennel. An anti-inflammatory injection and a peaceful night will I hope, do some good.

Friday 24th April

I leave five minutes earlier than usual today to release last night's casualty who seems fully recovered this morning. His rescuer has marked where she picked him up, because releasing him there gives him the best chance of survival. Rehabilitating wild animals is always tricky, but a quick return to home territory gives the highest chance of success. The little bunny hops smartly off down the banking, white bob-tail bouncing in time with his movements. In country areas such as this, some people spend a lot of time killing such creatures which are regarded as pests, but it is a good feeling to think that his life has been saved this time. A house martin swoops and soars across the fields as I return to the car - a sure sign that summer is not far away.

Further evidence that the weather is improving comes during morning surgery in the shape of a cat with sunburnt ears. Typically, this occurs in cats with white ears, just as in fair-skinned humans. Initially the ear tips become pink and scaly, but, as in humans, this can progress to cancerous growth. One preventative option is to keep the cat in during strong sunlight; another is to apply sunblock cream to the areas at risk. This amuses many owners but is definitely worthwhile.

Another client this morning is Mr Keith, a local contractor. For someone in what must be a stressful occupation, he is always wonderfully laid back - in no hurry, all the time in the world for a chat. It seems that the local osteopath asked to borrow his fork lift truck recently and Mr Keith drove it along, expecting to be moving some heavy equipment. In fact, the fork lift was required to suspend a race horse above the ground while the osteopath carried out certain manoeuvres. This sounds rather drastic, but apparently the horse is now very much better. This osteopath has a good reputation and it would be very tempting to dispense with spinal surgery in favour of manipulations, but it is hard to give up the devil you know for an unknown (to me anyway) therapy.

Tonight, we remove half of Chloe's stitches before she gets silly and unco-operative. She has recovered *too* well from her pyometra op. Tomorrow or the next day, Alison will try to slip her muzzle on before coming in and we will remove the rest; softly,

softly..... as they say.

Apparently our AWOL cattle have been recaptured. They returned again to converse with their mates and were ambushed after some nifty footwork by Colin and his tractorman. Julie laughs when she hears the tale - there is a 'feral' cow in the woods where she rides her horse. She comes across it almost every day, quite happily cudding away with no intention of joining the herd.

Having spent most of yesterday evening trying to herd creatures *into* a field, we have spent this evening chasing one *out*. A roe deer has jumped into the red deer pen and cannot get away. This happens occasionally and requires one of us to discretely guard the gate against red deer escape while the others attempt to herd the roe through it. The panic-sticken animal does not understand the plan and charges frantically around the pen until at last it happens upon the open gate and bounds to freedom. The last we see of it is his striking white, heart-shaped rear disappearing into the woods. There are many roe deer around just now; they regularly graze on our back field and we frequently catch a glimpse of that unmistakable rear retreating through the trees. The dogs have given up chasing them - they are far too fast.

Thursday 30th April

This week is turning into a cat virus week. Several times the dreaded vague symptoms of depression, high temperature and precious little else have reared their ugly heads. If there is no response to symptomatic treatment in those patients, then lab tests are necessary. Such a blood test has picked up feline leukaemia virus in one of Sheila's cats - Tim, a sickly young male with laboured breathing. The name 'feline leukaemia virus' is somewhat misleading as the virus can cause not only leukaemia but a variety of other conditions - suppression of the immune system, anaemia and various cancers. In little Tim's case, the virus has almost certainly caused a tumour of the thymus; his outlook is hopeless so he is painlessly put to sleep. In a sizeable population of free-ranging cats like Sheila's, it is inevitable that several nasty viruses will be present and will cause problems from time to time. Both FeLv (feline leukaemia virus) and FIV (feline immunodeficiency virus) depend on close contact between cats for spread of infection, so the shy, unsocial cats are less likely to become infected. Some cats can throw off the infection but most are doomed. Cats with FeLv will generally not survive more than two years at the very most, but, like humans with HIV, cats with FIV can live for years until their immune system fails and they become prey to all manner of unpleasant illnesses. It is always a tricky moral situation when FeLv or FIV are diagnosed - it may be possible to treat the symptoms for varying lengths of time, but the patient constitutes a risk to any other cat with which it comes in contact. This produced a dilemma for the owners of Big Sam, a middle-aged cat, when he became unwell six months ago and tested positive for FIV. He recovered well after several days of treatment, but his owners felt guilty about allowing him outside especially since some young cats had moved in nearby. Staying indoors over winter was perhaps no hardship, but now the weather has improved, he tries to escape at every opportunity. Sam has had two further bouts of illness from which he recovered, but he is ill again today. The grim faces of his owners show that they have come to a sad decision; his bouts of illness are becoming more protracted and he is not happy being confined indoors so the time has come to call it a day.

We have diagnosed yet another deadly feline virus this week - feline infectious peritonitis (FIP). This virus is something of a diagnostic minefield. FIP comes in two forms - *wet* FIP and *dry* FIP. Both are fatal, although the course of the disease is longer with the dry form. The disease is caused by a corona virus for which it is possible to blood test for signs of infection. The diagnostic problems arise from the fact that there are several types of corona virus and if the blood test picks up infection with the virus, it is not possible to tell whether the one present is the killer disease or another, less harmful, one. The blood results need to be analysed in conjunction with the clinical signs before coming to any firm conclusions. Our patient this week has had several bouts of fever and depression and is sitting hunched up in his basket. Antibiotics and other supportive treatment have helped in the past, but now he seems worse than ever, producing copious diarrhoea and losing strength in his hind end. FeLv and FIV results were both negative, but he produced a high titre to corona virus. Coupled with the symptoms, a diagnosis of FIP is very likely and he too is put to sleep. The worry is not over for his poor owners as they have two other cats. Although fine at present, it is possible that they too may fall ill in the future. A blood test can tell whether they have been infected with virus but not whether it will develop into the fully blown disease. Cat viruses really are a major pain.

A long, relaxing walk up the hill is called for this evening to escape the depression that diagnosing FeLv, FIV or FIP brings. It is a glorious day and the river is sapphire blue against the backdrop of snow-capped hills. The flowering oil-seed rape mimics an alpine meadow. Our swans have finally abandoned their stance in the rape; for a time only their necks were visible above the growing crop, like white periscopes in a sea of green. The geese have definitely gone and more house martins and swallows have been seen. The changeover is usually quite abrupt - geese go; swallows and martins come: in autumn, the order is reversed. I saw the first pipistrelle bat of the year last night. Panting slowly up the side of the deer fence, I stop to watch three hares cavorting in the field below. Being quite far north, we get mad April hares instead of March ones. These three are leaping, boxing and literally haring round in tight circles in their wild mating antics.

Honky the stag looks surprisingly naked - he has shed his antlers. The remainder of the walk turns into a search for the discarded headgear. We have found them every year since Honky first came to replace the old red stag and the hunt has become an institution. A callow youth in the early days, his first antlers resembled long curved stilletos with only a solitary branch near the base. Now he is a magnificent beast and each antler is two foot long, nearly eleven pounds in weight with six branches (or points) from the main shaft; a six pointer - a prime stag. I feel quite proud of our big pal; he must feel much better not having to carry that lot about. Holding the antlers high to repel the dogs' attentions, I triumphantly bear them home to show Jay. We will compare them with last year's and see how much he has grown. A cheerier end to a rather depressing day.

Friday 1st May

Today has been encircled on the calendar and imprinted on my mind for a while now. I have been asked to give a talk to the students at the nearby veterinary college. It has been hard to devote much time to my presentation with the pace of life being as it is and I had kept this morning free of routine work to marshal my thoughts, practice the speech and leisurely make my way to the college in good time. BUT this was not to be. For the last few days, a little cross collie - Ben Briggs - has been attending the surgery. He has had diarrhoea and is running a high temperature which refuses to respond to treatment. A blood sample has yielded little fresh information and we have to admit that we don't know exactly what is wrong with him. Last night, Ben had a fit and began to exhibit an array of worrying neurological signs. Linda administered several drugs and installed him in a recovery kennel on a drip, but this morning his condition has worsened. He is unable to stand, or even to sit up without support. His best chance is for him to go to the vet college where they have the expertise and equipment to perform the extra tests which we feel he might need. So, most of the morning has been spent contacting Joan Briggs, then the vet college, then Joan again, writing up all the relevant notes and preparing the little dog for the journey. He looks anxious as we stretcher him to the car and install him next to an equally anxious Joan. We all suspect that his outlook is probably bleak, but Joan wants to give him every chance. We will be crossing our fingers and toes for the next few hours.

Morning surgery is also particularly busy today, especially as we are now running horribly late. One call sounds intriguing: 'I've just come in and my dog's legs have separated from his body.' Resisting the temptation to be humorous, Gillian suggests that he is brought to the surgery as soon as possible ('Bring his legs as well!') The poor old dog is in a sorry state, there is no muscle left in his hind legs and he does the splits as he tries to walk. The combination of an exceptionally long walk and a thorough soaking in a downpour yesterday has reduced him to this. Painkillers will improve matters a little, but his owners will have to change his lifestyle somewhat in the future; he is an old man and will have to take life a lot easier from now on.

All too soon, it is time to leave for the city. A quick change of clothes and into the car, dropping the pager off at Linda's on the way. The talk goes better than expected; I am not a natural speaker and would rather face a brace of savage Rottweilers than stand in front of an audience, but today has been so busy that there has been no time to get nervous. Some intelligent questions from the audience, then - *at last!* - free of the nagging anxiety that has been lurking under the surface for the last few weeks. *Don't give up the day job.* Before heading home, I stop off to see Ben in the small animal hospital. It really is a coincidence that we are both here on the same day. He has had several tests and the most likely theory is that he has suffered a haemorrhage within his spinal cord. This condition is rare and appears to occur for no apparent reason. Ben is still unable to stand and the specialist thinks that his outlook is poor, but more test results are still to come and he will remain under treatment in the hospital over the weekend. More finger and toe-crossing is in order and Joan Briggs faces one of the longest weekends of her life. It is really a scary thought - one minute you are fine, then the next a spinal bleed leaves you paralysed.

Tuesday 5th May

The drive to Clayfern is particularly beautiful at this time of year. Whereas April colours the valley yellow and green, May is the month for pink. Campion and cow parsley grow in profusion from the verges and driving through the town, its origins as a fruit growing centre are betrayed by the abundance of pink and white blossom in many gardens. A stop is required at Abbeygate Farm to allow the goose to take her goslings across to the pond, closely followed by the Muscovy duck with her yellow and black ducklings.

The pleasant start to the day continues with a call from Joan Briggs - Ben is a little better and has managed to stand unaided for a few moments. If he continues to improve, he may get home for the weekend. This is great news - Joan loves her little dog - but this will hit her hard financially. The battery of tests and the intensive care will be costly. We decide to start a fund to help pay for Ben's treatment; both Joan and Ben are popular, so hopefully we might be able to ease the load a little.

More rabbits in today for vaccination against myxomatosis. Rabbits are becoming increasingly popular as pets and the veterinary profession is getting to know more and more about them - their behaviour and their diseases. At the turn of the century, horses were the main subject of study, then farm animals gradually assumed more importance. Small animal medicine was often considered no more than an irritating diversion from large animal work. Nowadays, the situation is almost reversed with more vets involved in small (or companion) animal work than with farm work. Cats are no longer regarded as small dogs and rabbits are gaining major attention. They are pleasant creatures who have had rather a raw deal in the past. This morning's owners have an added task for me - to sex their latest litter of babies. Small bunnies can sorely test your accuracy and I spend plenty time dividing the brood into male and female groups - then double check on returning them to their box. It is not uncommon for owners to end up with unexpected litters when two 'females' are put together. Opening the door for the assorted children carrying assorted boxes from the surgery, Mrs Cassidy finally enters the waiting room. 'I expect their name was Warren!' she comments drily. Mrs Cassidy is bringing our job for the morning - a cat demat, common at this time of year. Many long-haired cats refuse to allow their owners to groom them and obviously cannot cope themselves, developing felt-like matting over various areas of the body. This is uncomfortable for them and gives parasites plenty of scope. As Muffin is not known for his patience and placidity, he is sedated before we set about him with the clippers. Clippers are safer than scissors as the mats form very close to the skin. Muffin is badly matted, the whole coat clumped together and coming away in one piece - much like a sheep's fleece, leaving a bald but more comfortable cat. We are left with a magnificent black pelt which seems a waste to throw out so a scurrilous plot is hatched. After a quick spray with insecticide, the fleece is ceremoniously wrapped in tissue paper and put into a box with the following label:

The Acme Baldness Company Bespoke Hairpiece

It's as simple as ABC! Keep in the warm; keep out the wet; blend in with Border Collies! bring back the Ewe of the sixties!

On her way home, Julie anonymously delivers the parcel at shepherd Andy's door. It has to be admitted that he is a trifle trichologically challenged. We will now wait in dread of repercussions.

The rest of the day passes uneventfully and, taking advantage of the evening, we set off with the dogs heading for the woods at Peeswit Point. On the way we pass legions of hairy caterpillars on their way across the road. These are creatures on a mission - unfortunately a suicide mission for many. I think they eventually become tiger moths - we call them hairy bears. The woods are gorgeous at this time of year. Fresh new leaves are everywhere and underfoot are swathes of bluebells, wood anemones and miniature violets. The birdsong is slightly resonant under the canopy - as if in a cathedral and the whole effect is very peaceful and relaxing. Shards of sunlight dancing on the water penetrate the trees as we near the point. The view here is stunning: we have emerged onto a grassy bank - the river is almost a mile wide here and although we are bathed in evening sunlight, a mist is descending on the hills on the opposite side. The tide is in and we have the beach to ourselves. Perfect! We scrunch up the shingle beach while the dogs chase waves and retrieve various objects to their hearts' contents, then retrace our steps as the sea haar slowly closes in. On the way home, the smoke from our small group of cottages rises lazily into the night air. Although the days can be warm, the nights are still cold and the woodburners will be going for a few more weeks yet.

Relaxed after our walk, we settle down with mugs of hot chocolate but the peace is shattered by a phone call at 9.40 pm - Lucy - a nine year old Labrador is fitting continuously. Ten minutes later, they carry the jerking, slobbering creature into the surgery. She is soaked in saliva and urine and grunts as her legs thrash spasmodically. Such epileptiform fits look agonising for the patient, but as far as we are aware from human epileptics who behave in the same way, the patient loses consciousness from the moment the fit starts until it ends. The trouble is that Lucy's fit is not ending - she is in what is called *status epilepticus*. This is a very serious situation: the body temperature rises, the patient becomes dehydrated and exhausted and death will inevitably occur unless the fitting can be stopped. Immediately, I insert an intravenous canula and inject a dose of diazepam. Inserting a canula into a jerking, convulsing leg is far from easy, but her owner does a sterling job of keeping it relatively steady. There is no response to four doses of diazepam. We have to stop the fitting or Lucy's heart will fail. After a hurried discussion with her owner, I give her an anaesthetic injection, thread an endotracheal tube into her windpipe and connect her to the machine to receive oxygen. At last the spasms subside. It is now 10 pm; Lucy's temperature is 107°F (normal is 101-102°F) and her heart rate is 230 beats per minute (normal is 70-120). Her body is under tremendous stress and it is vital for us to reduce her temperature. She is connected to a saline drip to combat dehydration and the ECG monitor is attached to warn of heart irregularities. We soak her with wet towels and direct the fan straight at her. It is going to be a long night. Lucy's owners go home now as there is nothing further for them to do, I just need to monitor her and wait. At 10.40 pm her temp is 103.3°F and heart rate 180. I switch the fan off and stop the cold towels. Over the next hour, her temperature drops to normal and her heart rate returns to normal range. She has had no more anaesthetic but is still out for the count. Reactions to anaesthetics and similar drugs can be exceedingly unpredictable in fitting patients. At midnight, Lucy's temperature is continuing to drop and it is necessary to take active steps to warm her up, wrapping her up in warm blankets. Her normal body thermostat is completely up the spout and it is up to me to keep her stable. There is also the worry that she may begin to fit again as the anaesthetic drug wears off. You can't relax for a minute with these cases. From 2 am, her temperature and heart rate remain stable and she shows some signs of returning consciousness - but no more fits as yet. At 3 am., she is returned to her kennel and I return to the house to doze for a few hours. We have a baby alarm which is left by the kennel, the receiver stays by my bed and should alert me if Lucy begins to fit again.

Wednesday 6th May

7 am: Not much change in Lucy - temp. and heart stable, still flat out.Between our other tasks during the morning, Julie and I are kept busy maintaining the drip and keeping the patient dry and comfortable. She has passed urine, a sign that her kidneys are functioning as normal. Good. At 2.30 pm her owners visit and at 3 pm, she lifts her head. At 4.30 pm she laps some water. At 6.30 pm she can stand unaided and totters a few steps before eating some recovery diet. Shattered, I judge that her owners can cope with her tonight, so home she goes with a supply of phenobarbitone tablets. She will be on these fit suppressants for the rest of her life. I hope that the last twenty four hours will not have been in vain.

On a lighter note today, I was surprised but pleased this morning in Clayfern to find an envelope through the door containing some money from Hector in part payment of Lena's bill. During evening surgery, Gillian received a panic-stricken phone call from Hector: *had we banked the money? If not then please could he have it back as the car had failed its MOT test and needed vital (expensive) work to keep it on the road!* I thought it was too good to be true.

Saturday 9th May

This weekend sees Julie and I off to another conference. This one is held in a market town only an hour from Clayfern so travelling is easy and it is a low cost way to keep up to date. The subject this year is Ophthalmology - the study of eyes and their complaints - a favourite topic of mine, so I am looking forward to the day. Our marathon session with Lucy has left me a little jaded, but hopefully I'll perk up as the morning progresses. Lucy is doing well so far, no more fits, still quiet but getting more normal from day to day.

Ophthalmology is full of exotic sounding names such as *symblepharon, epiphora,* even *iris bombe* (pronounced bombay*)* which keeps us general practitioners on our toes. Years of using simple language to explain matters to clients have taken their toll and it requires thought to remember what such technical terms mean. Veterinary medicine as a whole is also increasingly awash with conditions shortened to initials - FLUTD, PRA and HGE to mention but a few and I occasionally need to covertly read further into an article to discover what it is talking about. Today's lecturers are excellent and add some colourful language of their own - the *spot welding* effect of a laser on a detached retina; the *jack hammer* effect of a technique known as phaecoemulsification which effectively breaks up and removes a cataractous lens.

Ophthalmology is a very visual subject. The views into the eye are spectacular and often strikingly beautiful - frequently reminiscent of scenes from outer space. There can be violet blues, turquoise, greens, yellows and flaming orange all covering an area at the back of the eye no bigger than one inch diameter. It is all too easy to drift off into a daydream while staring at such images and it requires effort to keep concentration going. The chap next to me actually falls asleep - a conditioned response to many years spent in warm, dark lecture theatres.

A look round the commercial exhibition and a chat to old friends completes a pleasant morning and there is still time to enjoy what has become a beautiful sunny day. There is plenty of wildlife up our hill this afternoon. Fintry chases two roe deer from the flowering rape field and all three disappear at speed over the brow of the hill. She comes back converted into a yellow Labrador by the rape flowers. The roe deer are at their most territorial just now as their young are due next month. Fintry's two have probably been chased off from a superior territory in the woods. Sitting at the stones, the foreground is carpeted with forget-me-nots, violets and small white flowers giving the area an alpine effect. Even the stones are covered in various shades of lichen - orange, white and browny-grey - a sign of clean air apparently. The crickets are 'cricking' which they only do at temperatures of more than 60°F - official confirmation that it *is* warm. Rabbits and a hare are also chased by Fintry and, on the way home, a large red squirrel narrowly escapes up a tree leaving two baffled dogs staring skywards, seemingly unaware that the squirrel is four trees farther along already. The only snag about walks with dogs is that our best views of wildlife tends to be of their rear ends as they disappear into the distance. On the way home by the deer fence, a brief encounter with Honky reveals that his new antlers are growing already - two inch knobs protrude from his forehead covered in soft furry vascular skin.

In the evening, I pop into Clayfern to visit Ben Briggs, home from the vet school yesterday. He is cheerful and pain free and although still very unsteady, can walk a few steps like a puppet being worked with strings. It is marvellous to see him back as none of us really expected him to survive. I show Joan how to carry out physiotherapy on his limbs to keep him in shape and she will keep walking him a little each day.

On the way home, a freshening wind is whipping the blossom from the trees like a pink snowstorm and pink drifts lie at the side of the road the last of the blossom for another year. Approaching home, the sky is streaked with several layers of colour - *just like the drainage angle of the eye through a goniolens,* I muse, turning into the drive. I think I must be tired!

Tuesday 12th May

A busy ops list today, much of it routine neuterings. To amuse ourselves, Julie and I indulge in a game of Mrs Cassidy's Tennis. This mind-expanding exercise originates from a memorable consultation with Mrs Cassidy which went something like this:

K. 'When did you first notice that he wasn't well?'
Mrs C. 'Well, on Tuesday I went to Stramar then on Wednesday, I went to the W.I. at Drumdurn.'
K. 'So perhaps Thursday?'
Mrs C. 'He's got a funny look in his eye.'

K. 'Is he eating or drinking?'

Mrs C. 'It's not like him at all...........'

And so on! The object of the game is to reply with a completely unrelated statement and is surprisingly difficult.

After much practice,we can achieve rallies of up to nine or ten. An example:

> J. 'I'm going to Stramar tonight.'
> K. 'I prefer green.'
> J. 'Thursday.'
> K. 'I wouldn't mind a BMW.'
> J. 'Marks and Spencer.'

The morning passes pleasantly enough until Julie reports a hitch with our autoclave (steriliser); it seems to have developed a fault. We swing into our usual problem-solving mode which basically involves pressing as many buttons as possible, then switching the machine off, then switching it on again. We observe its operation from behind the door frame, armed with a broom handle to switch it off if it does anything peculiar. Strangely enough, this seems to correct the fault but I resolve to get an engineer to service the machine as soon as possible. Operating at twice environmental pressure and heating water to 135°C, it doesn't do to take any risks.

'I must get it serviced,' I declare, 'I wouldn't have a leg to stand on if it blew up some patients.'

'Or arms or hands either,' jokes Julie like a flash.

Playing Mrs Cassidy's Tennis is obviously improving her response times.

Amongst our ops this morning, there is a cat's ear flap to be removed - cancer is eating deep into the outside edge and amputation is the only answer. The end result looks particularly smart, having been stitched with material no thicker than a human hair acquired courtesy of an aquaintance who is a plastic surgeon. The cat is handed out to his owner wearing a plastic collar which prevents tampering with the wound and we congratulate ourselves on a job well done. Pride comes before a fall, they say ...

The day's operations carry straight through until after four pm. Just time to whip the dogs into the back field for a quick run. The dogs gambol and play in the lush grass and the clock speeds round to evening surgery time. As I head to the car, I realise to my horror that the pager is missing, probably dislodged when playing with the dogs. No time to search for it now, I just hope it doesn't rain before I can search for it. Typically, tonight I have an appointment at the hairdresser's. While I'm there, Jay rings with an emergency call - the ear flap cat has got his collar off and has made a mess of his wound. It is bleeding, could I please return the call. The hairdresser waits patiently while I talk to the owners. By now, the bleeding has abated and the owner feels happy to keep an eye on the situation tonight and will bring the cat back in the morning. I apologise to the hairdresser, commenting that ear wounds can bleed like stuck pigs. 'You don't need to tell me *that!*' she retorts, poised for action with scissors at the ready. A worrying thought. A speedy exit to go on the pager hunt is thwarted by yet another emergency call, a vomiting dog. Not serious however and at last, I am free to search for the pager. By now it is nearly 9 pm and a soft mist is descending on the valley. The dogs are thrilled with the unexpected outing as we retrace our steps up the field. The grass is knee high and very wet, encouraging large black slugs to the surface. Unfortunately, in the fading light they bear a slight resemblance to the shiny black pager case and several false hopes are raised before I realise my mistake. Eventually, I use the mobile phone to order a test page, standing in saturated vegetation straining my ears for the familiar beeping. It is ironic - most times I dread the sound, now I am desperate to hear it. The usually appealing rustic noises - foxes barking, birds singing, sheep and cattle calling - assume cacophonous proportions and I only dimly catch the tail end of a beep. Even the dogs are a little bored by now. Eventually, the search is successful and we all squelch homewards. The end of a very long day.

Wednesday 20th May

A trip to the dentist today. Like me, he used to work in a large practice in a city, but has forsaken the financial rewards and stresses for life in a smaller pond. We agree that we enjoy our work more when not perpetually tired and interesting cases become challenges - not problems. We swap one or two anecdotes about mutual clients and I escape with only one filling.

In the main, veterinary dentistry is much more basic than the human variety involving less restorative work. There are veterinary specialists who carry out more complicated procedures and we are lucky to have one only an hour away to whom I recently sent Duke, a young Labrador with badly damaged teeth after a frenzied attack on a steel door. Rather than remove all his canine teeth, he has had root canal treatment to prevent infection spreading into the roots and the final appearance is excellent. It was not cheap however - it's lucky that he is insured.

Kippen has had his annual shearing today, courtesy of Gillian. His lovely dark coat is gone and he looks strangely pale and naked, like a shorn sheep. He is rechristened the silver ghost and friends are pre-warned so that they can try not to laugh and hurt his feelings. Whatever he looks like, he feels very much better and it is well worth doing.

Yesterday and today have been quiet at the surgery. Most other businesses in Clayfern are peaceful as well. This phenomenon occurs quarterly for a few days - when the telephone and electricity bills coincide. The lull never lasts long and is a pleasant break which we quite look forward to.

Unfortunately, our walk options are limited at this time of year. Thigh-high grass and crops are no fun to walk through unless bone dry and nettles are rampant in the woods so we have to stick to the track round the hill. Fintry derives some stange satisfaction from haring through the wet crops at high speed becoming covered in yellow rape blossom. Cow parsley and campion cover the sides of the track and the swallows are taking advantage of the insects attacted by the crops. The barley heads are formed now and the field moves in waves like a green sea as we pass. The year seems to be thundering by. Before long we will be thinking about trips to the real seaside.

Monday 25th May

Another bank holiday - except for Clayfern. The traffic is lighter on the way to morning surgery so *someone* is obviously not working but most of Clayfern is - apart from the bank. Even the kids are at school - they have *next* Monday off. Very confusing.

The first patient of the morning is Boots McKelvie, a young cat whose eyes have suddenly changed colour according to her owner. In fact, Boots has a condition known as *uveitis,* an inflammation of the *iris* - the coloured part of the eye. She is well in herself, but several serious infectious agents can give rise to this condition so we decide to take a blood sample to check for the main four possibilities. The little cat is the apple of her owner's eye and has already been fully vaccinated, spayed and microchipped. She also has the most beautiful nature. 'In that case, its almost bound to be something serious,' Gillian comments quietly as we take our blood sample - she is all too aware of Murphy's Law. We send the little cat off with steroid eye drops to be administered several times daily. The lab results will be back in a few days. Let's hope that Gillian is wrong.

Finally, I admit a long-haired cat for a demat. This one is the opposite of Boots - a particularly stroppy individual and I have prepared for the job by borrowing one of Sheila's crush cages. These are indispensable for dealing with feral cats, the movable side holding the cat firmly against the outer side through which an anaesthetic drug can be injected. Immeasurably better than being squashed under heavy blankets - with the risks of possible escape, or damage to the operator. A truly wild cat is much harder to handle than a difficult dog, having claws as well as teeth at their disposal and they can inflict serious injuries. Not to be taken lightly.

The demat goes without incident, but the day deteriorates

from then on - Sheila has been busy. She has had a call from a local farm overrun with cats, an all too frequent scenario. Cats have an awesome breeding capacity; three or four unneutered cats one year can transform into an unruly colony of twenty or thirty the next. Food is insufficient, diseases flare, the worn out females begin to produce sickly or dead kittens and the colony becomes progressively unhealthier. There is frequently a depressing lack of responsibility from people at the centre of these situations - 'Not my cats', 'Someone else's problem' are commonly heard comments. Sheila's mission is to try to sort out the problem (even though they are not her cats either). This involves rehoming young kittens, neutering the adults and returning them to the site if this is possible. So today, we have eight cats to neuter and return. There are also fourteen kittens to be checked over - they are hopefully young enough to tame and rehome. The adult ferals are in a sorry state. They have been caught in humane traps but are not surprisingly upset at being confined and the cages are flooded with urine and watery faeces. They have been drinking the calves' milk and severe diarrhoea is the result. The surgery is filled with four sodden reeking traps containing sodden, reeking cats. They are not in the best of condition; there is obviously not enough food for twenty two cats. The day wears on as we neuter, worm, de-flea, treat minor ailments and clean up continually. Each cat has the tip of its left ear removed to identify it as neutered. It is possible to tell that a male cat has been neutered from the outside, but many females have been operated on unnecessarily when this simple precaution has not been taken. At last, the cats are all done and Sheila departs to settle them in her barn overnight. She will monitor the farm where they live, advise the owners on feeding and check occasionally to make sure the cats are looking healthy. It is very fortunate that people such as Sheila exist, to take on the responsibility where others will not.

Thursday 28th May

Our summer season is well on the go and cases are coming in thick and fast. Seasonal itchings, vaccinations, demats and war wounds from fights or encounters with wire or glass make summer our busiest period. Good weather often seems to go to some clients' heads and trips to the vet come last on their list of priorities. We stayed open half an hour late last night to see a client who reported her cat was being sick but couldn't make it to the surgery during normal hours - she neglected to say that the cat had been being sick for *two months*. Gillian had a request for two 'emergency' groomings today - the owners are moving house tomorrow, hardly an unforseen situation. It has become quite common to receive calls after surgery hours as everyone in the family has been too busy to bother trying to attend during surgery hours. After working a ten-hour day, it is a little irritating to be asked to attend to routine cases when it would be nice to be relaxing - after all, the phone can herald an emergency call at any time of the night anyway. Most of our clients are considerate, but we seem to be having a run of folk who are just plain difficult. Of course, things always seem worse when you are tired and constant busy surgeries and out of hours calls do wear a person out.

Yesterday evening surgery produced a genuine emergency - Jake Lafferty, a twelve-year-old Labrador - not eating, not drinking, vomiting and desperately quiet and dejected. His owner had noticed that he was drinking a lot earlier in the week, but was now refusing both food and drink. A dribble of urine on the floor almost certainly gives us the diagnosis - the sample is loaded with glucose and substances known as *ketones*. A blood sample confirms the diagnosis - Jake is diabetic. Not only that, he is *keto-acidotic*. When the body cannot make use of the glucose in the bloodstream (as it is lacking insulin to allow the glucose to get into the cells), it attempts to produce an alternative source of energy by breaking down other body tissues such as fat. This breakdown yields toxic by-products - ketones - which are released into the blood making the patient feel nauseous and unwell. If Jake was to have any chance of survival, aggressive treatment was necessary. So, last night, he stayed in the surgery. Jay helped while I inserted an intravenous catheter and ran copious quantities of fluid into him. His veins were very hard to catheterise but the fluid was vital so I spent most of the evening sitting by his kennel to ensure the drip ran smoothly. He lay with his big head on my lap while I listened to the radio and caught up on reading veterinary articles. After four hours, he was much brighter but his glucose levels were sky high, so he was started on hourly injections of fast-acting insulin. Before each injection, it was necessary to check his glucose levels. Most dogs do not object to the insertion of an ultra-fine needle to collect a drop of blood, but Jake proved a real big baby - every sampling produced major sulks - his head was removed from my lap and he retreated to the farthest corner of the kennel. I resorted to applying local anaesthetic cream before each sampling. After three hours (i.e. 1 am.) Jake's glucose level is within normal range - probably for the first time in days - so we can switch to injections every six hours. Unfortunately, extreme vigilance is still important to make sure that the glucose level does not drop too far and starve the brain of energy. A hypoglycaemic episode such as this can lead to coma and death if not treated promptly. The rest of the night was therefore spent desperately trying to catch some sleep between the frequent shrilling of the alarm clock which heralded another sampling session.

At eight this morning, Jake was considerably brighter than his vet, accepted a good breakfast and was switched to a longer acting insulin. He has gone home this afternoon. He will be fed at 4 pm to coincide with the peak insulin activity. Coincidently, his owner is a diabetic so explanations are very much easier than usual.

Luckily, the rest of the day has not been wildly busy. Our only operation is a feral cat who looks like she has sprouted wings. Once anaesthetised and removed from the crush cage, the protrusions are identifiable as two of the plastic rings which hold beer cans together. The cat has somehow got both front legs tangled, leaving two plastic circles sticking out above her shoulders. The plastic has cut deep grooves through the soft skin of her armpits. We hope these will heal now that the plastic is removed, but will have caused the cat much needless pain and fear. Carelessly discarded non-degradable materials such as this can cause many problems for both wild and domesticated animals. At least domestic animals are spotted early, but wild creatures may die a lingering death through injuries inflicted. There are many examples - many wildfowl have limbs literally amputated by gradually tightening lengths of plastic fishing line; and I have seen a fox starved almost to death when its lower jaw and tongue got caught in an old tin can. A more amusing incident befell my old adversary Bugsy Smith, an unpleasant, snappy little terrier. His lower jaw became stuck within a glass fish paste jar and Bugsy's attempts to bite were translated into a series of dull clonks. Even after an anaesthetic, it took several minutes of lubricating and manipulating before the jar eventually slid off.

Good news about Boots McKelvie, our cat with uveitis. Her eyes are clearing and all the tests are negative. This puts her into by far the largest category of causes of uveitis - idiopathic - a medical euphemism which means that the cause is unknown. Even in this advanced day and age, there are still a surprisingly large number of idiopathic conditions, showing that we don't always know as much as we think we do.

Friday 29th May

The situation that all single-handed practitioners dread has occurred today. A bout of suspected food poisoning has left me unable to work. Although also affected, Jay gets on the phone to try to find a locum at short notice. In this job, we cannot just put up a closed sign. Both Linda and Moira are already occupied, but we manage to contact Alastair, an old friend, who kindly sets off immediately on the hour's trip to the Fern surgery. Coping with the situation requires planning with the precision of a military exercise. Gillian greets clients at Clayfern and either reroutes them to the farm surgery if the case is pressing, or arranges another appointment for tonight or tomorrow. Everyone is very understanding; 'There's a lot of it about,' confides old Mrs Bruce, 'all the dogs in Strathdollar have it!'

After another phone call, Julie arrives early to explain the delay to clients arriving at the farm surgery with animals booked in for operations. Through a nauseous fog, I consider yet again how lucky I am to have Jay. Being attached to a vet is never easy - above-average separations and divorces bear testimony to the trail of broken appointments, delayed meals and cancelled outings that are the lot of the vet's other half. Alastair arrives and, after a briefing from Julie, makes a start on the day's ops list. Exhausted after a sleepless night and relieved that all is under control, I lapse at last into a deep, dreamless sleep. After half a day, I am recovered enough to manage evening surgery and Alastair departs for a prior engagement. I am incredibly grateful to him for coming. Evening surgery is packed in accordance with Sod's Law as quoted by Gillian -

'There's nothing like an off-colour vet to guarantee a full house.' Finished after what seems an eternity, I retreat to languish in front of the woodburner for the evening. It is quite amazing that we are nearly in June but still need the warmth of the fire in the evenings.

Saturday 30th May

Another packed surgery but thankfully no pressing emergency cases to eat into the rest of the day. The good news is that Jake the diabetic Labrador is still doing well. He is in this morning - as he will be for the next few days until we work him up to the optimum dose of insulin. The routine is the same each day - his owner, Colonel Lafferty, collects a urine sample first thing in the morning then feeds Jake half of his daily food allowance before coming to the surgery where I check the urine sample, possibly take a blood sample, then instruct Colonel Lafferty on the technique of drawing up and injecting the insulin. Life is so much easier for human diabetics such as the Colonel - he has pre-loaded insulin pens for himself so is a little rusty on drawing up the correct dose, but is learning rapidly. Over the last few days, we have been intrigued by the variety of containers in which our urine sample has appeared. So far, there has been a jar of Gentleman's Relish, an oak-matured Stilton and a vintage port miniature.

Feeling still a little weak and feeble after surgery, I venture forth for a walk with the dogs - nothing too strenuous, just for some fresh air. The grass verges have been cut and the fragrant smell fills the damp air. A sudden mental alarm sounds - *When did the phone last ring?* Our telephone cables are vulnerable in this neck of the woods as they merely lie by the fence at the side of the road. Several times a year they are cut, either by mechanised verge cutters, drain diggers or even the snowplough. Once the problem is discovered, the telephone company can transfer surgery calls to the mobile phone and a repair team is dispatched with reasonable speed, but the whole procedure is a nuisance and we worry about missing important calls. It is not unusual for locals to be seen directing the repair crew to the precise spot where the damage has been done. We have all complained frequently about the lack of cooperation between the council and the telephone company, so perhaps they have done something about it. I remember that the phone rang this morning so, reassured, continue on our way.

A short walk today, just a quick trip through the woods, passable only thanks to the wonder of wellies! With the flair of an expert, Fintry locates yet another rotting lower limb from some unfortunate deceased creature - not so much a case of 'What have you got?' as 'Who have you got?' An undignified struggle ensues to prevent the bones from becoming a foreign body in a certain dog's stomach. Although supposedly a retriever, Fintry does not perform the whole sequence - she is happy to retrieve her quarry but unwilling to give it up. Once I have prized the revolting object from her jaws, it has to be put somewhere that the dog cannot reach, usually in the branches of nearby trees. As I attempt to clean my hand on some wet moss, I wonder what foreign tribesmen might make of a walk in our woods. Perhaps the carefully arranged exhibits might actually mean something to someone versed in voodoo! As to other dogs they probably think this is a wonderful place where bones grow on trees. Horribly aware that this might be the wild imaginings of not a well person, I head swiftly homewards to the sanctuary of the settee.

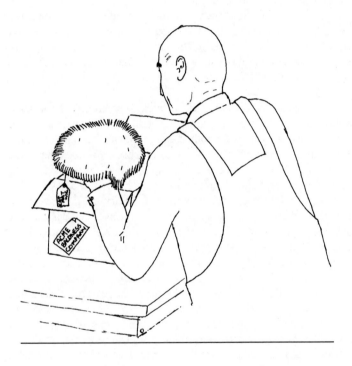

Tuesday 2nd June

A beautiful dry day, just right for an early morning walk before work. Up the hill with the effervescent fruity smell of hawthorn in the air and the blossom strewn like confetti on the track. At the top of the incline is the stamping ground of an unusual dark coloured cock pheasant. His red head atop the most beautiful dark green plumage makes him easily recognisable. It would be nice if his offspring are similarly coloured. As usual, he dithers frantically as the dogs approach then squeezes through the fence in the nick of time. It cannot be too traumatic for him (or he may have a very poor memory) because he will be there again tomorrow just as he has been for the last few weeks. Through the woods and on to the far side of the hill just in time to spot the white rear of a roe buck disappearing into the oil-seed rape. The flowers are fading from the crop and, with the cow parsley on the verges, the effect is of an alpine meadow. Swallows are fairly skipping over the tops of the fields and in the distance, gorse-covered hills contrast with the dark green wheat fields and the lighter tracts of barley. The dogs track through the long grass like creatures from the African veldt. They are not tall enough to notice a large dog fox passing in the opposite direction further down the field. He is so large that at first I thought he was another dog. Passing the deer field, from a distance, Honky looks as if he has Mickey Mouse ears - his antlers are already about six inches long and are covered in soft, velvety tissue which carries an excellent blood supply and is sensitive to the touch. The whole scene this morning is achingly beautiful and I feel very tempted to try to capture it in a painting. Perhaps I can fish out our assorted watercolour paints some time. This will cause long-suffering groans at home - my nearest and dearest are all too used to my sudden enthusiasms for home-based hobbies to pursue during our busy periods when we don't stray far from the surgery. They are resigned to the 'that looks interesting' comments following a browse through *Country Living* magazines. Such interests usually last long enough for expensive equipment to be acquired, then they gradually fade from our lives. It says a lot for the veterinary profession that it has kept me intrigued and interested for over twenty years.

Unfortunately, the walk turns out to have been the best part of the day. There is some bad news about a little bitch who we spayed recently for the local charity. The poor girl had been kept in a shed and used as a puppy factory for years. When she began to produce dead pups, she was smartly dumped on the charity. We saw quite a lot of her with her terrible parasite-ravaged skin then, once she had improved, she came in to be neutered last week. While still under treatment for her skin, she was re-homed with a marvellous family who adored her and life seemed to be looking up for her at last. When we spayed her, we noticed a lump on her tongue and took a biopsy. There seemed to be a core of tissue extending from the side of the tongue which I hoped was a reaction to a foreign body penetration, but the results came through today - a malignant tumour, highly likely to have spread elsewhere. Life can be very unfair sometimes. All we can hope is that she has the best few months of her life before secondaries make their presence felt. Already depressed by this, I have also had to put to sleep a young cat diagnosed with feline leukaemia. What is worse about this case is that the cat was one of a litter of four abandoned on the surgery doorstep when they were only a few days old. Seemingly healthy, they went to the local cat shelter and in due course were adopted by new owners. Over the last year, three of the kittens have fallen ill with the leukaemia virus and have either died or been put to sleep. This was the last. This shows how devastating this virus can be - like a time bomb it can stay hidden in the body for up to two years before wreaking its awful effects. In an ideal world, it would be nice to screen all strays for all the fatal viruses before re-homing, but few charities can afford to do that.

Gillian and I complete our gloomy day with a visit after surgery to put an old dog to sleep. Nothing dramatic, just an old, old fella whose owners have decided that the time has come. Keeping him alive will only mean misery and pain. It requires a lot of love to make this decision and our role is to make sure that his last moments are peaceful. This is quite stressful for both of us as we want everything to go smoothly. Gillian holds his leg while I trim up over a vein and prepare to inject. Thankfully, he makes no attempt to struggle while the injection is given and his owners cuddle and whisper to him as the drug takes affect. After being brave for him, once he is gone, they are distraught. Gillian wipes away a tear and I struggle with a large lump in my throat. Our job is to do the deed properly and in action we cannot afford to be emotional, concentrating solely on the technical details. Once our task is completed, we can be human again.

There is a grim satisfaction in allowing an old patient to die peacefully and with dignity and we are not too despondent as we return to the car, but today has been miserable and we both feel jaded and depressed, only wanting to get home and forget about veterinary work. As we drive down the village, someone waves energetically from the pavement - a triumphant Joan Briggs with a jerky but very mobile Ben straining on the lead. In a day full of clouds, a silver lining at last.

Friday 5th June

There is a touching reunion in the waiting room this morning between Jake, our diabetic Labrador and Midge, an elderly collie recovering from a stroke. They live close to one another and have been inseparable for years. In their youth, they had a litter of pups together and several of their offspring are now our patients. In a small town such as Clayfern, both humans and animals are often closely related to each other.

After the canine Darby and Joan, the next patient is Lily, a neat little cat belonging to Mrs Jenkins. They live with her son's family and an assortment of pets. Recently Lily has gone bald along her back leaving only stubble dotted with small spots. This is a common occurence in cats and ninety per cent are usually due to an allergy to fleas. I am having trouble convincing Mrs Jenkins of this - her Lily has *never* had fleas! Such a diagnosis is taken as an insult to her standards of hygiene and we have reached an impasse. Lily sits patiently on the table while I try to persuade Mrs Jenkins to at least try some flea treatment. Mrs Jenkins is obviously deeply sceptical about this provisional diagnosis and the consultation is not going smoothly at all when suddenly I spot the familiar form of a large brown flea scuttling across Lily's bald back and speedily point it out to Mrs Jenkins. Saved in the nick of time. Mrs Jenkin's antagonistic attitude completely collapses and we become joint allies in the battle against the devil fleas.

These last few days have been really pleasant: surgeries in Clayfern have been brisk but not hectic and the operations at the farm surgery have been straightforward, leaving time to keep up with paperwork *and* have a pleasant break in the afternoons. Today it is windy and the barleyfield moves in waves as we wander along the road. Dog roses and elderflowers are coming out; the dog roses are delicate pink-white flowers with such a short lifespan and the elderflowers are delicious when made into elderflower champagne. Climbing up the track to the woods, I count nineteen different types of flowers. This has become a habit; as the year progresses, incredibly, more and more flowers appear and it is fun to try to beat the previous day's record. There is a marvellous warm, resiny smell in the woods and the sunlight penetrating the trees is alive with tiny winged creatures zigzagging erratically in the beams of light. After a leisurely sunbathe in a mossy clearing with the dogs foraging nearby, we amble slowly homewards. On the way downhill, we meet our neighbour with a new dog. Kippen's attempts to look fearsome do not quite pay off due to his haircut. He looks like a Mohican with a short swathe of hair erected over his rump and the new dog is not impressed.

The fire has finally gone out today. Hopefully we can do without it now until autumn but nothing is ever guaranteed with our Scottish weather.

Monday 8th June

This week we are joined by a schoolgirl, Catriona, on work experience. We put up with this invasion with fortitude as earlier generations of vets put us with us. The students are at the stage of choosing their intended career options and it is worthwhile for them to spend time with us to see whether their idea of the job coincides with the reality. Even for seasoned vets, it can be either the best or the worst job in the world depending on what kind of day (or week) you're having. Some students can be a pleasure to have, while others are a pain.

We have to take a little care explaining our actions and thoughts to the student - they need to know that our rather black humour does not indicate a lack of compassion, but is only a method of coping with some of our bleaker moments. We don't shield the student at all and the first putting to sleep can be a daunting experience for them. Some almost reappraise their choice of career before your eyes.

Morning surgery is brisk with an interesting variety of cases and afterwards we progress slowly down the High Street stopping at bank, Post Office and chemist. The nice weather has brought everyone out and every few yards, we have an exchange of pleasantries with clients. There are dogs parked outside several of the shops - they are patients and also merit a brief greeting. The drive back to Fern is beautiful - burgeoning vegetation crowding the verges, contented livestock in lush fields and the river like a millpond reflecting the distant hills. So far, our student is seeing the best side of a country vet's life, but the worrying spectre of THE OPERATIONS looms on the horizon for an apprehensive Catriona. It is almost traditional for the novice student to feel faint at some time during the day's ops and Julie and I are expert at picking up the symptoms - the sudden silence, the shuffling and swaying and the draining of all colour from the face. Catriona copes well until a particularly bloody tooth extraction pushes her towards the edge. We gently suggest that she takes a seat outside, puts her head down and has a drink of water. Not only are we interested in the student's wellbeing, but we are also keen that she does not faint either onto expensive equipment or into the surgical field. I suspect that it is more the heat in the ops room and the fear of 'making a fool of themselves' that causes the symptoms rather than the actual sight of anything nasty. Once the worst has happened, most students settle down and become genuinely interested in the proceedings.

One of today's operations is a dog castration. This poor dog lives in a street where three unneutered bitches come into season one after the other. This means that for a considerable time the unfortunate dog is miserable with unrequited lust. He can't settle, will not eat and makes repeated attempts to escape in search of true love. Keeping an uncastrated dog anywhere near entire bitches is a real form of torture. This little dog has an amusing history - there is a clue in his nickname 'Bobbit'. Round about the time when the American Mrs Bobbit amputated her philandering husband's manhood, our Bobbit nearly did the same on a barbed wire fence. Luckily he did not damage the urinary tube and a marathon stitching session successfully reattached his doghood. The only evidence is a white scar extending a full 360 degrees round the organ. Perhaps this is the dog equivalent of tattooing - after today's operation, he will not impress the ladies at all!

Catriona is impressed with Julie's dexterity at restraining our patients, but she seems less agile than usual today - there is a large bruise on her leg sustained when falling over a sack of cat food. She comments on a wound on my hand and before long we have embarked on a tour of our other self-inflicted injuries - my burn from a close encounter with the cooker, her cut forehead from walking into a door and more. We reassure Catriona that such lapses do not, we hope, reflect performance in the operating theatre.

The next operation is an excursion into simple plastic surgery in an attempt to correct an eye condition known as *entropion*. This occurs when the eyelids roll inwards bringing eyelashes into contact with the surface of the eye causing much irritation and damage. A simple skin tuck is taken behind each eyelid allowing the lid to be pulled back into a more normal position. Care needs to be taken not to remove too much skin otherwise the eyelids turn outwards exposing too much of the eye's surface and cause further problems. This operation is one of several which seem to emphasise the difference in perception between owner and vet. Many years ago, my first entropion operation went extremely smoothly and I was particularly pleased with the final result. On disharging the patient however, I was greeted not with enthusiastic acclaim but horrified dismay. With the hair shaved from round the eyes, semicircles of dark stitches and some oozing of fresh blood by the wounds, it has to be admitted that the patients do not look their best. Many a young vet has carefully saved a large infected womb or excised growth to display to the owners only to be rebuffed with vehement refusals even to look at (let alone admire) the trophy. Several years on, I now have a good idea of what sights particularly upset owners and try to prepare them by showing them some photos in our special photo album. This contains before and after pictures of our more gruesome procedures - eye removals, leg amputations and the like. Owners can see that, once any blood staining has worn off, the stitches have been removed and the hair has grown back, the final effect is really not too bad. While we clear up, our student has been leafing through the album with a bemused expression on her face. Hopefully, she is now ready for anything. Several routine neuterings later, we are just in time to return to Clayfern for a brisk evening surgery. A shattered Catriona totters home at the end of her first long day. If every day is this busy, this week will either make or break her.

Tuesday 9th June

Off to yet another conference this morning. The official title is 'Small Rodents, Lagomorphs and Ferrets.' The fact that an entire morning is devoted to these beasties is an indication of how popular they are becoming. Rabbits (lagomorphs) are the third most common household pet after dogs and cats. The lectures are excellent with some interesting highlights - a slide of a gerbil attached to an ECG machine shows that it can be done. You always come away from these meetings with at least one nugget of totally novel information. For me, today's classic is that pineapple juice can be useful in breaking up gastric hairballs in rabbits. Now who found that out? The scientific name for such hairballs is also a classic - *Trichobezoars* - guaranteed to stop any conversation.

As if a morning devoted to furries isn't enough, on our walk, Fintry retrieves a young rabbit with myxomatosis which I humanely dispatch. They can be pests to farmers but they don't deserve to die in such a miserable way. It is chilling to realise that this disease was originally introduced by humans as a control measure. Nowadays we can vaccinate pet rabbits against myxomatosis. Even although they are kept in hutches, it only needs a flea from an infected wild rabbit to pass on the infection. The vaccine is still fairly new and is not as effective as dog and cat vaccines. Vaccinated rabbits can still show limited signs of the disease - occasionally producing raised nodules - so-called 'lumpy rabbit disease'. At least these rabbits live and the nodules usually fade with time. We encountered such a rabbit last year. Although lumpy, he remained bright and eating as normal. One day, his owner phoned - 'His nose has fallen off,' she reported. Many clients exaggerate, so we waited with interest to see what had really happened, but for once, the report was accurate. A large nodule on the top of the rabbit's nose had sloughed off, taking skin with it and leaving a cavity in which naked bone could be seen. For once, I was flummoxed. There was not enough skin to slide into the defect and our owner was not too keen on the thought of skin grafting. We agreed to keep the area scrupulously clean and monitor the situation closely. Sure enough, after two months the cavity had healed over and, apart from a marked indentation and no fur, looked almost as good as new. Throughout the healing phase, our rabbit remained cheerful and unconcerned.

This evening, I have to give a talk to the local youth club. As I hate speaking without any props, I resort to slideshows when possible. In our last practice - which ironically was close to a big city - I spent much time dealing with sick and injured wildlife: squirrels, swans, badgers, foxes, birds of prey - we saw them all. This led to an interest in the rehabilitation and release of the treated animals which in turn led into an interest in radio-tracking techniques for keeping tabs on the ex-patients after release. This provided unique opportunities to obtain photos of wild animals in their natural surroundings. Some of these slides are loaded into the projector for the talk. It really doesn't matter what the speech is about - the audience are totally enthralled with the animals. Strangely, I have treated less wildlife in this rural setting. This is probably because in a highly populated area, the animals are in closer proximity to humans and inevitably come to harm; not necessarily intentionally, but as a result of run-ins with man-made hazards such as vehicles, fishing lines and rubbish. It is certainly much more pleasant to view healthy wildlife in its natural state as we do every day. After the talk come the inevitable questions: 'What is the smallest/biggest/nastiest animal you've ever treated?'; 'What's the largest operation *you've* ever done?' The biggest was certainly a Clydesdale horse many years ago, the smallest is probably a frog or maybe a bat. But that's another story.

Thursday 11th June

Yesterday and today have been quite quiet, possibly due to World Cup fever. This is a little unfortunate for Catriona, the schoolgirl, but useful for Gillian and me as we can attend to the 'housekeeping' tasks which go by the board when we are busy. As the window display in Clayfern badly needs revamping, we decide to feature a seasonal topic - parasite control. At least after cutting out innumerable pictures and articles of interest to add to the display, Catriona will leave us with a sound knowledge of how to prevent flea infestations. We continue with the parasite theme when a cat is brought in with bad ears. Ear mites are the likely cause and a dollop of wax popped onto a microscope slide clinches the diagnosis. Under the microscope, the fierce crab-like parasites are revealed, still feasting on the debris present. They look like monsters from a horror film and Catriona is suitably impressed.

Before we return to Fern, we need to visit one of Edith McNaughton's girls, one has a *really* bad eye. It is often hard to decide the speed of response necessary for Edith's calls as they all sound urgent, so I decide to go sooner than later. Today's drama is an simple case, easily sorted with a tube of eye ointment. The settee and table are covered with World Cup information and we spend the rest of the visit discussing the finer points of Scotland's performance yesterday. Perhaps an unusual interest for a seventy year old, but Edith certainly likes to keep her brain active. Catriona is learning many lessons this week, not only about veterinary work.

As usual, any gaps in our operating schedule are ably plugged by Sheila who has been busy trapping again. This time it has been necessary to catch the feral cats living in an old factory before the demolition men move in. There are seven cats to neuter - obviously all related - all grey with pointed little faces like muskrats. Four of them also have squints! They are lucky; they are to be re-homed on a pleasant farm in the next county. Although it is a warm day, Sheila is wearing ski trousers, perhaps for protection against particularly nasty cats on her evening job? I never get round to asking her but the real reason becomes painfully clear in the evening when I arrive at the farm as requested to put the hens away at dusk. The nettles and thistles round the duck pen are four feet high and EVERYWHERE!

Friday 12th June

Still fairly quiet today, a reasonable morning surgery but only an X-ray to perform at the farm surgery. Bess the mongrel was chasing rabbits earlier in the week when she suddenly screamed and pulled up lame. She is holding up her right hind leg and the stifle (knee) joint is swollen and painful. This is identical to last year's experience when she injured the left hind leg. Today she will be given a sedative and painkiller combination to allow me to fully examine the relaxed leg as well as to take the X-ray. Sure enough, the cruciate ligament is ruptured. Our owners go to wait in the car while Julie and I do it. The blind in the X-ray room is drawn to allow accurate focusing of the beam of light which corresponds to the X-ray beam. Once a satisfactory picture is taken, Bess is brought round with another injection and the blind is raised. Like smoke from the Vatican chimney announcing the election of a new Pope, this is a signal that we are ready to pronounce and Bess's owners return swiftly to the surgery to discuss treatment. They know the routine from last year - Bess will return in a few days to have the damaged ligament repaired.

It is time for another learning experience for Catriona and we set off up the hill. She should experience *all* aspects of the vet's life. Little do we know what a unique sight she is about to see. As we follow the deer pen, the herd are lying only yards away. With amazement, I see the first baby deer of the season. It is unusual to see them at all for the first two to three weeks of life as their mother hides them in a secluded part of the pen. This one is very young - no bigger than a whippet, brown body dappled with dark spots and a pale head - courtesy of Honky, the white stag. His little ears are back as he attempts to stand, shaky back legs first then the front ones - they look so thin that they might snap at any moment. He is still tottery as he tries unsuccessfully to suckle from his mother and he takes a brief chase round a nearby, unimpressed hind before mother relents, busily nuzzling her youngster's white rear end to push him into the correct position. He could run right between his mother's legs at this age. We are so thrilled to watch this spectacle and incredibly privileged. The proud father is supremely indifferent. His antlers are now about ten inches long (high?) and look like furry candelabras on either side of his head. All in all, Catriona has had a very varied week and it seems to have strengthened her resolve to try for a place on the veterinary course. At least we haven't put her off. Who knows, in a few years, she may be looking for a job with us.

Scanning the deer pen with binoculars late in the evening, I see another small white calf amongst the thistles. Who knows how many more are secreted throughout the pen. Being white is certainly not an advantage; if we can see the youngsters, then so might others. Right on cue, a large dog fox trots across the pen and is chased off by an agitated hind. It is unlikely that it would attempt to take a baby deer, but even so, both Jay and I watch anxiously until he crosses into the next field and heads towards the woods.

Sunday 14th June

Although it is Sunday and theorerically 'emergencies only', this morning has been busier than some of our routine surgeries in Clayfern last week. First is a dog having trouble breathing - this sounds worrying over the phone, but in fact is no worse than an irritation of the nose causing what is known as *reverse sneezing*. This rather impressive effect occurs when the dog breathes in sharply through its nose in short bursts and can sound really alarming, but anti-inflammatory drugs should settle it down. Next, a dog who collapsed when playing with a friend. Such collapses can be either due to a heart or neurological problem, or even some illnesses such as diabetes. Because of the circumstances in which the collapse occurred and as the patient has a previous history of heart trouble, this is the most likely explanation. As is often the case after an unexplained collapse, the dog seems absolutely fine in the surgery. We discuss possible further tests before she is taken home to rest. Next again, a potentially serious emergency - a little Jack Russell Terrier has been in a fight with a bigger dog and is bleeding copiously from a neck wound. The towel and the owners are soaked in blood. Luckily, on carefully loosening the towel, the bleeding appears to have abated. The throat is a high risk area for surgery, crammed as it is with major blood vessels, nerves and other important structures and I would rather not operate if it is not necessary. The terrier's vital signs are fine so we opt for careful medical management with antibiotics, painkiller and a very mild sedative, together with a padded bandage. The throat is also not an easy area to bandage - too tight and the unfortunate animal is nearly throttled when it bends its head; too loose and the bandage slides down. With the bandage in place, the owners return home to keep their charge warm and quiet. Any worries and the surgery is only a phone call away. A final stitching of a cut pad and our busy morning is ended. We are rushing now to keep a lunch date with friends.

Even in a hurry, the the drive towards Clayfern is lovely. The sandbanks in the river are on the verge of being submerged by the tide and the herringbone pattern of the invading water glistens like silver in the sun. Dark stands of rushes are growing on the far river side - they are used for thatching and several cottages in the area sport cosy looking thatched roofs. Apparently, such a roof should last at least eighty years, although running repairs are occasionally necessary - often with straw. We pass our little mascot on the bends at Abbeygate Farm - a white baby rabbit. He has been there every day for over a week now and we dread finding him run over one day like so many of his fellows. Like our white deer, white creatures have the disadvantage of being very apparent to predators like the buzzard who regularly sits on a nearby fence post. Luckily, buzzards are lazy birds - why go to the trouble of killing prey when cars can do it for you. Baby rabbits are frequently surprised by cars coming round the bends, so he has a regular supply of fresh food without having to make any effort to catch it. Locals mention a particular rabbit hole nearby which regularly produces white bunnies. It also sheltered the pups resulting from Jake the diabetic's liaison with Midge the collie. Midge vanished from home in late pregnancy and was eventually found two weeks later, hoarding her pups down the rabbit hole. Such tales from clients and small dramas from everyday life often give special significance to local landmarks. Thus we pass over a deep gouge in the tarmac and remember its cause - where a runaway tractor landed after crashing through the fence above. It then continued through the fence on the far side and landed on its nose in the field. Luckily the driver had jumped out and no cars were on the road at the time. Then the gate oddly bent in the middle - the result of a fallen tree last winter. We are soon going through the woods where one client had a terrifying experience. Many bats fly near the woods on summer evenings - one smacked into our client's windscreen near dusk, then, with apparently deadly intent - but probably really due to aerodynamic effects - the deceased bat slid slowly across the windscreen before suddenly whipping round the corner, through the open window onto our client's chest. It says a lot for his *sang froid* that he neither had a heart attack nor ended up in the ditch.

Lunch is rather a rushed affair - our friends are on their way to the airport and have only a limited time to spend with us. They own a large veterinary clinic and view our low-key country lifestyle with a mixture of envy and horror. Left to our own devices, we spend the afternoon pottering in the garden - not a common pursuit for us but strangely satisfying once we get in the swing of things. In the late afternoon, I take a break to walk the dogs to the river for a cooling dip. They have stayed with us in the garden and look uncomfortably hot. The air is rich with the humming of insects and swallows swoop low over the fields executing breath-taking turns, sometimes flying low along the track then banking steeply at corners like a dam-busting squadron delivering their payload. An interesting incident occurs as we wend our way slowly homeward - although there is no wind, suddenly a swirling column of rape seed petals shoots upwards, rotating in ever widening circles until the petals are hurled across the track and all becomes still again. The whole episode lasts only a few minutes. This must be a mini-tornado – (these are apparently not uncommon in this region) - but what an eery effect. I rush home to tell Jay and this will be added to the many snippets which give 'home' such a sense of identity. For evermore, that will now be the corner of the field which had the tornado and will be incorporated into daily conversation: for example - 'I saw a fox today, it was past the corner of the field where the tornado was, but just before the rotten treestump.'

An hour or two more of gardening and we have both had enough, but are reluctant to move indoors on such a lovely evening. The perfect solution is to have a barbecue. In next to no time, we are piling into the car with disposable barbecue, dogs and the basic ingredients of our evening meal. Once up the hill, we head for the perfect spot - a grassy knoll under the pine trees overlooking the valley. In keeping with our tradition, I take the excited dogs for a stroll through the woods while Jay starts the barbie, then all of us - dogs included - stuff ourselves on delicious chargrilled fare, eating much more than normal; it always tastes so much better outside. The green woodpecker giggles in the background and the deer keep a watchful eye on us from the safety of their pen. The smoke keeps the insects at bay and we sit long into the evening, chatting and relaxing, sipping on bottles of beer and watching the sun cast a golden pathway across the river as it sinks lower behind the hills. As the sun sets and the barbecue dies, we finally stir, pack up our rubbish and head for home, so relaxed that even getting into the car seems like an effort. All four of us will sleep well tonight. Our friends can keep their big busy surgery - we wouldn't swap for all the tea in China.

Thursday 18th June

Another schoolchild for work experience today - 'seeing practice', as it is called for vet students. There is not much that a newcomer can actually be allowed to do if only here for a day or so: they invariably just watch all that is going on. We try to give them a taste of all aspects of the work, from the first contact at reception through consultations to further diagnostic tests and operations. We explain the equipment and show it in action to give an idea of what goes on behind the scenes. There are one or two things that the student *can* do - 'It isn't *all* glamour!' we chorus as they mop up a large puddle of wee. When we have a bright, enthusiastic pupil, it is a pleasure to instruct them, but it can be a strain having a shadow for every second of the day. Thank goodness for the last generation of vets who put up with me and my colleagues so stoically many years ago.

Today, we have only routine neuterings - five cat spays and two dog castrations (the knock-on effect from yet more bitches in season in Clayfern). It's hard to know if our student is bored watching the same operation, I can't remember if I was. During routine operations, Julie and I often have increasingly surreal conversations. Today we are dwelling on what Julie would do if I suddenly collapsed during an operation - 'Give you a good kick!' is her first thought. We work on an amusing (to us) scenario similar to that in films such as *Airport* where the pilot falls ill and the stewardess successfully lands the plane, talked down by another pilot in the control tower. We visualise Julie connected to another vet on the phone:

Vet 'First check your instruments.'

Julie 'Oxygen 1.5 litres per minute, 2% halothane, pulse ox. 98%.'

Vet 'Excellent. Now pick up the funny looking instrument that looks like blunt scissors - NO! NOT THOSE!'

Like the walrus and the carpenter, we talk of many things during long ops sessions. The student thinks we are very strange, but it keeps us amused.

A quick exit from evening surgery to attend a committee meeting of one of the animal charities. It is surprising how quickly the monthly meetings come round. Although on duty, I have my trusty pager and Stramar is only twenty minutes away. Emergency calls are pretty infrequent, but tonight I get bleeped - a dog which has been vomiting repeatedly since lunchtime providing an honorable excuse for leaving the meeting. It looks like an acute reaction after eating something 'inappropriate'. The dog is only a pup and 'rubbish in - rubbish out' is a common scenario. Some injections, a special solution to replace lost electrolytes and I am off home. It is a beautiful night and I linger in the garden, watering the plants, pulling the odd weed, not really wanting to go indoors. At this time of year, it is light so late that it seems a waste not to be outside. There are several deer calves in the pen now - old enough to be abandoned for long periods by their mothers. Honky's legacy is apparent, the small white bodies are easily spotted on the hillside. As the night wears on, the older calves join their mothers and play between their legs. Even at 1 am, the northern sky is still light - a pale turquoise topping the deep orange and crimson hugging the hills over the pale metallic blue of the river. Songbirds are singing in the crops and a frog croaks hopefully by the pond. It is hard to go inside when life is carrying on outside, but exhaustion eventually forces us to retire.

Saturday 21st June

Julie and I depart sharply after morning surgery is over. It is the church fete in the village of Duncraig today and Jay is judging the small pet show. A thunderstorm hits Clayfern as we leave. I hope it doesn't travel up the valley to the fete - everyone has worked so hard to plan the event, which is to raise funds for orphanages in Romania. Our home is roughly equidistant from Clayfern and Duncraig, a quiet little village with no shop or pub, but a lively community spirit giving rise to many *ceilidhs*, galas and other events. Balloons adorn the fences as we approach the manse where the fete is being held. We park in the nearby field and hurry along the lane, too late for the pet show, judging by the baskets and boxes being returned to cars. Jay sees us coming and meets us by the gate. The entrants were three rabbits, two hamsters and one hen, all of which have received a rosette (all diplomatically the same colour). The third rabbit, our friend with no nose, received a special award for bravery.

Pet shows are fraught with hazards for the unsuspecting and

I am secretly pleased not to be judging today. I can still remember the mutterings and aghast expressions at a bigger show when I awarded first prize to a hamster. Many small children with the family dog obviously felt spurned, but this hamster had great presence. Crystal, as she was called, lounged to the manner born in a hammock fashioned from an old toilet roll. Novel toys of all shapes and sizes were strewn around her cage, including an interesting creation reminiscent of a fairground helter-skelter. Such dedication by her young owner had to be rewarded, but she was not a popular choice and I slunk from the hall in deep disgrace. Since then, I have avoided such events wherever possible.

The fete is a delight. Most of the faces are familiar as clients and friends and we chat happily at every stall. We buy homebaking, bric-a-brac and plants; try our hand at the tombola; and guess the weight of the cake and the bear's name and birthday. The bear stallholder wonders whether our veterinary expertise might give us an advantage when it comes to guessing the age (Obviously it did, because we won.) Over soup and rolls, we watch the local kids - unrecognisable with painted faces - try their luck on the greasy pole and shooting for goal. If village life was always like this, no one would ever leave. And perhaps the minister really does have contacts in high places, because the rain holds off until the very end.

Monday 22nd June

Well, the day after the longest day - downhill all the way now until Christmas. Perhaps it's just as well. The long light nights are exhausting. It is hard to think of going to bed when it is so bright outside. There are seven baby deer now and they can be seen out even more now, especially at dusk. Often they play together, running round the pen like creatures possessed. Another snag of the light nights is that patients and their owners are also out and about late, increasing their chances of getting into trouble. At 11 pm last night, there was such an emergency case - Bruce the retriever was playing 'rounders' with the family and got hit in the face with a cricket bat. The bat made contact with the chin, knocking the entire bottom row of incisor teeth up and backwards. Painkillers, antibiotic and a mild sedative have given him a relatively comfortable night and our job today is to sort out the mess. With his dislodged teeth, he reminds me of Fintry's appearance when she proudly carries old pine cones; both look rather grotesque. Under anaesthetic, treatment involves filletting the detached teeth from the adjacent soft tissue, removing two broken tooth roots and stitching the remaining tissue over the cavity. The operation goes very well; Bruce should heal uneventfully and will no longer be frightening small children!

Sheila has brought in a stray white cat with crusty, peeling ears. She is worried about ringworm, an extremely infectious fungal infection which would be virtually impossible to eradicate should it get into her feral colony. I think the answer lies more in the fabulous weather that we had over the weekend - the ears are sunburnt. I can sympathise, the skin looks very similar to my shoulders. The treatment for both of us is the same: soothing cream and stronger sun screen next time. We also need to attend to Axilla the cat today. She is the cat who got tangled up in the plastic rings holding beercans together. At first, her wound seemed to be healing well but it has ground to a halt recently, so we loosen the skin edges from the underlying tissue and slide them carefully together, making sure there is not too much tension over the wound. Wounds in this area can be difficult to manage; I was reading an article the other day where the author successfully used a bridge of vascular tissue from within the abdomen to encourage such a defect to heal - intriguing stuff but hopefully not necessary here. Axilla is also a stray and her new name reflects her affliction - *axilla* is the medical term for armpit.

During the day, an unpleasant smell has pervaded the surgery prompting much checking in occupied kennels for 'accidents'. The animals are blameless however, the cattle shed at the farm is being mucked out and the resulting muck heap is perfuming the air for at least a half-mile radius.

The grass verges are being cut by the council today. Evidently they have heeded our pleas as, fifty yards behind, the tractor is tailed by a phone company van. We smile to ourselves as both slowly wend their way round the corner and up the hill.

What weather effects we have seen today. Rain clouds gather across the river and rain spills to earth via three water columns just as if three taps were turned on in the sky. Later the entire eastern sky becomes a mass of rainbow hues like a multicoloured curtain. Not typical summer weather, but this is not without its advantages - we do not yet have the plagues of flies which can make walks a misery; we don't have to water the garden so often and rainy spells keep us indoors attending to paperwork. After tea, the sun comes out, so dogs and I wander down the track towards the river. The smells of summer are rife - the musty, yeasty barley and the sweet smells of dog roses, honeysuckle and the newly mown track. Smells are incredibly evocative and yet so fleeting; they cannot be captured like sights in a photograph or sounds in a recorder. They come round at their allotted time and stir the memory like old friends, then we have to wait for another year to experience them again.

Thursday 25th June

Farming is much to the fore at this time of year. The grass is being cut for silage and any road journey can be extended by lengthy spells stuck behind tractors. Today is a special treat. Both Jay and I have the day off and are heading for the Royal Highland Show near Edinburgh. This is Scotland's biggest agricultural show lasting four days with something for everyone. There is just so much to see; as we enter, the first attraction is a larger than man-sized wood sculpture being fashioned with a chainsaw. Nearby, two loggers race to beat each other to the tops of poles towering above the showground. Apparently they can climb eighty feet in less then fourteen seconds - I can hardly do that distance in that time on flat ground!

First port of call is the food hall for a late breakfast. All manner of samples are on offer. We taste a stirfry after a cookery demonstration, try sausages, cheeses, chutneys, jams, shortbread and a heady variety of both alcoholic and non-alcoholic drinks before ambling through avenues of agricultural machinery worth a second mortgage to watch the sheep-shearing demonstration. Not only are power clippers used, but they do hand shearing as well - round the neck, down the undercarriage and over the hind leg to start with - as far as I have ever got before my back locks in excruciating agony; I can only salute these guys in wonder. A chance encounter in the craft tent with a lady at a spinning wheel sends me off with renewed enthusiasm to dig out the spinning wheel at home, bought with the intention of presenting friends with Christmas presents spun from their pets' own hair. At the time, Jay pointed out that my lack of knitting skills would restrict these to either scarves or ties and a failure to master spinning techniques caused a swift loss of interest in the project. Jay has heard it all before and, with a heavy sigh, steers us towards the show ring to watch the heavy horses.

The bookstands by the ring are a joy to investigate - who could not be tempted by such thrilling titles as *Incubating at Home* or even *Better Dry Stone Walling*. A trip to the resident Scottish Agricultural Museum is fascinating. Some old veterinary instruments and treatments are on view and we learn that the attractive pantiles which adorn many a roof near home were originally no more than a novel way of using up surplus drainage tiles manufactured nearby. After a final meal of steak sandwiches, haggis and crepes, we head for home. What a super day. We now have two new nicknames - I am Wabbit and Jay is Puggled (expressive Scottish words both meaning 'totally exhausted').

Although our legs are aching, we take pity on poor Kippen and Fintry who have been alone all day and wander slowly down the track. Once again the sky is amazing - a brilliant ivory sun sends beams of light into nearby clouds turning them a dusky orange. To the east, banks of white clouds gather like Arctic icefields, while overhead and behind us, purple and grey clouds swirl round a solitary patch of clear blue sky. We watch until the sun sets then turn wearily for home, shattered but very contented.

Saturday 27th June

The sun is beating down as I arrive in Clayfern for morning surgery. Today is Games Day (Clayfern's Highland Games) and the village is feverish with anticipation. T-shirted and shorted youths are parading the streets already; pipe bands are tuning up; and the local hostelries are bracing themselves for one of the busiest days of the year. Clayfern is usually a quiet little place, but on special occasions like the Games and Hogmanay, the locals certainly know how to party!

Surgery is surprisingly busy considering all the excitement outside. One little dog is feeling very sorry for herself - she was bowled over by a bigger dog yesterday while carrying a stick in her mouth. Today, she squeaks when she tries to open her mouth. This rings warning bells for us - stick injuries are common. The most frequent scenario is that the dog runs on to the sharp end of the stick and the tissue at the back of the mouth is penetrated. The most spectacular case I have seen was a dog who simply would not open his mouth at all. Under anaesthetic, I removed an eight inch stick buried up to the last inch in the back of the throat. Miraculously, no major damage had been done. Another common result of a stick injury is the dog who is brought in with a large abscess in its throat. In this situation, a likely diagnosis is a foreign body from a stick injury anything up to several months ago. Usually, draining the abscess will resolve the condition, although we very seldom actually find a piece of wood. The exception was a Labrador who was discharging small pieces of wood out of a burst throat abscess. The owner vaguely remembered the dog yelping when retrieving a stick six months previously. Luckily our little dog today was seen to have an end of the stick protruding from each side of her mouth before and after the tumble and a good look in her mouth reveals no injuries. I suspect she is just bruised and treat her accordingly. We will recheck her on Monday to play safe.

We finish promptly; a quick change into T-shirt and shorts before loading the dogs in the car and heading for Peeswit Point. The woods are cool and damp underfoot after the rain earlier in the week. Buttercups, wild strawberries and campion cover the ground and a mass of honeysuckle obscures the pine trees. The smell is wonderful and the air resounds with the steady hum of bees. The tide is in and a fresh breeze cools the beach. All three dogs rush straight into the water, Kippen and Fintry to swim while Jonno only paddles. I am kept busy throwing sticks, one each for Kippen and Fintry to swim for and a little one in the shallows for Jonno so he doesn't feel left out. Sticks thrown in water are not so hazardous as on land. Fintry can outrun Kippen on land but not in water - Kippen swims like an otter, using his heavy tail as a rudder and becomes a pirate, winning the race to all the sticks and snatching them from Fintry's grasp. Nice to see the old dog getting all the breaks for a change.

Once home again, I try unsuccessfully to book a locum for next weekend so we can travel to see friends holidaying on the West Coast. Everyone seems busy so we have to give up the idea. A little frustrating perhaps, but it is so glorious here at present that neither of us are really too disappointed.

Jay has been working today, so we meet in Clayfern to enjoy the remaining moments of the Games. It has been a sweltering day and the slopes overlooking the grass arena are covered with families lounging on tartan blankets, faces and arms like lobsters; there will be some sore people tomorrow. The beer tent is crowded as usual and the stalls pitched on the perimeter are doing good trade. The finals of the cycle races are under way - serious stuff, contestants travel countrywide to compete at all the local games. A great cheer goes up when a Clayfern lad snatches victory by the skin of his teeth. Even more cause for celebration later! We will not be joining the crowds tonight. We enjoyed our barbecue so much the other night that we have invited some friends to join us for another. Even up the hill the sound of music wafts up the valley from Clayfern - the village will be like a ghost town tomorrow!

Monday 29th June

Today we have three dogs in for routine surgery - each is called Sam. This has made post-op comforting very economical: every so often we just have to say *'It's all right, Sam'* in soothing tones and everyone is reassured. Julie has to be careful to give the right information to the right owner when they ring for progress reports. Today we also have an old cat, Perky, for intensive treatment. Perky has been quiet and refusing to eat for the last week. This morning she is jaundiced - her skin and membranes as yellow as a daffodil. This suggests several possible diagnoses and we take a blood sample to help pinpoint the problem. She is put on a drip and I also want to insert a *nasogastric tube.* This passes through a nostril down her gullet into her stomach and enables us to administer a semiliquid recovery food directly into her stomach. If a transient infection is involved, simply giving supportive treatment may effect a cure. She is an elderly cat however and it is very possible that something more serious is going on. A mild tranquilliser relaxes her before I pop local anaesthetic drops into her nose then begin to insert the tube. Cats tolerate this procedure surprisingly well. We flush the tube with saline to check it is correctly placed before attaching it firmly to the cat. For this we use *Superglue.* The glue tube is blocked and getting glue out becomes a messy business. Julie's fingers become glued to the cat as well as the tube: she looks as if she is turning into a werewolf when we detach her. We must buy a new tube tomorrow. Perky will now receive four feeds a day directly into her stomach. She is such a good cat, we hope the treatment is successful - at least it should make her feel better until we get the results.

Next we have a cat's teeth to attend to. Removing back cheek teeth can be tricky and is often made easier by placing the patient on their back. Julie helps with a hand on the cat's chest to keep her steady and a hand holding the bottom jaw open. 'Have you got a spare hand to keep an eye on the tube?' I mutter and wonder why Julie is giggling. Mission accomplished, I leave Julie to monitor the patients and depart on a visit to see an old dog belonging to one of my client's mother. Mother has gone into hospital for a while and daughter Carol is left with Fred. Fred is a delightful old fella who can barely walk fifty yards. For years, Mother and Fred have shared Mother's food and Fred is grotesquely fat. He is also incredibly hairy. Otherwise he is in good condition for an old chap, so we decide to improve matters for him. It will not be easy, but the rewards will be great if we succeed. I calculate how much slimming diet he should eat and instruct Carol to feed him three times daily. If possible, she will also take him for a short walk several times daily. Little and often helps more in the slimming stakes. Time and time again, we see the proof that slimming is good for overweight pets. Dogs crippled with arthritis can often come off medication when they lose half a stone. Our friend Tammy MacTavish the massive terrier could hardly walk, coughed frequently and dribbled urine wherever she sat. In all, Tammy shed nearly one third of her body weight, lost all her symptoms and became a new dog. A groomer will also visit to shear off Fred's coat. He might look silly but it is quite incredible how much relief a haircut can give. It makes sense if you imagine spending all summer in a fur coat.

The first of the hay fields has been cut today, a much needed different walk for the dogs and me. An enduring vision of summer is sitting in the new mown hay in the evening sun, smelling the wonderful aroma and watching the swallows swoop and dive in endless loops, their manoeuvrability the envy of pilots everywhere. The dogs catch the mood and play joyfully, emerging like scarecrows from under the cut hay. As I sit peacefully, three cars draw up by the house. The relaxed mood evaporates instantly. What disaster could necessitate *three* cars? A dog fight with three participants, a multi-animal traffic accident? Adrenalin pumping, I am poised to rush back to the surgery at the first chirp of the pager when the cars move off. Puzzled, I ring Jay from my mobile phone. No panic, the cars are on a treasure hunt and one task is to find the name of the vet's house!

Tuesday 30th June

An unexpectedly early start today. The phone jars us awake at two am. Someone has accidently shut their kitten in a door and it sounds near death. Worse is to come - the owner has no transport and no money for a taxi. There is no choice but to visit. It is remarkably light at 2.30 am. as I pull up at the cottage. The door opens to reveal a kitten trotting purposefully along the hall. 'We phoned back but you had left' explains the owner. That will have been popular at home, I think as I examine the kitten. This reveals no problems so I get to go home quicker than anticipated, not sure whether to be irritated or relieved. A bit of both really: kittens are remarkably resilient with impressive powers of recovery. Only a week ago, our charity people rushed into the surgery with a kitten who had fallen from a fourth-floor flat. Apart from a bruised tail, from which it recovered in days, the kitten was unscathed.

After the initial shock, it is quite pleasant to be out at this time of morning. The sky is lightening already and all manner of wildlife is out and about. A barn owl flies in front of the car and rabbits and a fox cub are in turn caught in the headlights. At home, the baby deer are playing, charging around the pen in ever increasing circles. It is quite strange to think of life going on for these creatures while we are tucked up in bed. Several years ago, I was lucky enough to follow badgers with radio-tracking equipment and have spent many nights watching them rootling in gardens while the householders slept totally unaware of their nocturnal visitors.

The problem after any nocturnal expedition is getting back to sleep again. It takes a hot chocolate and a long read before my eyelids begin to droop and all too soon it is time to get up again.

WEDNESDAY 1ST JULY

Bad news for Perky today. Her lab results are truly dreadful. Her liver is badly damaged and is not working at all well. We would need a biopsy to find out exactly what is affecting it - it could be tumour, or one of several liver conditions that cats can get. Neither her owner nor I are keen to attempt this; in a younger cat perhaps, but not in an eighteen year old. Despite the intensive treatment, she is going downhill fast so we make the decision to put her to sleep. She goes very peacefully and will be buried beside other members of her family whom she has outlived.

Another patient lightens the rather sombre tone after the deed is done - Cilla is an ancient crossbred terrier belonging to Mrs Black. For the last week she has been drinking excessive quantities of water and needing to go out to urinate in the middle of the night. This could be a symptom of several diseases, but Mrs Black is particularly worried about diabetes because Cilla's mother suffered from this condition. Mrs Black has been asked to bring a urine sample to the surgery when Cilla comes for her appointment because testing this can give us information that is useful in helping us come to a diagnosis. She certainly does not appear to be diabetic, in fact both urine sample and dog check out reasonably well. There is a trace of blood and protein detected on the urine test strip, which, combined with the symptoms and examination of the patient, leads to a provisional diagnosis of *cystitis* - an inflammation of the bladder. I dispense some antibiotics which should do the trick and book Cilla in for another appointment in a few days to keep an eye on her progress. 'It's not everyone who gets to test Cilla Black's urine sample!' comments Gillian as the scruffy, bandy-legged creature makes her way through the door. After our sad start to the day, this is enough to send us into fits of giggles. In fairness, the more famous Cilla is considerably better looking than her canine counterpart.

Along with the next feline patient, our client carries a cardboard box with rather sad contents. Her cat Sally produced three dead kittens last night. The kittens are a reasonable size but are naked, no fur at all - obviously they are premature. Sally seems fine, but I can feel another kitten in her abdomen. It is hard to say if it is alive and this presents us with a dilemma - the uterus has been open to the outside so there is a risk of infection, but there are no abnormal discharges and Sally seems bright and lively. Her owner is desperate for her to have a kitten. The ideal solution, if the owner agrees, is to send the cat to our neighbouring veterinary practice for an ultrasound scan. Such equipment can be very useful but is totally beyond the budget of a small practice such as this. Our neighbours are a large mixed practice who need the scanner for their farm and equine work. They are always happy to scan any of our cases. So off Sally goes and soon the results are telephoned through - a beating heart has been detected in our mother's womb. We decide to give Sally a course of antibiotics and monitor her carefully. Her owner has instructions to contact the surgery if the cat seems even a little off colour. Let's see what the next few days bring.

At the farm surgery, the rest of the day is spent neutering innumerable cats from our two charities. As always at this time of year, they are inundated with unwanted cats and kittens. We have been operating on twenty to thirty a week for the last few weeks and this usually continues into the summer. I'm sure that both Julie and I go to bed at night counting not sheep but cat spays.

Monday 6th July

The surgery is well and truly in its busy season and we have seen several emergencies over the weekend. One is Kim, an old Boxer with a pyometra (infected womb). This is such a satisfying operation to carry out; the patient feels sick and ill beforehand, but we are able to remove the entire source of infection in one go and usually the dog will feel better quite soon afterwards. Kim has an intravenous drip running throughout the day to flush toxins from her circulation. Some patients need intensive treatment for several days post op, but this little bitch looks happier only hours after surgery. Post-operatively, Julie has spent some time trimming out Kim's matted coat and combing dead hair away, filling two carrier bags with the results, so the dog will be feeling considerably fresher as well. We have been spending so much time neutering these days that it is a good feeling to have made a patient feel so much better. The effects of neutering are rather more for the animal's long-term benefit than the immediate.

Our final operation has been looming all morning. In the kennel sits an old dog with one of the worst mouths I have seen - full of rotting, infected teeth. The revolting smell is detectable over six feet away from the dog and we have not been looking forward to getting much closer. As well as having to put up with the appalling smell, taste and discomfort, the poor dog has had no cuddles from her family for months. We resort to the old trick of anointing ourselves with menthol cream below our nostrils to mask the stench, swallow hard and swing into action. After an hour, thirty six of her forty two teeth have been removed and her breath is considerably sweeter. She will probably take on a new lease of life after today. Changes that her owner has attributed to ageing are actually due to the chronic pain and infection from her mouth.

It has been rather pleasant today to have two fairly long procedures instead of ten or twelve short ones as is common on our neutering days and we both agree it has been quite relaxing. The surgery smells considerably better at the end of the day with one patient relieved of a stinking womb and the other of her stinking teeth. A major clean up is in order before any further surgery takes place. We have deliberately scheduled nothing else for the rest of the day. The results of our labours - the rotting teeth and infected womb are disposed of separately as is all our clinical waste. Bits and pieces of patients, soiled swabs and bedding, used syringes and empty drug containers are all required to be packaged carefully, clearly labelled and collected by a specialist firm. This involves surgeries in not considerable expense.

At last, it is time for a walk. It is very warm today and the tar is blistering on the road. The barley is turning golden and the hedgerows look very lush. More and more flowers crowd the side of the track – thirty one counted today on the way up to the thinking stones; not the record yet, but close. The clover in the field smells of honey as we approach the stones. Although beautiful, this is not the best time of year for walking. The crops are too high to walk through, the woods are besieged by nettles and the hay meadows are overgrown with different grasses which impart a purplish hue to the verges. The recent rain and the cuckoo spit from insects ensures a thorough soaking if one ventures off the track. Because of the damp weather, there is a profusion of slugs, snails and black beetles underfoot and each dog and human walks with their personal flock of flies. Stopping for a breather at the stones is no pleasure with the flies out in force. They are bothering the deer as well, ears are flapping constantly - and what ears! We call them 'the wingnuts'. The young deer are growing rapidly and are spending most of their time with the main herd now. Only Honky stays aloof, tortured with more than his share of flies attracted to his velvety antlers. In the wild, the stags and the hinds stay in separate herds at this time of year, only coming together during the rutting season.

On the way home, we pass our neighbour 'That must be a grand scent you're wearing, lass,' he comments, 'You're attracting all the flies'. Then after a reflective pause, 'Mind you, so does a dead sheep!'

Kim the pyometra - or pyo as it is known in the trade - stays overnight. She is much brighter than before and polishes off a good supper. She sniffs the air appreciatively when out for a final wee and snuffles around the hedge. The sun is nowadays setting almost directly opposite the cottage and the evening skies are a continually fascinating vista. Pink and ivory streaks blend with indigo and violet and darkness never quite seems to fall. Tonight high clouds reflect a steely blue in streaked patterns. These are so-called noctilucent clouds. They catch the sun all night at this time of year. Watching this magnificent spectacle, I am in no hurry to rush Kim into her kennel and she enjoys a thorough inspection of the small front garden before finally being taken back to bed.

Tuesday 7th July

Out in the garden early with Kim the pyo. While she is investigating the hedge, two minibuses pass, carrying the berrypickers to the local fruit farms. This is quite a prolific soft-fruit growing area. Somehow, we never see P.Y.O. fruit farms in quite the same light as other people. Kim's owners pick her up before morning surgery and are thrilled with the change in her. A good start to the day.

More good news in Clayfern - overnight, Sally has produced a normal, healthy kitten who is dubbed 'Ultra' in honour of the machine which first advertised her existence.

Even better, Hector has called in to pay off some of his bill. This is an unexpected surprise as Hector has been in a spot of bother recently. He and his partner in crime, Eck, have been caught poaching on the upper reaches of the River Clay. Acting on a tip-off (probably Eck and Hector boasting in the pub), the local gamie and his henchmen staked out the targeted stretch of water. The two miscreants took to their heels when powerful searchlights were switched on and took cover in the bushes by the river bank. ''Ach,will you jist come oot Hector man,' shouted the keeper in exasperation. Back came the unforgetable utterance 'But it's no'me!' Anyway, their case is coming up soon and they will undoubtedly both receive a hefty fine. Although we are ranked below car repairs and domestic bills, I am quite honoured that paying the vet takes priority over court fines. In fact, I am ashamed to say that we have in the past thoroughly enjoyed the gift of a sizeable salmon in lieu of more conventional remuneration (In my defence, I had no idea where the fish came from). There is a follow-up to this tale; apparently, the night following the incident, Eck drowned his sorrows excessively, mistook his wash house roof (which is set into the hill) for the back terrace and ended up draped round the chimney stack on top of the roof. The story would have ended there had not a well-meaning holiday-maker mistaken him for a potential suicide and called both police and fire brigade. An indignant Mrs Cassidy filled in the details for us in the surgery the next day; wakened by the flashing lights and commotion, she flung open her window and yelled 'Ach jist jump ye daft gowk and let us get some sleep.'

'That was a bit unkind, Mrs Cassidy,' said Gillian.

'Well, it was only aboot ten feet up' came the no-nonsense reply. The finale was something of a non-event. Wakened from his drunken stupor by all the activity, Eck sobered up rapidly at the sight of the boys in blue and was escorted off the roof by the local bobby. No one seems to know whether he will face an additional fine for disturbing the peace (or Mrs Cassidy at least).

Neutering day today for the charity and we have a batch of cross chihuahua pups, eight altogether. An advantage of doing 'job lots' is that they can recover cuddled in together, which is less stressful than alone in a kennel. We do have to watch carefully that they don't lie on top of each other. As usual after trimming up the op. site, Julie uses a portable vacuum to remove the loose fur. The patients are so small today that we joke they might disappear up the nozzle. The ops go smoothly and within an hour of the last stitch, they are playing amongst themselves. While we are operating, the hay is being baled. This is an intriguing procedure: the tractor tows what looks like a large tin drum along the rows of cut hay. Every several hundred yards, the procession stops, the back of the drum opens and 'lays' a big cylindrical bale ready wrapped in white nylon mesh. The whole valley is alive with tractors which will work late into the evening to beat the bad weather forecast for tomorrow.

After evening surgery, the freshly baled hay becomes a powerful magnet for my motley crew. Every bale has to be inspected and jumped on by Fintry the youngster. Kippen contents himself with jumping onto my vantage bale and enjoying the spectacle of the daft Labrador hurling herself on and off each bale in turn and generally going 'crackerdog' through the cut grass. This is a bittersweet moment - Kippen was exactly the same as a young dog. Jonno resists all encouragement to join us on the bale. Although he seldom participates in the fun, he catches the happy tone of the evening and enjoys being part of the gang.

Thursday 16th July

We have almost a replay of last Monday's ops list - but all in the same dog! It is definitely the season for all sorts of pyos. The patient today is Kelly, a sixteen-year-old poodle. She has shown symptoms of an infected womb before but they have been held at bay with antibiotics. At her age, her owners felt that major surgery would not be fair and luckily, the drugs did the job at the time. Inevitably, the symptoms have recurred and are failing to respond to medical treatment. Faced with the prospect of her either dying or having to be put to sleep, we have decided to gamble on surgery. It will be risky, but for her age, she is in remarkably good condition. After pre-meds of a mild tranquilliser, antibiotics and a painkiller, I slip a canula into her vein, administer anaesthetic and connect a drip. The uterus is a large, swollen bag of pus almost on the verge of bursting - better out than in. The owners and I decided to really go for broke and attend to Kelly's teeth as well. We would not normally carry out dental extractions at the same time as a surgical procedure in case any infection from the mouth is dislodged and passes to the op site, but her teeth are so horrible that they are also better out than in. Most are loose, but are concreted in place by large chunks of tartar underneath which are cheesy deposits of pus mixed with hair and food debris. The smell is horrendous but the job is soon done and Kelly is tucked into her kennel wrapped up in a warm, woolly blanket.

A constant feature in the farm surgery at this time of year is the drone of tractors in the background, busy with seasonal tasks. Today, the set-aside ground behind the house is being mowed. Good news for us walkers - more places to go. The colourful mixture of grasses, thistles, daisies and clover is beautiful, but has been too dense and wet to trudge through recently. In the evening, we all go to investigate the mowed field. Fintry is ecstatic, flushing pheasants from remaining islets of vegetation and rolling energetically in the mown grass. Our neighbouring farmer is out in his tractor, retrieving a round hay bale which dramatically escaped earlier today. It bounced over the fence on to the road, clipped the back of a passing car and landed in the next field. Luckily, the driver was not hurt but certainly badly shaken up. It can be a dangerous business, living in the country.

The field from which the bale came has been colonised by flocks of seagulls and rooks, largely segregated into their own species. Two oystercatchers fly overhead whistling shrilly to each other. They are attractive black and white birds with distinctive red beaks and legs. They are quite frequent visitors from the nearby coast. A lapwing or *peeswit* also wheels in the sky, jinking and dancing in its crazy flight, also calling with its slightly fuller whistle - a clarinet to the oystercatchers' flute. We don't see so many of them nowadays, but in the past, they were more common, a fact illustrated by the name of one of our favourite spots - Peeswit Point.

Friday 17th July

Kelly the 'pyo' has been in the surgery overnight. Medically, she seems to be doing well, but she is behaving like a little lost soul. On trips to the garden, she only looks round anxiously then relieves herself on returning to her kennel. She has eaten overnight but will take nothing in my presence. Her owner tells me that she has never been away from home in all her sixteen years, so I decide to send her home this morning. Medically it might be prudent to hospitalise her for longer, but psychologically she will be better off in familiar surroundings. Just like old people, old animals hate changes to their usual routine. Her owners are told to call us if there are any changes for the worse and we will check her in the surgery tomorrow.

There is a visit on the books today. This is to examine an old collie belonging to the Guthrie brothers. These two old boys are known in the village as the *Glaikit Guthries* (roughly translated as the daft Guthries). Sadly, they are just suffering from the early stages of senile dementia and it is debatable whether they are capable of managing on their own. Their collie, Meg, has grown old with them and it is certainly a wonderful home for a healthy dog as she wants for nothing and is spoiled shamelessly. Unfortunately, the brothers now tend not to notice if there is a problem with the dog

until it is well advanced. They have called us today, thus it is with trepidation that I approach the house. The door is opened by the younger brother, Albert. He has obviously cut himself shaving as his face is festooned with bloody strips of tissue paper. With his gap-toothed grin, he resembles a character from a horror movie. Grinning from ear to ear, he ushers me into the living room where Meg is lying flat out on the settee next to an anxious Alfred. My heart lurches; *Please don't let it be anything serious.* Fortunately, the problem is no more than an inflamed ear, probably brought about as a result of the brothers' bright idea of giving Meg a bath. In the ensuing struggle, I suspect that a fair quantity of soap found its way into the sensitive ear canal. Apparently Meg's reaction to the bath was so vigorous that it is unlikely she will be getting another. Always genial, after the work is done, the brothers invite me to partake of a tincture. They may be a little lackadaisical about feeding themselves but the drinks trolley is always well stocked. However, it must be very frightening to be gradually losing one's sanity, so good luck to them if it makes them feel better. I am rather
alarmed to see a can of woodworm killer next to the bottles. 'Watch you don't drink any of that', I joke. The brothers smile vaguely but I don't think they quite get the point. *At least, they will be well preserved.* The brothers escort me to the door and wave energetically until the car disappears round the corner. It is so sad to see them gradually deteriorating. I resolve to drop in occasionally whenever I have a spare moment.

Otherwise the day's workload is uncharacteristically light, just some cats to see for Sheila. She is inundated with calls to help trap unwanted cats and is totally depressed by the news of another cat charity's 'technique' for reducing stray cat numbers in their area. They are trapping the cats, then releasing them - unneutered - at rubbish tips on the outskirts of town. For stupidity and cruelty, this really takes the biscuit. The cats have been torn from familiar surroundings and released somewhere strange with unknown food supply and shelter. There will doubtless be local cats on the sites who will forcibly defend their territory. It is quite incredible that so-called cat workers can be so stupid.

The weather has been so changeable recently, one minute

sun then torrential rain. Everyone is wondering what has happened to long, sun-drenched summer days. Today is sunny but windy - useful for keeping the flies at bay and drying the surgery washing. Fleecy vet-beds and bright woollen squares flap gaily on the line. The latter are knitted or crocheted by kindly clients and are so helpful in the surgery where we have a high turnover of bedding. They are beautifully cosy and brighten the place up as well.

Picking up Jonno at the farm, I chat to our neighbour who is tinkering with the combine harvester, getting it ready for next month's harvest. Pigeons coo in the rafters and in the roof of the airy barn, the swallows have built their nests. These are impressive clay domes with a small entrance hole. Parent birds continually swoop through the barn into the nests to feed their voracious young. Some adolescents can be seen perching precariously on the telephone wires, no doubt taking flying lessons. The farm cats watch them hopefully from their sunbathing pitches by the door. Trust cats to pick the best spot - on straw bales out of the wind. Nice life for some!

My favourite summer flowers are now in full bloom; the verges are full of red poppies, ox-eye daisies and pretty blue cornflowers. They look gorgeous with the golden barley in the background. The first of the wild raspberries are out along the track and Kippen has his own method of P.Y.O., gently dislodging the berries from the cane. There are wild strawberries too, but these do not seem to impress the dogs - good! They are *my* favourites, much sweeter than shop-bought berries.

Saturday 19th July

A routine morning surgery: some booster vaccinations and itching dogs but nothing too taxing. The last patient is Kelly, who is carried into the surgery in her owner's arms. This causes a twinge of anxiety, but when she is deposited on the floor, she dances round her owner squeaking and yipping in excitement. She is brighter than she has been for months. The gamble to send her home has paid off; it is only necessary to remove the i/v canula (left in place in case she required more fluid), supply more antibiotics and make an appointment for stitch removal next week.

We now have a mystery to solve: a racing pigeon was brought into yesterday evening's surgery. The bird was just back from a long race and appeared to have a half-inch length of white string protruding from his leg. The most common problem with string or twine is when it wraps round the leg, sometimes cutting right to the bone, but this piece is at an odd angle. Perhaps there is a small hook under the surface? The only way to find out is to investigate under general anaesthetic. First a pre-med injection to dry up secretions in the windpipe, then an anaesthetic is injected into a wing vein. Racing pigeons are used to being handled, so he goes smoothly to sleep. Then he is placed on a heated pad and a special face mask delivers anaesthetic gas. The face mask is homemade from an old syringe case and is invaluable for anaesthetising small creatures; it is unusual for most anaesthetic equipment in that it is wonderfully cheap. Gently grasping the string, I incise the skin under which it disappears. Almost immediately, the 'string's' appearance changes, taking on the familiar shiny form of tendon. It looks as if a sliver of the outer edge of the tendon has been shaved off and the skin has healed round it. The rest of the tendon seems intact, so there is nothing for it but to cut off the abnormal tissue and stitch the bird up. He recovers rapidly in a warm kennel and is ready to go home by mid-afternoon. Once the swelling has settled down, I expect him to be able to use the leg as normal.

Tonight we are expecting guests for supper, including Sue of duck-bottom fame who will be staying for a few days, but as usual I find time for a quick walk before preparing the food. A pleasant surprise awaits at the corner of the woods - this is the territory of our handsome dark green pheasant who has been dubbed Farquhar (or perhaps it should be Pharquhar). We have been feeling sorry for him recently as he is such a solitary bird, but his wonderful plumage has obviously worked its magic and at last Farquhar now has a mate, swiftly christened Francesca (Phrancesca?). I cannot wait to tell Jay - we will be waiting with bated breath to see whether the offspring will inherit their father's magnificent colouring.

In the evening, we manage a barbecue in the rather fleeting summer sunshine. The cottage is an entomologist's dream at this time of year - moths, assorted flies, beasties and beetles are rife. Many are intent on 'Ending It All' in bowls of salad or cream despite fervent attempts to keep everything covered. Luckily our friends are made of stern stuff and regard the inevitable foreign bits as extra protein!

Monday 20th July

Both Jay and I have tried our best to have some free time while Sue is here. The poor woman has so often been faced with the alternatives of either coming to work with us or spending time on her own. Both have their attractions - but not all the time. There is only morning surgery to do - then Linda is taking over for the rest of the day. Mrs Cassidy is uncharacteristically first into the surgery. Being slightly disabled, early rising is not her forte, but she is looking quite anxious, something is obviously afoot. She has a couple of hens who scratch around in her back yard, but this morning one is hopping on one leg - unfortunately, it is hopping faster than Mrs Cassidy can hobble! As she only lives a few doors away, it is no problem for Gillian to go to catch the invalid, the surgery is quiet and I can manage on my own for a while. After what seems an inordinately long time, Gillian reappears, triumphantly clutching the patient in a cage - 'Here we are - the original Chicken in the Basket!' Very funny, Gillian. Although only using one leg, the hen had led Gillian a merry dance through the garden, one of the town's original orchards which extends for several hundred yards of dense undergrowth. Luckily, the bird is exhausted as well as Gillian and sits quietly while I examine her leg. Sure enough, there is a break. 'Please do what you can for her,' pleads Mrs Cassidy, 'She's my favourite.' 'Ever Ready' as she is known, is an ex-battery hen who was found wandering at a busy roundabout after falling off a lorry. She has a lovely nature, clucking gently when spoken to. It is quite sad that she is so taken with human company, when humans have not exactly treated her magnificently in the past. Some padded gutter splint secured with bandage provides a light but rigid support and Ever Ready does not seem distressed in the slightest. Having preferential treatment while restricted to the wash house will be right up her street. The mystery of Mrs Cassidy's early start soon becomes clear: 'I'm in a rush today,' she confides, 'I'm off on the bus going to thon big religious convention in Edinburgh. Not that I'm going to be converted, mind, but it's a day out.'

For once, no emergencies complicate the swap-over with Linda and we escape - the remainder of the day our own. First a snack lunch at our 'local', a cosy little hostelry in Drumdurn. As usual we discuss the vagaries of local business with the owners; like us, they too experience the 'all or nothing' phenomenon that occurs all the time here - no customers until the waitress goes off duty then a sudden surge and so on and so on. It is comforting to compare notes while Sue, no doubt, makes a mental note *never* to venture into a job which involves serving the public. It may come as a surprise to think of veterinary work as a service industry, but this is indeed the case. Being good with animals is not the only qualification required, because every animal comes with at least one human attached. This often comes as a shock to prospective vets, but it is as well that they realise the reality sooner than later if they are to survive in this job.

The rest of the day is a treat for us all: a leisurely trip up the glen for Sue to revel in the majestic scenery, then a surprise - we draw up by a drystane dyke and make our way over a meadow and down through a cool pine thicket. At the bottom of the valley a small river gurgles over large rocks and widens into a deep pool known as the Dapple Linn. As a child, I would cycle here with my pals in summer for a swim. After the exhausting cycle up the glen which left us hot and sticky, it was bliss to slide into the icy waters. Then we would clamber back onto our bikes with anaesthetised limbs and peddle like fury back down the glen in a desperate attempt to return our body temperature to normal. The water temperature is even more of a shock to the system as adults, but eventually we are all fully submerged and the pain gradually wears off as circulation to the extremities is cut off. The resuscitation technique is also slightly different for adults and involves a few medicinal sips from Jay's flask followed by a hearty meal at a loch-side restaurant at the bottom of the glen. What a super day.

Tuesday 21st July

Ops, ops and more ops today - all routine neuterings and one unwelcome call - Ben Briggs is unwell again. Ben is the little dog who was rushed to the veterinary college with a suspected spinal haemorrhage. Against all odds, he survived, although he still walks like a puppet worked with strings. His initial symptoms were frustratingly vague, just a 'hingy' animal with a high temperature. He is the same again today and both his owner Joan and I are a little nervous. We decide to keep him on antibiotics and watch him like hawks. Joan simply cannot afford more tests - she is still paying the first vet college bill - and it is unlikely that there is much more that can be done in the way of treatment. It is humbling that even with the most extensive of tests, some conditions remain for ever undiagnosed (or diagnosed at post-mortem which is not what we want at all.) We are going to have an anxious few days till we see how things go.

The television and other media have been much to the fore today. There have been a spate of TV adverts for special dog biscuits and a flea treatment which certainly bring potential customers flocking in. There is also a surfeit of veterinary documentaries on the TV which is something of a double-edged sword. They can certainly make it easier for us to explain complicated conditions and treatments - the owners have already come across it on the TV - but can sometimes be irritating. If a television presenter with no qualifications pronounces on air then this is regarded as gospel - such is the power of the media. Then again, this is not particularly new - it has long been our cross to bear that the next-door neighbour's or the milkman's opinions are often taken to heart more than the vet's.

Sue has been left to her own devices today and has kindly made the evening meal: 'I was going to go on a cycle run this afternoon, but couldn't find the bike you said was in the shed,' she mentions in the passing. Initial puzzlement turns to amusement when we realise that she has overheard us talking about the wasps' nest in the shed - otherwise known as a *byke*. She also needs help with working out when to collect her photos: 'They'll be ready the morn's morn' explained the shop assistant. This means that she can pick them up tomorrow. At this rate, we will need to provide her with an interpreter!

In the evening, we all go for our usual walk. What strange weather we are having; some sun but not enough, high winds and lots of rain all within the space of a few hours. It is a talking point with everyone. We all pine for glorious sundrenched summer days and farmers worry about the harvest. Although it is almost harvest time, the crops are not ready and many have been damaged by the wind and rain. In some areas, whole fields look battered and dishevelled.

It is almost like autumn tonight, with a slight chill in the air. Already, there are small berries forming on the hawthorn and bramble bushes, green nuts on the beeches and small green apples on the orchard trees. The valley is a patchwork of green and tan. The tide is out and the steel grey sky is reflected in the ripples left on the sandbanks. Sheep are calling in the distant fields - the high-pitched calls of the lambs and the gruffer tones of their mothers - and woodpigeons are cooing in the woods. All seems well with the world. The burn which we pass by is in full spate, gurgling and spitting down to the river. Everything is beautiful as ever, although perhaps not entirely as expected at this time of year.

Friday 24th July

Another autumnal day dawns. There are wreaths of mist obscuring the hills and seeping through the woods and rooks are congregating on the mown field behind the house, cawing mournfully to each other. They don't normally appear here until later in the year - perhaps the wet, humid conditions are producing a good food supply on the ground.

This weather is causing problems at work. I see the first

berry bug case of the year. This parasite is also known as the *harvest mite and* causes intense itching in its victims both animal and human. Today's patient is a West Highland white terrier, a good subject in which to demonstrate the parasite: it looks like bright orange powder between the dog's toes. Under the microscope, the powder transforms into large, satanic crab-like aliens. Luckily, anti-inflammatory treatment to bring relief and a suitable insecticide to deter the mites will do the trick. Not very dramatic perhaps, but that little dog will feel a whole lot better soon.

The next patient's condition is also linked to the weather but is not so easily cured; a collapsed rabbit is deposited on the consulting table. A familiar smell gives a clue, seconds before the diagnosis is plain to see. The poor creature has been flystruck and is infested with maggots which are squirming in and out of the skin under the tail. Early cases can be treated, but this poor beast has gone into terminal shock due to toxaemia and is too far gone to be saved. The only option is to put him to sleep. Humid conditions are perfect for blowflies which lay their eggs in any warm, wet environment on the animal. Rabbits or sheep with soiled rear ends, or animals with open wounds are the usual victims and good hygiene and extreme vigilance are necessary to nip the problem in the bud. Too late for this fella, unfortunately. All veterinary staff detest maggots and they are given a good blast of insecticide after the rabbit is dead. Disgusting creatures.

A happier Ben Briggs is last into morning surgery. The antibiotic course seems to have done the trick. We are not sure what these episodes add up to, but can only thank goodness that he seems back to his usual self.

I am looking forward to one of our surgical cases today. A small black cat, Jeremy, had been missing for a week, only returning home last night. Appalled at his appearance, his owners rushed him into yesterday evening's surgery. Instead of his usual bright eyes, he has a large deep ulcer or erosion in the centre of each cornea (the clear front of the eye). The surrounding corneal tissue is cloudy and obscured by a tangle of tiny red blood vessels and both eyes are discharging greenish-white infected material. This is a serious situation requiring prompt attention as both eyes are in danger of perforating. There are many causes of corneal ulceration - trauma and viral infections probably being the most common - but few are as severe as this. There are normally no blood vessels in the cornea, so for an ulcer to heal, capillaries need to grow in from the periphery to provide healing materials for the defect, then regress when repair is complete. Jeremy's eyes have tried to heal thus producing the mass of blood vessels on the surface, but things have gone badly wrong. The cat is miserable and in pain - immediate action is necessary. After antibiotic and painkilling injections, Jeremy is anaesthetised and both eyes are gently cleansed with sterile saline. The plan for each eye is to produce a *conjunctival pedicle graft* - a strip of conjunctiva is dissected free, trimmed to size and sutured to the edges of the ulcer. As the graft is still attached to the conjunctiva at one end, the completed graft looks like a tongue of pink tissue extending over the corneal surface. A magnifying light and special miniature instruments are necessary for the delicate surgery which uses fine sutures - thinner than a human hair - to fasten the graft in place. The graft protects the damaged cornea and provides a blood supply to heal the defect. After a month or so, the tissue bridge is sectioned, leaving the island of transplanted tissue in place. The animal can still see through the surrounding parts of the cornea. Cross-eyed myself after working in miniature, I am pleased with the final result and am tempted to take a photo for posterity, but decide to hold off for a few days. Having a superstitious nature, this is too much like tempting fate and there is still a long way to go before Jeremy can be signed off. I explain to his owners that this is basically a salvage operation to save the eyes and there will be some scarring. He has an Elizabethan collar fitted to prevent him rubbing or scratching the eyes and requires two types of eye drops. He will return every few days to be checked before the tissue bridge is cut.

An evening off tonight and miraculously the cloud has lifted to give some weak rays of evening sunshine, a poor imitation of our usual summers but better than nothing. We drive to the East Neuk of Fife, the coastline between St Andrews and Leven which is dotted with traditional fishing villages - a quieter and less commercial version of Cornwall. Many happy childhood holidays were spent here and a walk round the familiar sights is wonderfully relaxing. The coast road is particularly scenic at this time of year with clumps of poppies and large daisies set against a backdrop of ripening corn and deep blue sea. The East Neuk is a windswept region and the roadside trees are sculpted into strange stunted shapes bending in the direction of the prevailing wind. We enjoy a supper of fish and chips while watching the colourful boats depart for the evening's fishing, then wander round the narrow streets before heading back home again ready to face whatever the weekend has in store.

Thursday 30th July

Still the wet humid weather persists. When the wind gets up, it can be chilly and we have occasionally needed the heating on in the surgery. As the farm surgery is a wooden building, constant sunshine can heat it up and maintaining an even temperature is rather like steering a large ship - changes need to be made well in advance. At this time of year, this mainly involves cutting off the heating early and drawing the blinds before the sun transforms us into a greenhouse. Mrs Cassidy's Ever Ready is in the surgery this morning - Julie has inherited her as the nursing has proved too much for Mrs Cassidy. She will join Julie's small flock when today's ops are finished. She has had a bandage change and is happily munching on a dandelion leaf. The bird is well named as she is ever ready with a soft clucking whenever one of us enters the kennel room. In fact, she is also rather a talented bird, mimicking various sounds in the surgery - so far, we have mistaken her for the autoclave; a purring cat; a snoring dog; and a running tap. Mindful of the possibility that we have a star on our hands, Julie has been attempting to develop Ever's talent by introducing her to a selection of other noises, rewarding any valiant attempts with more dandelion leaves. She has been spending far too much time in front of the bird's cage, brandishing the portable vacuum in one hand and a bouquet of dandelions in the other. I somehow don't think that Ever Ready will be our ticket to stardom, but at the least, we have gained a practice mascot.

As well as providing a stream of seasonal parasites and

itching patients, the weather seems to be adversely affecting our arthritic patients. Mild, dry summer conditions usually suit these animals but this year we are dispensing many more anti-arthritic drugs than usual. The problem is that no two arthritic patients are alike: one will do well on drug *x* while another with identical symptoms will show no improvement. This explains why there are so many anti-arthritic drugs on the surgery shelves. There are also a wide range of complementary therapies and supplements which can help, but the results are not consistent. After one owner sings the praises of - say - raspberry leaves, I mention them to the next few clients only to find that the results are disappointing. Changes in lifestyle are usually necessary for arthritic patients; gentle regular exercise instead of leaping about, walks on flat ground instead of hills and thorough drying after getting wet. Warm, padded beds, keeping slim and having haircuts all help to tip the balance in the patient's favour. Kippen acts as a barometer for other arthritic patients - when he is bad, I expect to see others. He is also a test pilot for any new treatments. He will always need anti-arthritic drugs, but the hope is that the dosage can be reduced. At present, he is on a food supplement which contains shark's fin amongst other things. At the price, we reckon it might be cheaper to go to Florida to catch our own shark. It does seem to help a little. Today, a magnetic collar has been delivered for him to try. There have been some good reports about these; whether Kippen will benefit remains to be seen.

One telephone call today heralds the arrival of a guinea pig which has 'gone off' its legs. Irreverent as ever, Julie remarks that this sounds odd - like someone who has *gone off* a particular outfit. The poor wee pig is in dire straits - severe pneumonia makes recovery unlikely. The irony is that this guinea pig was rescued by his present owner after a life of neglect in dreadful conditions, despite which he stayed healthy.. Now after two months of care and attention, he is at death's door. Life can be very unfair.

Another sad case today, a little cat with a very sore mouth. Her breath smells foul and on opening her mouth, I see that she is suffering from severely inflamed gums. This is known as *gingivitis and* is a major problem in cat medicine. Some cases are caused by

149

dental disease, others by viruses and many are never diagnosed, remaining an intractable problem. There are many treatments with which we try to control the condition, but total cure is seldom possible. It is often the case that when there are many treatments, it is because none are completely effective. The first step for Ellie is to take a blood sample for FeLv and FIV - if one or both are positive, then the outlook is bleak. If the result is negative, then step two is a thorough dental treatment. While we wait for the results, Ellie is given antibiotic and painkiller. Her owner has limited finances to spend on treatment and feels guilty, but even a millionaire could not buy a cure for Ellie. We just have to do our best and act in her best interests.

A walk along the mown hayfield this evening, attired in wellingtons and waterproof. Hard to believe that we are usually in shorts and T-shirts at this time of year. Everything is drenched and we are each followed by a individual flock of flies - this part of the walk is not really a pleasure. We go through the woods which smell wonderfully spicy after the latest downpour and the air is filled with the shrill cries of the buzzards. Four are gliding overhead. There has been much screaming from them recently, we suspect that the youngsters are learning to fly and perhaps the parents are yelling directions. Suddenly, Fintry dives into undergrowth and a pheasant erupts unsteadily into the air, alighting on a nearby branch. It is Farquhar! Thinking the better of a landing nearby, he sets off on a hazardous flight through the trees 'Oh Farquhar, be careful!' I shout, then feel rather foolish when Jay laughs. We are surprised to see him here but, as Jay says, its only several hundred yards as the crow flies from his usual spot - mind you, that's probably about tem miles as the pheasant flies.

Friday 31st July

Not entirely unexpected news about Ellie, the cat with severe gingivitis. She is looking more unhappy and has tested positive for feline leukaemia virus. Putting her to sleep is the kindest option. Although this is very sad, I almost feel a sense of relief.

Ellie's mouth was a dreadful mess and improving matters was a tall order. She has been spared the misery of this unpleasant condition and her owner has been spared the financial drain that prolonged treatment would have brought.

It has been a day for cat blood samples: one patient looks as if he may be hyperthyroid. The big black cat is losing weight despite eating everything in sight and his heart rate is exceptionally high. I can feel an enlarged thyroid gland at the base of his neck so the result is likely to be positive. If so, his owner will need to decide whether to opt for medical or surgical treatment, or even a trip to Glasgow for radioactive iodine therapy. There are several healthy cats on our books who have undergone one or other of these treatments. The final decision depends on several factors such as the state of the other body organs; expense; and the ability to give tablets three times daily. Our other blood sample is a cat with uveitis - inflammation of the coloured part of the eye. This can be due to a variety of infectious agents (which will be tested for in the blood sample) but many are idiopathic, meaning we don't know what is causing the condition. The outlook is variable depending on what the blood sample shows - if FeLv, FIP or FIV are involved, then the cat's future is poor; if the parasite toxoplasmosis is present, then it can potentially be treated. In fact treatment for this has been started already - it will do no harm and might do some good.

Also on eyes, Jeremy has been in for a check-up. His eyes look much more comfortable - the tongue-like grafts stretch from the top of each eye to the site of the ulcer. They appear to have 'taken' and are a healthy pink colour. The rest of the cornea is no longer opaque and the angry-looking blood vessels circling the defect have receded. Jeremy is a much happier cat and I am pleased with his progress. Unfortunately, it is difficult to impress anyone with my handiwork as both owners are squeamish about looking at eyes; even Jay cannot be persuaded to look closely.

A visit to check on Mrs Adams' Lacey continues with the ophthalmological theme. Mrs Adams is wonderfully independent despite increasingly poor eyesight. 'Its lucky that you didn't come on Saturday' she observes while holding on gamely to a recalcitrant

Lacey, 'I wouldn't have been much help to you then'.

'Why not?' I enquire curiously.

'Well,' she says, 'I must have fallen asleep when I was sitting in the garden and when I woke up, I couldn't see at all.'

'What did the doctor say? 'I ask in horror.

'Och well, I didn't like to bother him on a Saturday and I was better when it came to Monday.'

I can only marvel at such self-sufficiency. If that had happened to me, I would have wanted a doctor there by helicopter. As we round off the routine visit with a cup of tea, I notice a pile of large-print books awaiting collection by the library van - they are all horror stories. This sweet little old lady is a fan of the type of extreme horror tales which I would hesitate to read at all. They must have broken the mould when this resilient character was born.

The harvest has finally tottered to a start today with the swathing of the oil-seed rape. An odd looking light-weight vehicle carries out this task which involves cutting the crop to make it easier for the combine harvester to manage. The spindly tractor fairly hurtles up and down the rows of rape working late into the night. It is almost dark at 10.30 pm tonight - what a change from last month when we were often still in the garden or up the hill in daylight which lasted almost till midnight.

Tuesday 4th August

A new month and still no really good weather. The lack of a summer is now a major talking point with clients and aquaintances in the local shops. Someone remarks that so far we just seem to have had a green winter. Apparently, a weather forecaster has predicted that August will be good - this is not the result of painstaking scientific research, but merely invoking the law of averages which suggests that not all three summer months should be terrible. Today is windy with a grudging sun appearing at intervals from behind the clouds. In desperation no doubt, Colin has made a start on the harvest. The combine is lumbering through the large barley field between our house and the river. It will take two days to finish the field if the weather holds and the combine doesn't break down. Every so often, the tractor and trailer run alongside the combine to collect a load of grain then thunder along the road to transfer it to the big barn down at the farm.

Summer or no summer, the weather has not stopped the local cat population from breeding and today we are ploughing through twelve neuterings. It is not long before our first interruption: one young female cat has obviously missed the boat and has had three kittens before dying from unknown causes. The kittens have been reared by a neighbour and are now three weeks old. One kitten was found collapsed this morning and has been rushed to the surgery, not looking good at all. She is pallid, with laboured breathing and a sub-normal temperature – so no one is taking bets on her survival chances. We can only guess what reduced her to this state. The most likely scenario is a pneumonia following inhalation of milk. Some warm fluids are instilled directly into the marrow cavity of her thigh bone. This relatively new technique enables us to get life saving fluid directly into the circulation without having to get into a vein. Kitten veins are difficult to find at the best of times; impossible in a shocked patient. Other drugs are administered with a fine insulin syringe. The owner is an ex-nurse and will provide vital nursing care. In such cases, this is as important as the medical treatment given. The kitten will be warmed gently inside bubblewrap on top of a hot water bottle - not too hot as she is not mobile and cannot move if the heat is too extreme. If her temperature comes up, then some recovery food can be offered. Little patients like this have no energy reserves so this is very important. We will be crossing our fingers for her. Waving patient and owner off, we return to our neutering. Within minutes, an unsettling phone call is received - a pup has eaten a plastic scrubbing brush. Careful questioning reveals that he has chewed the brush up first and some fragments are scattered on the floor. However, he must have swallowed at least one third of it. There are no after effects so far, so we elect to practise masterly inactivity - his owner will inspect everything he passes and will be alert for any signs that all is not well. It is quite incredible how many potentially damaging obstacles can be eaten by dogs with no ill effects. Only a few days ago, an owner entered the surgery clutching something wrapped in tissues - it was a piece of broken crockery almost half an inch across. This had passed right through the dog's gut and appeared in her morning 'duty'. Other dogs have survived eating leather belts with buckles attached, plastic dishes, Lego (a popular one), coins and a watch. One irate owner had his wage packet eaten by his Gordon setter and had to be dissuaded from demanding immediate surgery to recover his loot. Only the fact that the cost of the surgery would at least equal the amount of lost money managed to change his mind.

It can be hard to decide which obstacles require surgical intervention. Generally sharp objects fall into this category, but every case has to be considered separately. We had a very sad case several months ago - a young dog was seen to swallow a small rubber ball but initially seemed to suffer no ill effects so the owners did not contact a vet. Several weeks later, the dog began to vomit and continued to do so for three days before they thought to do something about it. Unfortunately, by that time, the gut in which the ball was lodged was so badly damaged that it ruptured, peritonitis set in and the dog was at death's door by the time it was eventually brought to the surgery. The ball will have stayed in the stomach causing no harm for a few weeks, but once it found its way into the intestine, the results were fatal. The case was particularly depressing for us as, if the dog had been brought to the surgery sooner, immediate action would undoubtedly have saved him.

We have results for the cats' blood sampled on Friday. The

cat with uveitis has tested negative to all infectious causes of the condition thus falling into the idiopathic category. Luckily she is responding well to treatment with corticosteroid drops and will hopefully just get better without us ever knowing what caused the symptoms. Timothy, the black fella is definitely hyperthyroid and after much discussion with his owner, she has opted for surgical treatment. Linda will be operating tomorrow to remove both thyroid glands - cats seem to manage fine without them. Timothy will stay in for a few days to make sure that there are no problems with hypocalcaemia before getting home. The glands which control the body's levels of calcium - the parathyroid glands - are extremely close to the thyroid glands and trauma can cause them to shut down for a while. We supplement all our thyroid cases with oral calcium for some weeks post op, but some may require injections as well. Calcium is necessary for nerve cells to function properly. Low calcium initially produces a slight tremor or twitchiness. If left untreated, the patient can then progress to convulsions and ultimately death, so vigilance is necessary. Most cases have no problems, but you just never know.

My final patient of the evening is a welcome sight - the tiny kitten who was hovering on the brink of death this morning. She has staged a remarkable recovery and is now playing with her brothers in the carrying cage.

It seems to have been a long, 'bitty' day but it is finally finished. The dogs and I cross the road and slip through the fence into the freshly harvested field - a different walk at last. Soon pastures new will be appearing all round us as the harvest progresses. This happy state of affairs continues until Colin gets busy with his muck spreader or ploughs ready for the next year's crop. The dogs are enthralled with all the different smells by the field edge and gallop in ever increasing circles. We can walk right down to the river again. Luckily the tide is in as both dogs plunge straight into the water: mistime these walks and both dogs reappear with leggings of black smelly mud which welds to their bodies and will only fade after rigorous shampooing. We have walked to one of the old fishing bothies, a solid two-roomed affair built from thick blocks of stone. A large open fire place connects the rooms; it must have been cosy in front of the blazing fire waiting to haul the nets in. Now part of the bothy roof is gone and ivy threatens to engulf one side. Swallows have built nests in the corners of the rooms and swoop in through the windows at neck-breaking speed with impressive accuracy. The whole bothy looks in danger of being overgrown by vegetation - swathes of reeds grow within feet of the entrance; rosebay willowherb, Michaelmas daisies and thistles invade the tiny yard. It is sad to see it gradually disintegrate, but it is a peaceful spot in which to sit in contemplation while the dogs splash happily in the river. On the way home, a sodden Fintry rolls in the discarded chaff and emerges like a canine Worzel Gummidge. Banishment to the kitchen will be in order until they both dry out.

Tuesday 11th August

Tuesday has started early - at three am. to be precise - with a phone call from a distraught owner. Her bitch is having pups but there appears to be a problem. The first pup appeared just after midnight and Molly now has six live pups and one dead. For the last hour, she has been straining but there is no sign of another pup. Fearing the worst, I spend the time before her arrival productively. First, Julie must be located. She carries a pager at all times and answers quickly, before rushing to dress and drive to the surgery. I start checking equipment for a probable caesarian section. Instruments, drapes and swabs are already sterilised. There is a full oxygen cylinder on the anaesthetic machine and the vapouriser is full of anaesthetic liquid. Next, I gather together all the special drugs and equipment needed for the job - the usual and those peculiar to caesarians - towels for puppy revival, respiratory stimulants and a cage with a hot-water bottle for those we are satisfied with. When Molly arrives, it is clear that a caesarian will be necessary - the small bitch is obviously tired and is making no progress despite heavy straining. An internal examination reveals a pup's back wedged firmly across the entrance to the birth canal. Unfortunately, there is not the space in dogs to correct such a malpresentation - unlike in cattle or sheep where an entire hand and arm can be inserted into the womb. There is nothing for it but to carry out a caesarian. Jay also comes to help; as vet and nurse are dealing with the anaesthesia and surgery, it is very handy to have a puppy reviver as well. Molly's owner goes home to tend to the other pups and we make a start. A canula is inserted into Molly's vein to administer the initial anaesthetic injection, then a bag of fluid is connected. The exhausted bitch goes off to sleep without a murmur - no doubt pleased to have some respite from her unproductive efforts. The operative site is quickly shaved and prepared and a careful incision opens into the abdomen. A swollen uterus bulges into the wound. Another incision through its wall, then fingers hooked round the stuck pup and suddenly it is out in the world and passed to Jay who skilfully clears the pup's mouth and nose of birth membranes and fluid before holding him steady in a towel and rubbing him firmly with another. This imitates the bitch's licking which dries the pup and stimulates it into breathing. This pup is a little sluggish but after more mouth clearing and rubbing, an outraged squawk is finally elicited, gaining in strength and annoyance as the pup begins his first struggling movements. We are all relieved to have a live pup. Performing a caesarian to find only dead pups is a depressing affair, but with live pups it is a happy event. While Jay has been reviving the pup, I have been checking for more, finding two afterbirths but no more pups. I then stitch the breach in the uterus and close the abdominal wound. Julie reduces the anaesthetic dose as the op. nears the end, so Molly is conscious (although a little wobbly) within 20 minutes. She has had painkillers and a bag of fluid and will have appreciated the rest. The entire operation has only taken 40 minutes but we are far from finished. While Molly recovers in a warm kennel and the pup snuggles into his hottie bottle, the clearing up begins. Whelpings are not clean affairs and the surgery is awash with birth fluids and blood. Everyone sets to with good grace, still on a 'high' from the successful result. Jay and I clear the table and ops room floor, while Julie cleans then resterilises the instruments. Everyone is in good spirits and we joke happily while we work in concert, well used to the routine.

At last it is time for a welcome cup of tea. Molly is now alert and paying attention to her offspring's cries so we carefully introduce the pup to his mother, standing by to make sure she takes to him and is gentle. Instinct takes over and mother and son fall into the age old routine, Mother firmly cleaning and nuzzling while the pup begins his blind, shaky voyage in search of the milk bar. Some pups seem so stupid that it is a wonder that they ever manage to get a feed. We stand by quietly, drinking our tea and watching the happy scene. Molly's owner is summoned, given instructions and departs with the family. Julie also takes her leave and Jay and I try to decide what to do next. It is quarter to six, hardly worth going to bed - even if we did, it would take ages to fall asleep - so we opt for the next best thing - a cooked breakfast, then an early morning walk to the river through the barley stubble. The fields have been a hive of activity these last few days - first the combine, then the baler and finally the tractor towing the bales farmwards on the big trailer. The combine had a mishap the other day and was out of action for most of the morning. The culprit is plain to see as we go down the field - a large oval rock nearly three feet in diameter looms by the verge. It was not there when the field was sown last year, but the action of water and weather has brought it to the surface. This seems quite amazing, but it happens somewhere on the farm almost every year. The digger will be required to root it out and dump it out of the way.

The tide is out again and many birds are prospecting on the wet beach: a heron stands like a statue in the shallows, gulls and sandpipers root in the mud and a cormorant skims low over the water on its way seawards. Behind the house, the buzzards are still making a din and several are wheeling above the woods. I wish we could spend all morning pottering by the river, but today is guaranteed to be fraught. Jay and I are going on holiday tonight and it seems traditional to have a really hectic day before leaving. Today is already going accordingly with our early op. We have a full ops list and two unscheduled urgent cases - a pyometra which goes well and a spaniel tangled in barbed wire. Luckily, the spaniel's wounds are only superficial and are closed using the surgical stapler - a godsend for such tasks, so quick and easy after cleansing and infiltrating the wound with local anaesthetic. There is one tricky laceration by the side of the dog's nose, but the staple pulls the wound edges together well and the owner's daughter is thrilled with her 'punk' dog which matches her own body jewellery. As we plod on through numerous neuterings, three sets of results are faxed through from the lab - *another* task to be done before the close of day: owners to be rung, results discussed and decisions to be made regarding further treatment. The chances of leaving with everything in order and up to date seems to be getting rather remote. It is strange how everything seems to come to a head on the last working day before a break. I keep threatening to book an extra day off *before* we go away but have never managed it yet. By the time our locum appears, an evening in front of the TV seems infinitely more appealing than a long drive to our holiday destination, but - at last - everything comes together: the car is packed, Alastair is fully briefed and we finally set off for our annual break.

Tuesday 18th August

Home again tonight. It is after nine before Alastair has finished summarising all that has been going on and leaves for his next assignment. The weather is noticeably colder than it has been farther south and it is a shock to find it almost dark at 9.30 pm Across the river, lines of flames stretch in sections along the water's edge - stubble burning. Cases are unpacked, washing loaded in the machine and a list made of phone calls and tasks to do tomorrow. We go to bed, mindful that I am now back on call and there is always the possibility that we will not make it through the night without being disturbed. After a week of guaranteed unbroken nights' sleep, this is always a slightly sobering thought.

Wednesday 19th August

The dogs and I start the day with a walk to the river. There is a distinct chill in the air and rosehips, hawthorn berries and brambles are all ripening in the hedgerows. The harvest is only half finished but already our field is being ploughed. I hope for some more good weather so Colin can continue the harvest and leave the field unploughed for a while longer.

The day is quite busy: just catching up takes quite some

time. It takes half an hour just to open the last week's post which is swiftly sorted into do it now, do it later and rubbish. Needless to say, 'do it later' and 'rubbish' by far outweigh the first category. For the rubbish, we have our own personal shredder in Fintry who proudly mangles any paper left within reach. Then there are phone calls to return - nothing urgent but some clients, particularly the older ones, prefer to deal with their familiar vet rather than a locum (or 'locust' as one old lady calls him). Alastair has left everything in good order and, before too long, we can continue with the ops of the day.

The first case is a challenge - remove the ring from a rabbit's leg. The ring is not causing a problem at the moment, but the owner's friend has just lost her rabbit through its ring tightening up and obstructing the circulation. By the time the problem was discovered, the leg was almost gangrenous and the rabbit collapsed and toxic. There was nothing for it but to put him to sleep. The ring is made of tough metal, so removal involves sedating the rabbit then using a hacksaw to cut it off. Budgies too can have problems resulting from rings. We have a budgie patient whose leg was rubbed to the bone by its ring. He recovered remarkably well after it was removed. Luckily, most bird rings are made of plastic which is considerably easier to deal with. As we work, Julie updates me on Ever Ready's progress - the splint has been removed and she is using the leg rather like a child on a scooter. Yesterday, she tried a sand bath which was rather more like a sand shower as dust flew everywhere. However she seems contented and not uncomfortable, so we are reasonably happy with the result.

So far, the day has been quite relaxed but, as always, a phone call soon changes that - an anxious Edith McNaughton reports that once again Meeny may be having disc trouble. Sure enough, when I get there, the little dog is knuckling badly on both hind legs and is clearly experiencing back pain. Back into her cage she goes for enforced rest. I admit that I am concerned about her - this episode is more severe than the last when she was sore but showed no dysfunction. If she does not improve with rest - or if she gets any worse, then surgery to relieve the pressure on the spinal cord may be necessary. Edith is not keen on surgery, but I persuade her that it may be the only option - thank goodness she is insured. The poor dog is fed up with being in her cage but movement may make things worse. We will keep in close touch over the next few days till we see how the land lies.

In the evening, an expedition up the hill to see what has changed while we have been away. Some leaves are already changing colour and falling and the vegetation round the 'thinking' stones is overgrown and dotted with late summer flowers - thistles, vetch, ox-eye daisies and my favourite pale blue cornflowers. The baby deer are growing rapidly and now stretch to midflank on their mothers. They are now part of the main herd. Honky's antlers have shed their velvet, although one or two strands dangle from the points and his neck is becoming thicker and hairier as his hormones begin to prepare him for the rutting season. The flies are still active up the hill, pursuing us mercilessly throughout the walk. Another hazard at this time of year are the *berry bugs* which cause intensive itching in the most embarrassing nooks and crannies of the body - not easy to scratch in public. We fill a bag with fallen twigs for kindling for the newly lit woodburner, aided and abetted by the dogs who think this is a magnificent game, then collect wild raspberries for a supper treat. At home, we are beseiged by hordes of corn lice (or thrips) which invade *everywhere* in the house. Small insects less than a millimetre in length, they coat all surfaces and even work their way under the glass of framed pictures. All glasses and crockery need washing before as well as after, use. Needless to say that after the day's work, we feel as if we have never been away.

Friday 21st August

We have an extra day off today which seems something of an extravagance after having nearly a week away, but today was booked before the holiday was even thought of. When it comes to holidays, we are generally last-minute bookers as we are never sure until the last minute that we can afford to book a locum. Luckily July was busy so we splashed out. There is only morning surgery to do before Linda takes over, but I am quite edgy in case an emergency blows up which necessitates cancelling the day out.

Before surgery, I visit Edith and Meeny. There is no doubt about it, Meeny is worse. She is dragging her hind legs and is unable to control her bladder - the worst signs we could get. Luckily, I have prepared for this possibility and have checked that Edith's friend would be willing to take her and the patient to our orthopaedic specialist for surgery. A quick call to the specialist - who has been forewarned - and they are on their way. It is up to my colleague now and he is an exceptionally skilled spinal surgeon.

Molly, our caesarian from last week, is in during surgery to have her stitches out. The pups are doing well; they are almost double their birth weight and two nearly have their eyes open. Their mother is very proud indeed and the milk bar is in full production. She is eating like a horse - over the next couple of weeks, she will be guzzling nearly three times her normal daily ration to produce enough milk for the babies. Several of the pups are spoken for already. They will be staying in the locality, so I will see them grow into adults. Just like family doctors, we will care for them from cradle to grave. It is this sense of continuity which is so rewarding in general practice.

On this pleasant note, we leave to spend the day with friends. We head off for the coast to visit all our favourite haunts. The weather is beautiful for a change and everyone goes into the sea to a greater or lesser extent. The dogs have a wonderful morning chasing waves and 'rescuing' fronds of seaweed from submerged rocks. Kippen is like a puppy again. Later, we visit the local sea festival - we rummage through the boat jumble, taste local delicacies and concentrate raptly on the cookery demonstrations. The day ends with a superb meal of crab, lobster and plenty of wine. A wonderful day out - I am feeling really spoilt with all this time off.

Thursday 27th August

An early start to check on our in-patient - Mickey, yet another hyperthyroid cat. He was operated on yesterday and is due to spend a couple of days in the surgery to make sure that he has no problems with low calcium levels. Unfortunately, Mickey has had a balance problem from birth and evaluating him is proving difficult. As he totters towards me across the floor, I finally come to the conclusion that he might be better off at home. His owner knows the extent of his imbalance very well, so will be better placed to spot any worsening. She is at home all day and will be able to watch him closely and contact us immediately if she suspects a problem. The decision whether to hospitalise patients or send them home depends on several factors. If the owner is sensible and likely to be around, then I am quite keen to see certain patients go home. The animal will be more relaxed in familiar surroundings and a well-briefed owner will be alert to any deleterious changes.

We have a mixed bag for ops today. As usual,we have some cats to neuter for one of the charities. We routinely empty their bladders before operating and are amused to note that the bladders are becoming increasingly full as the day wears on. Our bitch spay also requires microchipping. The tiny microchip is only the size of a grain of rice and is detected by a special scanner which reads the chip's unique identification number. This is recorded on a national data base together with the owner's name and address. Thus if a lost microchipped animal is scanned, the owner can be contacted. Microchipping can be carried out on conscious patients with no trouble, but some owners prefer the idea of it being done when their pet is anaesthetised for a routine op.

There is time afterwards for a quick walk down one of our remaining unploughed fields. In the adjoining field, the tractor is ploughing busily followed by an enthusiastic and noisy crowd of seagulls. A neighbour mentioned recently that he occasionally also had a buzzard following the plough - yet more proof of what lazy birds they are. We pass hedges of rosehips, hawthorn and brambles before climbing down the banking on to the shore. We amble slowly along the water's edge. I look for attractive stones for the rockery while Kippen searches for balls and Fintry fruitlessly chases rabbits back to their burrows in the banking. There is a plastic safety helmet lodged by some driftwood. These turn up on the shore surprisingly often - one wonders what has happened to the wearer.

A phone message from Edith and a fax from the orthopaedic surgeon are waiting when we return. Meeny has had her operation and is due to come home tomorrow. Unfortunately, during the operation, there was a complication - some of the prolapsed disc material was stuck too firmly to the spinal cord to be totally removed, so Meeny's outlook remains guarded. Although she has recovered well from the surgery, she is still unable to walk. We will now have an anxious time waiting to see if she is going to make it.

Friday 28th August

An amusing start to the day in morning surgery. Fresh from watching a veterinary programme on television last night, our client enthusiastically set about removing a tick on her pet's neck with tweezers - unfortunately, it is a wart and, not surprisingly, proved reluctant to be dislodged. Coincidentally, the very next client has been putting ointment on what she thought was a wart - but is in fact a tick! Such confusion is not uncommon: occasionally, we will have a client wanting advice about a wart or tick on their pet's abdomen. There is much hilarity and embarrassment when we point out that, if they look really closely, there are five on either side - and that they are in fact nipples.

I have a visit this morning, a trip over the hill to see elderly Mrs Cross with her equally elderly terrier, Judy. This is a routine trip to clip Judy's nails - which takes five minutes - followed by coffee and biscuits with Mrs Cross which takes considerably longer. Although having reached the grand old age of ninety, Mrs Cross is very much 'all there' and we cover many subjects during our 'crack'. She has lived in this area all her life and her conversation is a veritable local history lesson. Today, she recalls the Saturday nights when she and her sisters would walk over the hill to our neighbouring farm. The bothy there housed several young farmhands and parties were regular events. No alcohol, of course, but everyone would bring some food - perhaps a dumpling, or some freshly baked scones. The walk over the hill is around five miles each way, so it is amazing that they had any energy left for dancing. Of course, all the farm bothies are gone now, just like the fishing bothies. Mechanisation means that the farms can be easily worked by only one or two men. Those bygone days must have been hard, but fun too.

I reluctantly tear myself away as today's lone operation is waiting at Fern with Julie. Sylvester the rat has a mammoth growth to be removed. He is elderly and his owner expected him to pass on before the growth grew to the extent it has, but Sylvester is still bright and perky and tripping over his massive appendage. From the rear, Sylvester and appendage resembles a motorbike and sidecar! Careful preparation is important for such a major task on such a small animal. The heating is full on and the room is hotting up as Sylvester gets his anaesthetic injection. I have had to estimate the weight of the growth and subtracted it from the total before calculating the dose required. We later discover that Sylvester weighs 240 grams and the lump 120 grams. Once asleep, he is placed on an insulated bed, the spotlights are switched on and his face is covered by a homemade anaesthetic mask fashioned from a plastic syringe case. Even his tail is wrapped in bubble wrap to limit heat loss. Some warm saline is administered under his skin to keep him hydrated and the op. begins. The growth shells out quite easily from the surrounding tissues, only one or two blood vessels to tie off, then out it comes. This leaves us with a large redundant sack of skin which is trimmed away (ignoring Julie's suggestion that Sylvester might like a rucksack) and the wound is closed. Still swathed in bubblewrap, the sleepy rat is placed on a warm water bottle and left to recover in a warm cage. So far, so good.

Some lunch while Sylvester comes round, then off to collect my friend Margaret and her new pup for a walk. Our local grocer, Jim is delivering her week's supplies when I arrive - we already met earlier this morning at Mrs Cross's house. His visits are vital for many people living off the beaten track as few buses cover this area. While Margaret gets ready, Jim and I discuss the merits of my new car - a four-wheel drive Tundra, just like his. In this area, they probably account for one car in ten. We are also over-represented by Jeeps, Landrovers and other 4 x 4 vehicles. Although not the most elegant of vehicles, the Tundras are work horses, as happy in fields or farm tracks as they are on motorways. Not surprisingly, the trip up our hill causes no problems and we are spared the slog up the steep track which is so uncomfortable for Kippen's old legs. We amble leisurely to the stones while the dogs initiate the pup into all the local scents and burrows. We have another novelty for him: there is an echo at the thinking stones - in her early days, the echo of my drawn out 'Fi..n..n.n..treee' would send our pup tearing off down the valley in pursuit. She is wise now and ignores any such commands. The new pup is initially galvanised with interest, but being a collie and therefore intelligent, soon learns that this is just one of these 'daft human games'.

After surgery, a visit to Meeny. She is so happy to be home and tries hard to come to greet me, but her poor hind legs drag helplessly behind. It is only a week post op. so there is hope yet, but it is sad to see her so powerless and Edith is obviously upset. One plus is that she seems to have regained bladder control, only passing urine when carried into the garden. There is nothing for it but to wait it out and pray that things improve. It does take time for inflammation to settle down and no two cases are exactly the same, but to be optimistic of her recovery, we would really want to be seeing a good improvement by three to four weeks post op. In the meantime, all we can do is keep the little dog's spirits up. Edith has been shown how to carry out physiotherapy on Meeny's legs and I have no doubt that she will carry out her instructions to the letter. I fervently hope that she does improve; I can think of no worse scenario than having to put her to sleep after surgery and weeks of fruitless nursing. In fact, I don't even like to think about it.

Saturday 29th August

A pleasant but brisk surgery this morning, the kind that are a joy to work - nothing serious; many conditions improving; and all owners happy and chatting in the waiting room. Jeremy, the cat with the corneal grafts is one of our patients. It is now five weeks since his surgery and it is time to cut the bridge of tissue which brought healing materials to the corneal defect. Some sedative, a few drops of local anaesthetic into the eyes and it is a relatively easy job to pass a blade of our fine scissors under the tissue and snip it off. There is now just a patch of pink tissue left in the centre of each eye. This should become less apparent with time. Although it is basically a salvage procedure, the surgery has been a success - the cat still has sight in each eye, they are painfree and the defects have been sealed. By chance, our next patient, Mac the Jack Russell terrier, also has a corneal ulcer acquired after a run in with next door's cat. Luckily, it is nowhere near as severe as Jeremy's was and Mac is sent off with antibiotic drops and an appointment for a check-up next week. A phone call from Sylvester's owner puts the icing on the cake. He has recovered extremely well and seems back to normal. His owner is absolutely delighted.

I'm glad that today has gone so smoothly as it is nurse Gillian's last day. Now that her children are older, she is returning to full-time human nursing - our loss, their gain. The surgery is almost like a family and it is unsettling when someone leaves. Gillian will be a hard act to follow. Mrs Cassidy comes in with a good luck card and a box of chocolates. Gillian is touched by this gesture. As Mrs Cassidy lives alone and is slightly disabled, she calls in occasionally for a chat and for help with some of the trickier tasks in her life such as chasing hens and zipping up dresses. 'Can you do me a big favour?' she asked one day, turning her back on Gillian (who wondered what was coming) and pulling up her cardigan - 'Pull up my corsets for me.' Gillian reached blindly into the depths, connected with elastic and gave a hefty tug. 'Ahhh, thats better!' exclaimed a satisfied Mrs Cassidy before going on her way. Our new nurse will have to provide the same level of service - I wonder whether to warn her or to let her find out for herself. First, I have to appoint someone. I am still reeling from the tremendous response to my small advert in yesterday's local paper and have already become familiar with the coy, self-conscious approach of clients *sans* animals, sidling in to enquire about the vacancy. This afternoon, tomorrow and Monday too are to be spent interviewing applicants. Many of the candidates are my friends and choosing is going to be difficult.

Three interviews later, I have had enough and head for the great outdoors. In a fit of enthusiasm, dogs and I aim for the summit of the hill behind ours, but are beaten back by head high bracken and nettles. This walk is obviously off limits until later in the year. Several falling leaves brush past us on their way down and the first whiff of the burnt smell of autumn tingles in my nostrils. A hint of mustard colour tinges the forest. I feel a thrill of anticipation - autumn is the best time for walking and the sights and smells are truly sensational.

A call comes through on my pager just as we are nearing home. An old Westie has taken a turn for the worse. He has been failing for weeks (bad heart, bad legs, more not working than working) and although some treatment bucked him up initially, the end result is inevitable. Today is the first time that he would not get out of his basket or even wag his tail when his owner, Big George, came home. Big George is over six feet tall and almost as wide and is generally regarded as the Hard Man of Abercromby, especially in the local taverns. Covered in tattoos visible through a skimpy singlet, he is not a man one would like to cross, yet here he is, breaking his heart over his little Westie. Most vets soon learn not to judge by appearances: the outrageous punk may nurse his kitten through thick and thin, while the elegant, well-spoken couple may have no use for their 'darling' if he comes down with something messy or inconvenient. One couple who attend the surgery will pay any amount of money if we will just take their pet away into a kennel when it is ill and return it when it is better again. Poor George is a little embarrassed to be in tears, but is too upset to really care. He loved his dog with all his big heart and the feeling was obviously mutual. Frequently a strange thing happens when an animal is put to sleep. Client and vet chat, reminiscing about earlier days and sometimes laughing at some remembered antic. Peculiar to see hilarity amongst so much grief. So George and I talk for a while, remembering Albert's past, then off the big man goes, cradling the little body tenderly in his massive arms. I don't envy what he has to go through over the next few days and I fervently hope that no one crosses him in the meantime.

Tuesday 1st September

A truly beautiful autumn day greets the first of the month. Warm sunlight bathes the golden stubble fields while wisps of morning mist thread delicately through the trees. The hedgerows are heavy with red rosehips, purple-black elderberries and brambles. The swallows are gathering on the telephone wires before swooping and diving across the fields in search of insects. Judging by the number of insects in our kitchen, they should be very well fed. The mild weather is also proving popular with parasitic insects - fleas and berry bugs are out in force and itching animals outnumber any other patients during surgeries. The bright orange berry bugs can often be found between toes, in armpits or other nooks and crannies of affected victims, while chestnut brown fleas are more usually glimpsed running for cover on the animal's trunk. We feel that we are under siege by insects. Cath, our part-time nurse, tells an interesting tale of her trip to Turkey. Apparently bus companies there are in fierce competition for customers and a perk offered by several is the presence on the bus of a small boy with a large spray for killing insect pests. Cath says that they were often reduced to taking a bus trip purely for the relief afforded by the boy with the spray - perhaps we should engage a local youth for the waiting room, several possibles have already tried applying for the soon-to-be-vacant nurse's post.

I have now finished interviewing and a decision has to be made. This is far from easy, but at last the best is chosen. I telephone to offer a surprised Alice the job. She will start this Friday. It is great to hear her so thrilled, but now I have to do the task I dread - phoning the unsuccessful applicants. They were all so good; I feel like a 'hatchet man' afterwards. Personnel management is definitely not for me. I can now return to pure veterinary work with great relief and redoubled enthusiasm.

We have a mixed bag to attend to at the farm surgery today. The first case is quite urgent: a ferret was rushed into Clayfern surgery, suddenly choking and coughing. Although the symptoms had abated when he arrived, he was still upset, especially when touched near the throat. We now need to anaesthetise him to have a good look. Visions flash through my mind of chicken bones lodged in inaccessible places. Will the owner want to pay for X-rays and major surgery? Or will we be faced with nothing to explain the symptoms - just a ferret with a cough? There is not much room in a ferret's mouth, but with the aid of a slim otoscope (usually used for examining ears), examination of the back of the throat becomes possible and 'Hallelujah!' - something is visible lodged at the entrance of the larynx. Grasping carefully with the aptly named crocodile forceps, I gently withdraw two pieces of conifer twig. Further inspection down the inch of windpipe that will accomodate the 'scope reveals no further obstruction. Hopefully we have retrieved the only foreign bodies present. The wakening ferret is injected with antibiotic and anti-inflammatory drugs and is wrapped up for recovery.

Next we have the inevitable cats for neutering, six altogether and each one in a different type of basket. There are wicker ones with short lengths of wood pushed through woven loops to secure the door; plastic carriers with an assortment of locks; and a homemade contraption made out of a washing basket lashed to a board with elasticated luggage straps. The latter requires extreme caution to avoid injury from recoiling elastic. Most veterinary workers could probably produce a Ph.D. thesis on the wide range of receptacles available. It reminds me (in a lateral sort of way), of earlier days in farm practice. The same principle applied to farm gates - each one different and a tribute to the owner's ingenuity.

Our final task is the repair of an umbilical hernia in a five-month-old kitten. A hernia occurs when the abdominal muscle layer is not complete and a sac lined with peritoneum - the thin membrane lining the inside of the abdomen - protrudes through the gap to form a bulge under the skin. Small hernias can be left, but this one is almost three inches long and allows abdominal organs to pass freely into the sac. There would be serious consequences for the kitten should the hernia contents twist, or even if he sustained a wound on the sac. Just a skin wound could allow his intestines to spill out of his abdomen. We have been aware of the hernia since the kitten was little, but have delayed surgery until he grew so that there might be more spare tissue to be utilised to close the defect. There are commercial products available - mesh made out of polyester - to provide a permanent patch over the defect, but the price is beyond our client's means. The kitten is anaesthetised, placed on his back and prepared for surgery. Cutting through the skin, the extent of the defect is strikingly apparent. I could - if I wanted - put four fingers through the gap at one time. A large hole for a small kitten. The contents of the hernial sac are dissected free and returned to the abdomen. Next, the edges of the hole are freshened before suturing them together. A strong synthetic suture material is used and tension stitches are placed to spread the strain. Julie and I joke - rather uneasily - that the kitten will have a 'sucked in' appearance as if held in by corsets. At last the job is completed. Amazingly the wound edges have come together, but the owner is advised strongly to keep the patient very restricted in a cage for the next week and to feed him several small meals daily instead of less frequent large feeds. We do not want any increased pressure put on the fresh suture line.

We are just sitting down for a much needed cup of tea when a phone call comes from a client seriously worried about her dog. Over the last two weeks, Lassie the collie has slowed down considerably, is reluctant to go for walks and is only picking at food. When she arrives, I am amazed at her weight loss since I last saw her striding out on a walk along the road. Examining her, a list of possibilities is automatically forming in my mind. Unfortunately, the list is still rather long at the end of the examination as there is nothing diagnostic to be seen - just a 'hingy' dog. In such a case, further tests are necessary to reach a diagnosis. The first step in Lassie's case is a blood sample which her owner will take straight to the lab to speed up the results. In the meantime, we administer some empirical treatment and arrange an appointment for tomorrow. She does not look well and instinct tells me that trouble is a brewing.

Wednesday 2nd September

Lassie's results do not bode well - there is evidence of severe liver malfunction. Yesterday's treatment has produced no discernible improvement. There are many conditions which can affect the liver ranging from inflammation to infection to tumour. An X-ray has shown neither an enlarged nor a shrunken liver and no obvious masses are detectable in the organ. We have now reached an impasse - to get a definitive diagnosis, a sample of liver tissue would be required. To obtain this would require either a full exploratory operation under general anaesthesia, or a biopsy guided by ultrasound scan. Lassie is in no state for an anaesthetic and her owner does not wish to be referrred to a specialist centre for a scan. As is often the case, we are left with the option of treating to see if an improvement is forthcoming. We will provide optimum conditions for recovery by giving supportive treatment. Lassie is admitted and put on an intravenous drip. Other drugs are administered and we will wait to see if there is any response. She does not appear to be in pain, but will be feeling lousy. Liver complaints frequently lead to the patient feeling rather like humans do with a hangover - nauseous and weak. The fluids should help to reduce the nausea and specialised food will give the liver the best chance of regeneration.

Having Lassie in the surgery inevitably produces extra work. Her drip requires frequent monitoring to ensure that it does not block or become twisted and the dog needs occasional trips outside to relieve herself. She also appreciates company and TLC (tender loving care - a mainstay of good veterinary treatment).

It seems only moments after I have finally sunk onto the settee tonight when an emergency call comes from Clayfern - a cat has come home with its stomach stained with blood and the owner fears serious injury. Even worse, they have no transport so I am doomed to travel into the Clayfern surgery. I am feeling seriously sorry for myself when I set out - there is definitely no rest for the wicked. This is my first trip into Clayfern in the dark since spring, but what a pleasant night. A crescent moon shines high above the town reflecting a silver pathway on the river. In the moonlight, a ghostly white form moves between the trees - this is our 'feral' sheep. She suddenly appeared in the neighbourhood over two weeks ago and has been living wild in the woods. No one knows who she belongs to and no one seems to be looking for her. She is frequently spotted strolling up farm tracks or grazing contentedly by the roadside. I resolve to bring her some carrots or potatoes when she next appears. Cat and owners are waiting at the surgery door and we rush straight into the consulting room. For someone so seriously injured, the cat seems surprisingly bright and waltzes across the floor searching for an escape route. Once detached from the window ledge, she is tipped over to expose her abdomen which certainly looks rather as if it might be streaked with blood. This is not due to injury however, but the result of water making contact with flea 'dirt'. As fleas eat blood, their waste products stain a rusty red colour when wet. Judging by her tinted underside, she is well infested! Amusing certainly, but hardly an emergency. There have been several letters in our veterinary magazine about similar 'false alarms' - the emergency lump which turned out to be a piece of pink chewing gum stuck to the foot; the leg slashed to the bone - or rather - a white lollipop stick attached to the fur by the remains of a strawberry lolly. In all these cases, the owners appear to have panicked without any regard to their pet's demeanour. Surely - they might think that the animal might be at least a little distressed if the leg was truly slashed to the bone. However, I cannot be too superior as I have committed a similar *faux pas* - one evening, we were awaiting the arrival of a dog seriously injured in a traffic accident. A client was just entering the consulting room when the outer door opened, admitting a lady carrying a small dog in her arms. Across the waiting room, it looked as if his brain might even be exposed, as a sinister red and white mixture coated his head. Hurriedly requesting our client to return to her seat, I ushered the 'accident' into my room. Although geared up for emergency action, incongruous facts flashed through my mind: Why does the owner look so unconcerned? Why is there another dog at her heels? Soon all was embarrassingly clear. Both dogs were coming in for their annual booster and during the car journey to the surgery, the big dog had been sick over the little one! All that was hurt was the little dog's pride.

Saturday 5th September

Before morning surgery, Lassie's owner arrives to take her home. It is very hard to gauge her progress - one minute she looks much brighter, the next she looks miserable. She has been on a drip for three days now and is certainly eating a little better. Her owner has decided to see how she is at home over the weekend - make or break time.

This is the first Saturday surgery for Alice, Gillian's successor. Jay has come in to help as Saturdays can be hectic, but we are let off lightly with a steady, friendly hour. The hernia kitten checks out fine and our ferret with the fir is back to normal. As yet, no Mrs Cassidy. Julie drops, in full of excitement - she has been to an antique fair this morning and has found a genuine old veterinary instrument to add to my collection. It was to be for Christmas, but in view of the circumstances, she has decided to give it to me now. The instrument consists of two bracket-shaped brass arms, hinged at one end. Protruding inward from each arm are several metal spikes and at the opposite end to the hinge, there is a screw which can be used to tighten the clamp causing the spikes to mesh together. This is a hernia clamp. In times gone by, the contents of the hernia were pushed back into the abdomen before the clamp was applied over the base of the loose sac of skin and tightened so that the spikes intertwined. The resulting inflammatory reaction sealed the hernia for ever. It doesn't do to imagine the unfortunate animal's response while the device was applied. Thank goodness,we have progressed since these days. The hernia kitten's owner regards Julie with deep suspicion when she explains the instrument's use. Alice, thankfully, seems to share our rather morbid interest and carefully places the clamp in pride of place in the display cabinet in the waiting room.

As usual, after our relaxing surgery, a walk is in order and we strike off towards the river. It is a still, misty day and as we pass by the farm, the deep rumble of the grain dryer can be heard across the field. At this time of year, Colin spends up to twelve hours a day loading and unloading grain into the gas-powered dryer. The weather has been too poor for him to finish the harvest as yet. It has not been the best of years for farmers really with beef and lamb scares and bad weather for growers. The season has been poor for countryside fruits as well. Usually at this time of year, the bushes by the river are heavy with damsons, sloes and wild cherries, but today only a few sloes are to be seen. It was frosty when the blossom was flowering, so there were hardly any bees around to carry out the necessary pollination. The only good autumn crops are the brambles which are black and succulent. They blossom later than the others and thus avoided the frost. As usual the dogs help themselves, gently prising the berries away from the prickly stems. Dainty, small-scale flowers are growing amongst the stubble - forget-me-nots and miniature pansies, while by the burn, milky white bindweed weaves amongst the willows - somewhat muted colours after the vibrant poppies and daisies of high summer.

Sunday 6th September

Today Jay and I have planned a quick trip to a local country fair to visit some friends who are exhibiting their garden wares. I have an ulterior motive - a requirement for a new pair of wellies since the old ones have sprung a leak. Our first stop is at an outdoor clothing stall which sports an impressive supply of green wellingtons in an assortment of styles. My new pair even come with an instruction manual, which causes gales of laughter amongst our friends. We are used to buying cheap and cheerful rubber boots, but apparently instructions are the norm at the more exclusive end of the market. The manual even gives the degree of electrical insulation provided by the soles - you never know when this might come in handy! Another exhibit catches my eye as we tour the show - a basket- making stall displays an array of goods woven from willow saplings. This seems like a good way to utilise the willow branches cut by the tractor at our river's edge. Jay sighs at the possibility of yet another hobby on the horizon - but at least it doesn't sound too expensive. The basket-makers are full of useful advice - ideally it is better to cut willow saplings later in the year when the sap has died back. Another display catches our friend's eye - the thatching exhibit. She lives in a thatched cottage whose roof has been recently mended, so she has a particular interest in the techniques involved.

Reeds for thatching also grow on our river's edge and are harvested by hovercraft - an interesting meshing of old and new technologies. Jay has volunteered to build an outdoor kennel for the semi-feral cat which has adopted our friend since her old cat died. As there are plenty of reed beds near home, Jay and I secretly decide to thatch the new kennel to match the house and take a close interest in how it's done. The finished article will be rather a fun surprise for our friend's birthday. Creative urges are running amok, but we are swiftly brought down to earth by the shrill bleeping of my emergency pager. An elderly dog is virtually collapsed after vomiting all day. We need to leave immediately and head for the surgery. At least we have had long enough for a good look around and to buy what we came for. It happens occasionally that we no sooner arrive somewhere than we are called back. This is particularly irritating if you have just parted with a hefty entrance fee.

Back at the surgery, my heart sinks as a limp, slobbery Effie Low is carried in from the car. This will not be dealt with quickly, allowing us to return to the fair. Effie is weak, dehydrated and unable to stand for long. There are several possibilities - acute gastroenteritis due to infection, poison or foreign body; infected womb; liver or kidney malfunction; pancreatitis; or even a tumour. First priority is to try to regain lost ground before we go in search of a diagnosis. Effie's owners leave and we get to work setting up a drip and administering useful drugs. She is ill enough to lie still on an X-ray plate while a film is exposed - nothing obvious shows up. It will be up to a blood sample to bring us to a diagnosis, but the lab will not be open until the morning. However, a drop of blood on a simple test strip does show elevated levels of substances normally passed out by the kidneys.

By teatime, Effie is a little brighter and manages the short walk into the garden to pass urine. This requires careful juggling with dog lead in one hand and drip in the other, but Effie's progress is slow and the trip is completed without incident. Testing the voided urine shows excess protein in the sample - which strengthens the case for kidney malfunction. This is how diagnosis goes, accumulating more and more information until we finally get an answer. After a few hours, the list of possibilities is shrinking: foreign body and infected womb seem less likely due to the negative X-rays and the blood-test strip and urine results point towards probable kidney involvement. The evening passes peacefully - Effie is more comfortable, sleeping quietly in the kennel while the drip runs smoothly into her vein. At least she has not been sick again, but her response to treatment and the blood results will dictate what her future will be.

Monday 7th September

Effie needs to be carried into the garden this morning and supported while she passes urine. She has also vomited a small drink of water - things are looking rather bleak, which is particularly disappointing after yesterday's improvement. We decide to hang on for the blood results but her owners are aware that her chances are poor. Again the unfortunate swansong effect has falsely raised everyone's hopes. As feared, the results show severe levels of kidney malfunction, so we concede that we are fighting a losing battle and end it for Effie with a lethal injection into her drip. Julie cuddles her while she goes to sleep for the last time.

Both of us are upset and the day turns suddenly sour. A pall of depression hangs over the surgery for a time as we work, but we gradually get back to normal as routine takes over. Unfortunately, today is destined to be miserable as, not long after Effie's demise, Lassie's owner telephones: after a week of hanging in the balance, Lassie's will to battle on has evaporated and there is no doubt that she is going downhill. Jane asks me to put her to sleep at home where she is reclining on the settee - not in pain but very weak. The deed goes smoothly and Lassie is gone as well. Jane is sad but philosophical as we carry Lassie to her resting place - an impressively large hole at the top of the garden. Incongruously, I wonder how she got the sides so sheer. We reminisce about happier days for a few minutes, partly to catch our breath: even after illness, Lassie is still quite solid and the garden is exceedingly steep. Then I depart, leaving Jane to grieve.

Feeling more like the Grim Reaper than a healer, I trail unenthusiastically in to evening surgery unwilling to take on any more misery or misfortune. Luckily, the first case is a new puppy for first vaccination. Three months ago, his owners were in the same position as Jane, saying a heart rending goodbye to an old faithful friend ravaged by cancer. However, time heals and life goes on (all the old cliches really are true) and now they have their hands full with a nine-week-old bundle of mischief. Just what the doctor ordered for all of us.

Friday 11th September

Today, we have a 'Big' operation to carry out and I am both excited and apprehensive about it. The patient is Don, an elderly black Labrador. Over a short time, he has developed an unpleasant ulcerated skin tumour on the front lower part of his hind leg just above his toes. A biopsy has told us that at least it is unlikely to spread, but we have the technical difficulty of how to fill the defect once the tumour is removed. A skin graft would be a possibility, but we have decided to try an exciting new product - a material produced from pig small intestine which acts as a scaffold, allowing skin to grow over the defect. Until yesterday evening, Don was the only operation scheduled for today, but when the terrier with the corneal ulcer - Mac - returned to surgery yesterday, I was dismayed to find that his ulcer had not healed. Usually after one week, blood vessels will migrate into the ulcer carrying healing materials, then regress leaving a perfectly intact cornea, but in Mac's case, there is absolutely no sign of any healing; the wound in fact appears to be slightly worse. There was nothing for it but to book him in for this morning. After anaesthetising Mac, the plan is to tidy up the ulcer edges, removing any loose tissue before performing what is known as a punctate keratectomy, rather a grand name for quite a simple procedure. It involves making small indentations in the cornea around the ulcer using the point of a hypodermic needle. This is supposed to encourage the healing response. Finally, the dog's third eyelid is stitched across the eye to form a protective patch. Antibiotic drops and painkillers are administered and Mac will return in a week for the third eyelid patch to be detached. Hopefully, healing should be well advanced by then. All fairly routine, but time is pressing on and we have not even started on Don yet. His will be a complicated procedure and we do not want to be rushing.

At last, we make a start. The tumour looks even more grotesque once the leg is shaved and prepared. The skin is remarkably tough and the first incision feels like cutting into gristle. It takes over an hour - and two pairs of scissors - to detach the abnormal oval of skin, only removing it at a painfully slow rate of about two millimetres per minute.

Eventually, it is removed and the hole gapes - an uncomfortably large defect ten centimetres long by six wide. Time to unpack the new material. When dry, it feels and behaves like thin parchment, but when immersed in sterile saline as per the instructions, it is more like wet tissue paper. It is quite a job to drape it cleanly over the wound free from large wrinkles but at last it is in place and I begin the slow task of stitching it to the skin edges. Finally we are finished; it only remains to carefully apply a special non-stick bandage and return Mac to his kennel. He has been under the anaesthetic for two and a half hours, a long time for an old dog. Operating for two and a half hours is also a long time for an old vet and nurse so as soon as we can leave Don for a few minutes, we retire for a restorative cup of tea. Unlike our usual operating sessions where we chatter most of the time, the need to concentrate today has kept us uncharacteristically quiet so we need to catch up.

During our short break, we return to a popular current theme - that of the worm-charming competition. A Chinese whisper suggested that such a competition was held in the neighbouring county and Julie assumed that my previous experience of comparing badger activity with earthworm availability might give us a head start. From a mere casual comment, the idea has grown in feasibility to such an extent that the whole surgery (plus several intrigued customers and friends) have been considering the ideal worm-charming method. As worms appear after rain, our initial plan was to water 'our' square; then Alice noticed a rich source of worms under a piece of roofing felt and this too was added to the plan. The mental challenge has exercised all our brains and I knew that the idea was gathering steam when the first words from Alice one morning were Hot water! As worms like humidity, this seemed eminently reasonable. Many suggestions have been volunteered - earth-pounding machines and *Viagra* to mention but a few. Edith MacNaughton suggested dog food, but the court is out on that one. As the idea snowballed, it occurred to us that this would be an ideal arena in which to advocate the worming of pets - a perfect publicity stunt for responsible pet ownership. As we spayed and castrated away, we even designed the campaign T-shirts: on the front - a picture of worms from a worming brochure surrounded by the legend - 'Fern Veterinary Surgery, the BEST wormers!' On the back - a hen (in the style of Ever Ready) pulling a worm from the ground ...'Better out than in!' It is really quite sad (not to say worrying) that such a topic can get even passing consideration in the thoughts of three supposedly mature veterinary professionals. Anyway, Julie has both good and bad news today. We have been unable to track down a local competition anywhere but her friend surfing the internet has unearthed a national competition in England. Unfortunately, it has just taken place. Initial despondency about this turns into keen anticipation when I suggest a surgery outing to next year's competition.When friends and partners are updated on this latest plan, initial consternation at our proposed absence next year is tempered by relief that we will be making fools of ourselves far from home territory.

Monday 14th September

There has been an element of the unusual during the first part of today. Our first case is rushed through the door the minute it is opened. Mrs Scobie's washing machine was no sooner switched on this morning than she heard a heavy clonking inside. Investigating, she was horrified to see her new kitten whirling round in the wash. After a moment's panic trying to open the door, she wrapped the sodden kitten in a towel and rushed to the surgery. Luckily, apart from being badly scared and extremely wet, the kitten seems to have suffered no ill effects. He is also remarkably clean. A correspondent to the Veterinary Record recently reported seeing a cat who had completed the entire wash cycle and had miraculously survived - as had its generous population of fleas. This made the point very clearly that more than washing is required to remove fleas from their victim.

Before beginning our ops list at the farm surgery, I have arranged to see a former neighbour's dog. The family are only back in this area on holiday, but their old dog has unfortunately gone into terminal heart failure and will have to be put to sleep. He and I are old pals so the deed is carried out easily and peacefully. I assume that cremation will be required but Angus the owner has other ideas. 'He was born here, so it's only right that he should come to rest here,' he announces 'Could you lend me a spade?' Thus it is when Julie arrives that she witnesses the deceased being carried by one owner while the other follows with a spade. It looks as if we have begun a new line in DIY funerals. They bring the spade back while we are operating, sad but satisfied that the dog is installed in one of his favourite spots on the hill.

I call in on Edith and Meeny on the way to evening surgery. Although cheerful and alert, Meeny's hind legs are still not working. It is now over three weeks since her surgery; ideally we should be seeing some improvement. Little prickles of anxiety thread their way round my heart and without panicking Edith, I try to introduce a note of concern. I don't want to upset her unnecessarily, but it is better in the long run if she is kept fully in the picture. We must look a strange sight, two sombre women sitting with a happy dachshund, dragging her useless hind legs, desperately trying to attract our attention. All fingers and toes to be kept firmly crossed for the foreseeable future. I leave promising to keep in touch as often as possible.

During evening surgery, both our ops from Friday are in for check ups. There is nothing much to see with Mac. The third eyelid is still firmly stitched across the cornea and the dog seems comfortable. He is booked in for stitches out in a week's time. Don is his bright and bouncy self as always, on the hunt for biscuits.

Once in the consulting room, he automatically takes up position by the worktop, eyes willing the jar of doggy treats to move in his direction. He is sporting a very smart fabric sock over his bandage, handmade by June his owner. The bandage is wringing wet and the smell is distinctly offputting. Foot bandages have a tendency to become somewhat 'ripe'when in place for any length of time, but this has only been on for three days, so I begin to remove the dressing with considerable trepidation. Don reclines on his side, June holding his leg while Alice feeds the front end with treats. We don't know exactly what to expect, but the graft is still intact and there is no sign of infection - probably as much as we can expect at this stage. This is going to be a long haul.

There is a strange car by the house when I arrive home - it has been a long day and I really hope that it is not an emergency, but Jay has opened up the surgery so it looks rather like it. Once inside, I can only see Jay, Alison, owner of the exasperating Chloe and her friend Mavis. Alison is taking photos of the equipment and Mavis is writing notes. What *are* they doing? Jay looks rather guilty. Eventually all becomes clear. Alison and Mavis are part of a local group whose hobby is to build and kit out dolls' houses - we call them 'The dolls' house six'. Jay has secretly commissioned them to make a scale model of the original surgery - the large shed at the bottom of the garden - for Christmas. I have rather ruined the surprise by coming home instead of attending the meeting which was scheduled for tonight. Never mind, I am absolutely thrilled and it will be exciting to be involved with the project from the start. It is absolutely incredible the detail which goes into these models; the miniaturists (as they are called) produce everything to scale and if they can't buy something, they make it. It is a wonderful hobby for a hoarder as they never throw anything out - 'Your earrings would make excellent curtain tie backs' muses Mavis idly. It is also amazing what can be bought - scaled down ops tables, oxygen cylinders, even sinks with hot and cold running water (although we all agree that the latter will not be necessary). Even a vet will be installed, dressed in my usual blue scrubs and wigged with hair similar to my own. Other people's interests are always fascinating and spending an hour or so in their company has probably proved more relaxing than the same time draped over the settee.

Tuesday 15th September

A bit of a downer this morning - Mickey our hyperthyroid cat with the balance problem is not doing well despite an excellent initial response. Quiet and even more staggery than usual, he is eating little and has lost weight. This is disappointing for a post-thyroidectomy cat - by this time, our owners are usually impressed with how much weight their pet has gained. It is almost three weeks since his operation and usually most problems have arisen and been dealt with by this stage. We admit him for intensive nursing and blood samples to try to pinpoint the problem. Luckily, Alice is going into Stramar and will drop off the blood sample at the lab so we can get an early result. In the meantime, we start treating with fluids, some calcium in case of hypocalcaemia, antibiotics and vitamins. Mickey is a sweet cat, no trouble at all to deal with and his owners are also lovely people. I feel bad incurring further expenditure for them but there is no choice.

The rest of the morning passes uneventfully and we are finished by 2 pm. Unfortunately, as walk time approaches, so do dense low clouds. Risking it, we find ourselves in the middle of a thunderstorm complete with forked lightning and cracking thunder. Perhaps the insulation value on the new wellies isn't as academic as we thought. However the storm is over surprisingly quickly and the vast purple grey cloud responsible for it moves away in a stately glide much like a mammoth airship. Quite impressive if we were not all so drenched.

Mickey's results are through when we get home; one or two values are abnormal including the calcium level which is below normal. Unusual to find this a problem so long post op, but the way forward is clear. More calcium is added to his drip immediately and tomorrow I will sort out a calcium supplement from the local chemist. The reason for the other abnormal values is unclear, we can only continue the treatment and hope all goes well.

Autumn is progressing steadily now - driving to evening surgery more leaves are falling and feathery rosebay willowherb seeds float by like a small parachute regiment on a mission. The sun is setting further to the west each day. Soon it will end each day behind the western hills and we will no longer have our evening sunset extravaganzas. Checking Mickey before bed, the night is inky black but the light of our nearest navigation buoy flashes into the dark, lighting the way for a boat which is moving silently downstream, lights twinkling, a ghostly apparition skimming the edge of the field as it continues on its way.

Wednesday 16th September

Mickey seems more cheerful this morning, has eaten a good breakfast and toileted enthusiastically afterwards. Unfortunately, this involved much energetic scraping in the litter tray with his front feet followed by the deposition of a large pile on the vet bed. There is obviously scope for improvement in his aim.

Although this is a morning off, I set off for Clayfern to find an edible calcium supplement for Mickey. Word has gone round that I have a different car and people are now waving again as I pass. The last few weeks have been rather lonely, my friendly greetings being met with blank stares. In this area, everyone recognises each other's cars; in fact, borrow a friend's vehicle and you automatically gain new friends.

After a discussion with Karen the chemist, we decide on a calcium supplement, working the dose out as half a tablet per day. Back at the surgery, I consider the best method of administration; the tablets are very large and Mickey is not easy to dose. They do dissolve however, so syringing the solution into his mouth seems like a good plan. For an imbalanced cat, Mickey's claws have no trouble connecting with human flesh so he gets wrapped in a bath towel before dosing commences. He is not impressed. The tablet is effervescent and obviously not to his liking. Cats will produce copious quantities of saliva if exposed to an unpleasant taste and back in his kennel, Mickey now resembles a rabid beast with frothy sheets of slobber reaching from mouth to floor. Oh dear! Back to the drawing board. Veterinary medicine manufacturers try to help in this respect and many products are now reputed to be palatable. So, we have beef or chicken-flavoured toothpastes and malt- or tuna-flavoured tablets. Not all animals read labels however. Dogs are less selective in their eating habits and secreting a pill in a titbit often does the trick. But even dogs can be awkward - I used my trump card recently on an arthritic dog who refused to take any pills. Expecting sighs of relief and gratitude from her owner, I removed the top from a medicated syrup and invited her to take a sniff. 'Honey', she breathed, 'Now that is the one thing she will *not* take under any circumstances'. You can't win them all. As effervescent tablets are obviously not going to do for Mickey, a search through the feline computer programme comes up with a promising alternative - a simple antacid which we have in our bathroom cabinet. That will do nicely for tomorrow. Problem solved - time for a walk.

With no risk of being called back for an emergency, we can go further afield today. I decide on a trip up the hill opposite the thinking stones, now accessible through a harvested corn field. Across the stubble we go, over the wall and into the woods. The dogs are skipping ahead, joyfully aware that we are off on 'An Expedition'. It is blustery and the trees bob and grab in the wind as we climb between them. Toadstools of every hue sprout everywhere - red, white, brown, black and lemon ones of all shapes and sizes. The broadleaf trees give way to silver birch and rowan as we climb and clumps of blaeberry and heather begin to merge into continuous springy carpets. The heather is in bloom - a beautiful purple. Soon I am purple as well from eating handfuls of the small juicy blaeberries. Passing by broom and gorse bushes, the wind rustles the dry seed pods like castanets and an intriguing rustling in the dry bog grass attracts the dogs. Suddenly, a group of young pheasants scuttle from the undergrowth and across the path. With their upright posture, long necks and rapid footfalls, they remind me of the velociraptors in the film *Jurassic Park*. Luckily these are not carniverous. I wonder whether any are offspring of Farquhar and Francesca - we once saw Francesca briefly with one gawky youngster but whether it was a Fergus or a Fiona was impossible to tell. We will have to look out for that familiar bottle-green plumage later in the season.

The top of the hill is rocky - an ancient volcanic outcrop overgrown with lichen and reindeer moss. It feels like the top of the world. It is in fact the site of an Iron Age fort - a dun. Familiar territory stretches in all directions as far as the eye can see: the river and mountains to the north, fertile farmland and a glimpse of sea to the south. The Iron Agers certainly picked good spots. There are several such hill forts in this area, each one providing an excellent walk (I occasionally think of writing a guide book on such walks - it could be called 'Dun Roamin''!) The dogs drink from hollows in the rocks and track through bracken down in the valley. They disturb a roe deer which lifts his head sharply before evading them easily with a few graceful bounds. Just sitting here is good for the soul and sets me up for the rest of the week.

Friday 18th September

Today's highspot is that Mickey has at last 'gone' in his litter tray. This has eased the strain on the washing machine and is also a hopeful sign that his coordination is improving. He is certainly much brighter and is eating well. We have had a few problems with the antacid tablets - which turn out to be fruit-flavoured and also not to his liking - but his objections are less than with the previous medicine and the daily doses are going in successfully. His owners are taking him home for the weekend and we will repeat the blood sample on Monday.

Don comes into Clayfern surgery for a bandage change; again it is sopping wet but there is no sign of infection and the graft is in place. He is sporting a multicoloured sock this morning, the same bright colours as worn by cyclists or surfers. This dog is definitely out to make a fashion statement. Replenishing the biscuit jar after he leaves, I hope fervently that all goes well with his wound healing. He will be a little niggle in the back of my mind until the defect is closed satisfactorily.

Calling on Edith again, I am dismayed to find no change in Meeny. That is now four weeks post op. and something should be happening by now. Occasionally I have used acupuncture and suggest to Edith that we could give this a try. She jumps at the idea like a drowning man at a straw, so I depart to unearth old acupuncture textbooks and needles, promising to return once I have refreshed my memory on the technique.

A trip to the river this afternoon leads to the discovery of a piece of driftwood bearing an uncanny resemblance to a duck. All that is missing is its beak. Jay cuts a piece of cardboard as a temporary measure and the hunt will be on for a beak-shaped piece of wood to complete the picture. The duck now graces the kitchen shelf along with other finds. We cannot decide whether to paint it or to leave it au naturel. There are real ducks amongst the reeds by the river now. Unfortunately, this morning the sound of shots echoed up the valley. The duck-shooting season began this month. Many of our clients are shooters and fishers - that way of life is a fact of life here, but I still feel sad for the ducks. From now the shooting season gathers steam and the surgery will see a steady trickle of dogs injured in the line of duty, often cut on wire or glass at the water's edge. Luckily, most wounds are superficial and gun dogs are amenable to be stitched or stapled under local anaesthetic.

Another highspot today is the unmistakable sound of geese flying over - the first time since spring when they left for their breeding grounds in Greenland and Iceland. We mostly get pink-footed geese here and we are always glad when they return. Their ragged skeins and off-key honking is a favourite autumn impression. Somewhat surprisingly, some swallows and martins are still here. The transition is usually abrupt - in autumn, swallows go and geese return; and in late spring, geese go and swallows and martins come. The mild weather may be delaying their departure. There are still plenty of insects and they are still doing their bomber squadron antics over the fields. Once they start gathering on the phone wires, departure is not far away. During their migration to Africa, they feed on the wing, so mild weather will give them a better chance of surviving the long, arduous trip.

An amusing call this evening - for us if not for the patient. A young male pup has got rather over-amorous towards a favourite cushion and subsequently developed the condition known as paraphimosis where the edge of the prepuce or sheath acts as a tourniquet preventing the enlarged penis from returning to its resting place within the sheath. Sometimes all will deflate naturally, but occasionally not and serious damage can occur to the exposed organ. Luckily cold compresses and some lubrication do the trick in this case. Much of the comic appeal of such cases result from the owners' discomfiture. Describing the condition to the vet causes much embarrassment and euphemisms abound. One dog was described as 'Having trouble with his tail - but not the tail that wags.' Try working that one out over the phone. In the surgery fridge, we have a stock of frozen pink elephants, the novelties used in drinks instead of ice and much joking can ensue when the dog's 'doghood' is approached with one of those. Tonight's owners are from farming stock not given to embarrassment at all, so the atmosphere is relaxed and good-humoured with several ribald remarks. An easy problem for 11 pm - not serious, easily sorted with several chuckles along the way.

Monday 21st September

Morning surgery brings in two of our ongoing cases: Don for yet another bandage change - dog still happy, bandage still very wet, nothing actually wrong, but no encouraging signs of healing so far. Nothing to be done, just keep going. Mac the terrier is also in for removal of the stitches in his third eyelid flap. Definitely bad news - instead of a nicely healed cornea, there has once again been no change and we are confronted with the same ulcer which if anything looks a little deeper than it was before. The situation is now more serious as there is a risk that the eye might rupture. Immediate measures need to be taken to save the eye. Mac is admitted for more surgery. This time I am going to graft a patch of conjunctival tissue on to the defect. If successful, there will always be a patch of opaque tissue over the damaged area, but the eye will be safe and Mac will be able to see round the sides of the tiny patch with no trouble. Once again, I look out the fine instruments and suture material and attach a magnifying loupe to my head. The latter consists of magnifying lenses on a plastic strip which fastens on to a leather headband. This makes working on such a small scale much easier. All the operating lights are trained on Mac's face as I begin the surgery. First, stay sutures are placed through the conjunctiva at the edge of the globe and grasped with artery forceps. Julie will hold these gently to ensure that the ulcer remains central in the operative field. Often as an animal becomes more deeply anaesthetised, the eyeball rolls downwards making it almost impossible to get at the area that you are interested in. The ulcer bed is again tidied up before a small piece of conjunctival tissue is cut free. This is placed over the defect and trimmed to fit. Now the difficult bit - stitching the patch down with ultra-fine stitching material. Even finding the unwrapped suture without the magnifying loupe is remarkably difficult. After almost an hour of such close-up work, I am feeling rather queasy and according to Julie have developed a manic stare. Luckily, this wears off as the day progresses. Mac is discharged with an Elizabethan collar to thwart any attempts at interfering with the graft; and an appointment is made for a check-up in a few days.

Now, a visit to Edith and Meeny to begin Meeny's acupuncture. The specialist has been on the phone and shares my gloomy outlook, but it is at least worth a try. Acupuncture has been used for over 3,000 years, originally by vets in ancient China who observed that finger pressure on certain spots eased symptoms of pain or disease. They found that the effect was improved if needles were used. The Chinese interpretation of why acupuncture works does take some swallowing for anyone trained in western medicine. The underlying Chinese principle is that energy runs throughout the body in defined channels. In disease, the flow is imbalanced and the accurate positioning of needles on points along the channels helps to restore the correct balance. Interestingly, acupuncture was on the curriculum of the first European veterinary schools and was widely practised until the early nineteenth century when advances in veterinary medicine caused its popularity to wane. Much research has been carried out to provide rational explanations (according to western beliefs) as to why it works and several theories have been proven. Acupuncture definitely does inhibit pain receptors and causes release of endorphins - the body's own painkillers. An electromagnetic effect has also been demonstrated but the significance of this is not yet clear. Amongst my books on the subject is a 'recipe book' which is incredibly helpful: it tells you which points to use for different conditions. So, with Meeny on the settee between Edith and I, we begin, the open recipe book balanced on the arm of the settee. Four needles are inserted along the spine on each side of the affected disc, one in the middle and several at remote points on each hind leg. Acupuncture points vary in size from pinpoint to almost tennis ball size, but a good 'pointer' as to whether the position is correct lies in the amount of 'drag' on the needle. I am confident that we are in the right place today - the drag on each needle is immense. There are no hard and fast rules as to how long the needles stay in, so I decide arbitrarily on five minutes. During this time, each needle is rotated from time to time to enhance the effect. As with most patients undergoing acupuncture, Meeny does not object as the fine needles slip in and lies quietly during the procedure. Edith chats happily while I gently twiddle needles. She has been making melon pudding. 'That sounds nice', I comment, whereupon she displays the pudding. 'The likes of you could use cream or something on top,' she observes. Thank you Edith, do I detect a slight insult there somewhere.

Friday 25th September

All three long-standing cases have coincided today; first, Don for another change at two weeks post op. Removing the smart 'country gentledog' oiled sock, the bandage is again sopping wet, but possibly a little less smelly. At last there is a thin rim of pink around the vast defect - new skin. Thank goodness, some progress. As often happens in life, every silver lining has a cloud and elation with Don's improvement is soon snuffed out by Mac's arrival in the surgery. Disaster. His owner's friend removed the Elizabethan collar for the dog to eat then forgot to replace it. He has obviously had a good rub at the eye it is inflamed and watering profusely and worse, the conjunctival patch is completely detached. Arggghhh! Nothing for it but to operate again. I performed the free graft fresh from hearing an ophthalmologist extolling its advantages, but this time, we'll stick with the old familiar conjunctival pedicle graft as performed many times before. Plan C! Once again, an hour spent staring fixedly through the loupe followed by a nauseous half an hour. From a routine case, Mac has worked up to a major worry - please let this work.

These days are being spent in a lather of anticipation and dread, waiting to see Don, Mac and Meeny. Needless to say, they also occupy quite a lot of off-duty thoughts. Life is not dull.

Finally, Meeny. She is five weeks post op. and as yet, no change. Again the acupuncture goes without incident. No melon pudding today but some rather tasty Viennese whirls. These frequent visits have their compensations.

Tuesday 29th September

A real autumnal morning. Haar cloaks the fields and river and outlines cobwebs on hedges to look like filigree lace. There is not a breath of wind and the hills on the opposite bank of the river are reflected as mirror images in the still water. The ghostly cry of a curlew echoes through the mist and a heron flies ponderously overhead like a pterodactyl. The whole effect is quite other-worldly. However, into the surgery and back to reality. Our first patient is Mickey for a blood sample. He is doing well, eating the fruit-flavoured tablets without too much persuasion. Next is a collapsed guinea pig virtually breathing her last on the table. The proud new owners were told that she was six weeks old, but she is much older, heavily pregnant and suffering from eclampsia, another life-threatening condition where body calcium levels drop too low. Although the condition is treatable if picked up early, she is too far gone and dies on the table. Her babies are also dead. Not a happy situation. Alice manages to cheer up the distraught young owners by helping to plan the funeral. Children often accept death more readily than adults, but the 'funeral arrangements' are often extremely important to them. As the family leaves with the guinea pig in a 'shroud' of paper towelling, it is the mother who is red-eyed and weepy, while the kids excitedly debate the merits of burial in the rose garden versus under the willow tree. Alice laughs when I tell her the tale of my former colleague's young son. Watching her treat a kitten, he announces, 'We're going to get a kitten when Flip dies, aren't we Mummy?' (Flip being an ancient but much loved spaniel). 'Yes, Jon,' came the answer. Short pause, then, 'But *when* will she die?' Clearly young children have not yet amassed the emotional baggage and taboos that come with being an adult.

Alice has been here nearly a month and is settling in well. Catching herself greeting a client, searching for the record card and answering the phone simultaneously, she suddenly felt that she had 'made it'. More confident in her role, she is enjoying meeting familiar faces - both human and animal - and is developing the perceptive approach vital to all good nurses. She has learnt that 'My dog has cut his foot' is not necessarily an emergency until you get the answer to the all important question 'When?' If - as is frequently the case - the answer is 'Four days ago', then the vet does not need to be recalled immediately to the surgery. Clients' ideas of what constitutes an emergency can be irritating or amusing (depending on how tired you are!). A good example is a call at ten last night: 'My dog's really ill and needs urgent attention.' After a short discussion of symptoms we say,
'Fine, bring him straight to the surgery.'
'Right, we've got friends in, so I'll just have supper with them and be along in about an hour.'
Most clients are apologetic for ringing at unsocial hours, but some display a singular lack of consideration.

Waiting at the farm surgery is our old friend Jake Lafferty, the diabetic Labrador. He is not eating and is distinctly off-colour. He looks dehydrated and thin, his skin shrinking over his old bones. As I admit him for fluids and further evaluation, I warn his owner that he may not buck up this time. Before blood sampling, we prepare his vein with local anaesthetic to prevent any sulking. His glucose level is far too high and his temperature is up. Diabetics are prone to infections and this is a common reason why things may go a little haywire. We work hard with him all day, checking his drip, taking blood samples and administering short acting insulin. By four pm he is more like his old self, sniffing the air while he wees on my heather. Tail wagging, he hurtles back to his kennel and scoffs the tea which Julie has waiting. Obviously feeling better. We'll keep him in tomorrow then send him home.

Mickey's last blood result is through - calcium within normal range. Hooray! We'll gradually reduce his supplement and re-test next week.

We have visitors staying this week; unfortunately their outings are limited because of the weather. As a mutual treat, they visit Jake in the evening. I have an ulterior motive - his catheter needs to come out. In the past, detaching the *Elastoplast* from his leg has resulted in major upheaval and heavy sulking. I'm hoping that the guests might distract him. Sure enough, we have the beginnings of the wounded soldier routine, but the chunks of pork from our supper cause a rapid change of heart and he reverts to the sunny character we know and love. He really is an old rogue!

Back in the house, my services are again in demand. The moist mild weather is bringing out spiders by the score - and the visitors are phobic. Spiders need removing from the bath, the walls and the ceiling all the most inaccessible spots. They have coined a new nickname - for this week at any rate, I am the Arachnovet!

<u>Wednesday 30th September</u>

An afternoon off, thank goodness, but first a trip to see Meeny. This is the third acupuncture session in ten days so we really should be seeing some improvement by now if we are at all optimistic. Nothing spectacular has happened but there does seem to be some power at the top of the hind legs and she almost seems able to move her knees forward a little. Edith is thrilled and insists there is great improvement. I am more cautious, but there is definitely some change. Reason enough to carry on anyway. Yet more silent prayers during needle-twiddling time.

Thursday 1st October

Alice is on her weekly visit to the farm surgery being instructed in the mysteries of anaesthesia and surgery. Some regular mornings here will enable her to be of help should Julie be ill or on holiday. In awe, Alice watches Julie prepare the ops room for action, lay out all necessary equipment and masterfully control an unruly dog while I inject anaesthetic into a vein. Julie and I have worked together for several years now and dovetail very nicely. She knows what I mean when I ask for the *doodas* or the *thingummyjig*. We have a similar sense of humour and a morning's surgery can be a pleasant way to pass the time - depending of course on what the surgery is. Today is like pets' corner. First, a hamster with a dislocated eye which is infected and sightless and needs removing. Over-enthusiastic grasping of the loose skin at the back of a hamster's neck can actually dislocate the eye. It can be replaced if caught early, otherwise irreversible damage occurs. The usual small-creature precautions are taken and Hammy is injected with a cocktail of anaesthetic drugs. Once safely asleep, it only takes a few moments to remove the damaged eye and suture the cavity shut. Then off he goes into a warm kennel, securely wrapped in bubble-wrap. Next, a rabbit to X-ray. He has an abscess on his face which I suspect is due to dental problems. An X-ray will tell us the state of the teeth and facial bones. Ten years ago, X-raying a rabbit was virtually unheard of, but rabbit medicine is becoming increasingly sophisticated and such techniques are now quite commonplace. Perhaps in a few years, we will also be X-raying hamsters routinely. Sure enough, the abscess seems to arise from the bone of the lower jaw due to a tooth root abscess. Treatment can be complicated and discussions with the owner are necessary before we progress any further.

Now it is Alice's turn to hold a dog for injection. Perhaps not the best choice, the energetic young spaniel is barely dented by the sedative pre-med and wriggles furiously on the table. Cries of 'Sit' have no effect and the situation is becoming fraught until I remember that this is a gundog. 'Hup, Jack! Hup!' has a magical effect. Who knows why shooters use this command instead of 'sit', but it certainly works.

Lunchtime soon comes round and we sit in the garden to enjoy our sandwiches. This is the first time that Alice has met Kippen and Fintry and she is truly shocked at their bad behaviour. Luckily we live four miles from Clayfern so most clients will not realise that it is a case of 'Do as I say, not as I do!' Both dogs watch every mouthful like spectators at Wimbledon. Thick, tenacious strings of saliva hang from each corner of Fintry's mouth as she sits six inches from Alice's lap. The saliva strings are fascinating and Fintry is talented with them. Thus we have - the *yo-yo* effect, the *pendulum* effect (surprisingly hypnotic) and - the piece de resistance - the *flycatcher* or *Tarzan* effect. The last usually results in success for the dog; a titbit is given to dislodge her for an instant while the victim mops their slimed clothes.

The nurses depart to clean the surgery while I steel myself for a dreaded job. The answering machine is playing up and it is necessary to record a new message. I am hopeless with technology and can be reduced to a quivering wreck by a gadget's refusal to play ball. Answering machine and human have had several skirmishes over the last few days, but today is the day of reckoning. 'I will keep calm; it's only a machine' I intone as yet another error message flashes on the display. Finally, I win through and the now-functional machine is left sitting malevolently on the desk. All vets depend heavily on telecommunications to keep in twenty four-hour contact for emergencies. It is amazing that we can land men on the moon but still cannot achieve one hundred per cent foolproof communications. Invariably a glitch occurs from time to time.

Innumerable advances in technology have improved the veterinary lot over the years. In relatively recent times, my vote goes to the video recorder and microwave oven. I can remember the frustration of faithfully watching weekly instalments of a TV drama, only to be called out during the final episode. The only hope then was to track down the repeat (invariably on at incredibly unsocial or impractical times of day). Similarly, in cases of dire emergency during mealtimes, one's food ended up dried beyond recognition in the oven. Nowadays, an abandoned meal can be swiftly reheated to its former glory in a matter of minutes. We even have a microwave at Clayfern surgery which some clients fondly believe is for staff snacks between customers. Not so - it is incredibly useful for warming fluids prior to administration and beats the previous method which required a frustrating five to ten minutes dunking in a bowl of hot water. Progress indeed.

Friday 2nd October

An emergency at the beginning of morning surgery has thrown the day askew. The waiting room is already filling up when an anxious family burst through the door, Dad carrying a twitching, jerking retriever in his arms. While the dog jerks uncontrollably on the table, they quickly fill in the background: Belle had ten pups three weeks ago and all has been going well until earlier today when she appeared staggery on leaving the whelping box. She also seemed somewhat twitchy and the family resolved to bring her to morning surgery when it opened. However her condition has worsened dramatically in the last half an hour. The diagnosis is easy - a classic case of *eclampsia* or *milk fever.* Belle has been an excellent provider for her large brood, producing vast quantities of milk. Milk is rich in calcium and, like Mickey and our guinea pig, her calcium levels have dropped below the amount necessary to keep nerve cells working properly. If not dealt with immediately, the condition proves fatal. The treatment is intravenous injection of calcium solution. Targeting a blood vessel when the patient is shuddering wildly is not easy, but thankfully as the needle slips below the skin, we see the tell-tale plume of blood which denotes a 'hit'. First hurdle over, but more to go. The injection has to be given very slowly - calcium slows the heart and rapid injection can kill the patient. So I am crouched over the foreleg which Alice holds extended with a vice-like grip, slowly depressing the plunger - aiming for approx. one ml. per minute, with a stethoscope plugged in my ears, monitoring constantly for any change in heart rate or rhythm. Each minute lasts an eternity - and all the while the bitch twitches and jerks, panting like a train. It is so tempting to slam the entire contents of the syringe into the circulation, but sadly not possible. After six minutes and six mls, Belle's panting finally begins to slow and the jerking eases. Two mls more and she lies quiet but alert, like someone roused from sleep. The poor girl will be exhausted. I am reluctant to withdraw from the vein, but in another minute she is trying to rise and even wags her tail. Alice and I release our holds on leg and syringe and massage life back into our cramped fingers while Belle laps greedily at a proffered bowl of water, jumps off the table and makes a circuit of the room, tail wagging furiously. It is almost miraculous how suddenly these eclampsia cases can recover. It is important that Belle's pups do not suckle from her full time from now on. We provide a puppy milk substitute and a feeding bottle as well as calcium tablets for Mum. Belle pulls her owners out of the door and we are left pondering the strange coincidence which has produced three low calcium cases in virtually the same week. We may see no more for a year now.

The waiting room is now packed but no one complains about the delay, appreciating that next time it could be their pet in need of urgent attention. Finally the last patient has gone and I need to rush to the farm surgery where more clients will be waiting. The road home is fraught with hazards which prevent an all-out dash. There has been so much rain this week that the ducks at Abbeygate have taken to dabbling in the puddles in the road. The Muscovy duck has taken her entire brood along the roadside. Unfortunately, they are small, yellow and charcoal coloured and blend in too well with fallen leaves, causing many anxious swerves when spotted at the last moment. Further along, our feral sheep saunters across the road to try her luck in the opposite stubble field. Still no one has claimed her, but she seems to be doing quite well on her own, showing no desire to seek out the sheep in neighbouring fields.

Home eventually, where cars are stacked like planes at Heathrow. Owners are chatting or walking patients along the verge, happily unperturbed at our haywire schedule. Julie has explained about our emergency at Clayfern and everyone asks how the victim is when they enter the surgery.

Some light relief in the afternoon. I am participating in a telephone survey, relatively frequent occurrences nowadays where practitioners are asked their views on a variety of topics. The surveys are often commissioned by drug companies to gauge the likely response to a proposed new product. I always find them demanding - it is not easy to suddenly work out how many dogs one sees in a month, let alone those with heart complaints, for example - but finally all questions are answered with time for the foreign interviewer to fill in some background information.

'Is the practice mixed or small animal?'

'Small animal only.'

'City or rural?'

'Rural.'

Then the priceless question

'And how many veterans are in the practice?'

'Oh- just the one!'

Tuesday 6th October

An RTA (road traffic accident) with a difference today - the victim is a duck. Some kind clients rescued him yesterday from the side of the road. He can only hop on one leg - the other thigh bone is badly fractured and the bone ends are overriding, so there is little chance of it healing naturally. We will have to repair the break surgically. Injured wildlife often present interesting challenges and ingenuity is required more frequently than in our usual species. With birds, there are several anatomical features to be taken into consideration, one being that they behave rather differently under gas anaesthesia. With animals, gas enters the blood stream only when the creature breathes in, but in birds, gas is absorbed on exhalation as well. This means that they can go from light to deep anaesthesia extremely quickly. Or, put another way, from waking up to near death in moments. The anaesthetist needs to know this and be extremely alert, or disaster can occur. In other respects, the anaesthetic procedure is not too far removed from normal - a drug combination sends our duck to sleep initially, then he is intubated and attached to the anaesthetic machine. Alice is anaesthetist today and is carefully instructed in the reflexes to check in a feathered patient. Next the surgical site is prepared - plucked not clipped - damping the feathers first to prevent the ops room looking as if a feather pillow has exploded. As it is, feathers still manage to get everywhere and will be turning up in the hoover or on the brush for days to come. I try not to pluck away too many as the bird needs his plumage for waterproofing and temperature control. Now the op begins. Bird bones are light compared with mammals and earlier vets' delight at mending bones conventionally soon turned to dismay when their patient either sank or failed to get off the ground. Today, I am using a technique which has been useful before. When trimmed down, the plunger of a syringe makes a light, sterile peg to insert into the broken fragments pinning them together. The X-shaped cross-section helps to stabilise the break and the addition of surgical steel wire in a figure of eight across the fracture site secures the reduced bones in place. All goes well and we replace our duck in a warm kennel having first wrapped him in a towel to prevent damage from uncontrolled wing flapping on recovery from anaesthesia. The Good Samaritans who found him are willing to nurse him until he is well again. He will remain in a cage for the next few days but will be allowed physiotherapy in the form of swimming several times daily. Birds heal faster than animals and it is important to keep the limb moving to prevent muscle wastage. Swimming is ideal as the water supports the weight while allowing the muscles to do some work. Psychologically, it will also do the duck much good. Feeding is not difficult as ducks will eat most household waste - especially when mixed in water. At a wildlife sanctuary at our last practice, we treated many swans. These big birds can get through a lot of food and the sanctuary operated on a shoestring budget. Luckily, the local cafe donated their leftovers - mostly bread and cereal - daily. Occasionally the remains of ham sandwiches would appear in the mix and we lightheartedly hoped that the birds would not develop a particular liking for ham and swoop on unsuspecting pigs when released.

Last op of the day is an elderly cat with bad teeth. She is a scraggy old girl so we took the precaution of blood testing her beforehand to learn of any additional problems which might compromise her safety under anaesthetic. The level of waste products normally cleared by the kidneys is higher than normal showing that her kidneys are not one hundred per cent. To deprive her of fluid intake on the day of her dental could tip her into acute kidney failure, so our strategy is to keep her on a drip during and after the much needed dental work. Her mouth is frightful and desperately needs attention; quite apart from being painful and unpleasant, the bacteria and toxins passing into her body will be hindering her wellbeing. All her remaining teeth are removed - not a long job as they are rotten and loose anyway. The drip runs smoothly and she recovers quickly from the anaesthetic. Painkiller and antibiotic are already in her blood stream and she looks remarkably perky when her owners collect her during evening surgery. The canula remains bandaged in place in case she requires more fluids tomorrow.

A late afternoon fax report brings yet more results for Mickey; calcium levels still normal. Good. So, we'll continue gradually reducing the calcium supplement.

A quick call on Edith and Meeny before surgery. Edith is thrilled with the improvement. Now when Meeny pulls herself along, her left back leg faces forward and she very occasionally goes 'up and over' on it, almost like a pole vaulter. *Something* is definitely happening. As always, excitement is tempered with the fear that this is the best that we will get. It would be so harsh to get so far then no further - at least we are heading in the right direction which is a great relief after almost seven weeks. A small spot of blood oozes when I withdraw the last needle; *'Well,* that's the first time I've seen you spill blood*',* says Edith mournfully. 'Oh for goodness sake, Edith!' I laugh,' It's only a spot, I'm hardly slaughtering a goat!' We both set off with uncontrollable giggles, with a puzzled dachshund sandwiched between us on the settee.

Don comes in during evening surgery; yet another soggy bandage but not as smelly as last time. The wound area is still extremely wet and there is a thin rim of fresh pink new skin. Again, heading in the right direction but pitifully slowly. Flushed from success with Meeny, I try some acupuncture on the defect. This simply involves inserting needles into the skin margin and twiddling occasionally. Don's owner June seems a little bemused but is willing to try anything to hasten the healing process. She was brave to allow the surgery to go ahead in the first place, as she knew it was fraught with potential difficulties and that the outcome was uncertain.

Final patient of the evening is Mac, sporting his well-worn Elizabethan collar. Thankfully, the corneal pedicle graft is still in place and the inflammation present post op. has settled down. At about five weeks post op, the tissue bridge will be severed leaving the eye with a discrete patch. So, that's all four of our 'long haul' patients on the one day. Mickey is great; Mac and Meeny look hopeful; and Don at least is better than he was. All in all, quite a satisfying day.

Wednesday 7th October

It had to happen sometime - four pups in for vaccination named Tinky Winky, Dipsy, Lala and Po after the children's television series, *Teletubbies.* Popular TV programmes have a lot to answer for and many unfortunate animals bear the reminder of some long-forgotten craze. Most Starskys and Hutches have died out now, as have Del Boys and Rodneys, but there are a still a few geriatric Turner and Hooches, Gizmos and Kylies. At the end of these animals' lives, the programmes will be but a distant memory. It is a social commentary on the transient nature of fame. Perennial favourites such as Bonnie, Sheba, Sam, Ben and Max figure significantly in the files and in this neck of the woods, appropriate, evocative names are frequently given to working dogs - such as Moss, Peat, Ghillie or Turf. Scottish names also have a pleasant ring - *Darra* (Gaelic for oak), *Dhu* (black), *Ruadh* (red). Non-Scottish locums can have language problems with some. For example, *Ceilidh* is pronounced Caylay. Like many folk, we are full of interesting ideas for names until faced with naming our own. Kippen came already baptised, but Fintry was originally Jaunty. As with children, it is worth remembering that the unfortunate animal is stuck with its name for life. Animals only respond to one or two syllables, so long names like Napoleon or Quasimodo can be a waste of effort. It is also worthwhile remembering the embarrassment factor involved with summoning your pet at night. Shouting 'Psycho!' or 'Sweetiepie!' from the back door will certainly get you noticed. Cat owners are often extremely enterprising at name picking and, as cats frequently come in pairs, clever combinations abound. We have records for two Siamese called Mao Zedong and Zhou Enlai and other two-somes such as Salt and Pepper and Neep and Tattie.

There is an emergency this afternoon involving a cat called Ceefor (C for cat!). Ceefor has just given birth, but in the owner's words 'The kittens are all stuck together.' When the cardboard box is placed on the table, we see a distressing spectacle: four kittens - obviously all alive judging by the frantic mewling - all struggling together in a writhing heap. Two are stuck fast face to face, held together by their entwined umbilical cords; the tail of the third and the hind leg of the fourth are also tightly tangled in this mess. With patience and delicate use of fine scissors, the puzzle is gradually unravelled. Extreme care is necessary not to damage the skin of the struggling, squawking kittens. Two cords need tying off then the kittens are apart for the first time in their brief lives. It would make a good story if they were Siamese kittens, but they are only mogs. The kitten with the trapped leg may be a problem - the bottom half of the leg is extremely swollen and cold; it may be past saving. I consider the options, but am encouraged by his alertness and slight movement made with his foot. We will give him a chance overnight, but if his leg is dead then the kindest option will be to put him to sleep. This situation only occurs rarely, only one kitten survived last time, attached by its cord to its two dead siblings - the stuff of nightmares.

More nightmarish images this evening, in an owner's mind at least. Her old Pekinese has *glaucoma* in her left eye and I have advised removal. Glaucoma occurs when fluid can no longer drain from the globe of the eye. This causes an increase in pressure within the eye which is initially painful, but soon the *optic nerve* is damaged irrevocably and the eye remains sightless and distended. There is evidence from human medicine that headaches can arise if the 'dead' eye is left in situ and most vets recommend removal in their animal patients. Although Daphne is no oil painting as she is, her owner dreads the thought of an empty socket. What she imagines is doubtless worse than the reality, so we play our trump card - the photo album containing pictures of procedures most likely to cause anxiety amongst owners eye enucleations (removals), leg amputations etc. We start with photos from immediately post-op. These tend to be the most 'sensitive' with the site shaved of fur, showing sutures and perhaps a little bloody. As usual, it does not look as horrific as Daphne's owner had imagined. By the six week post-op. photos, she is positively cocky. So much is fear of the unknown and it is our job to try to educate it away. Daphne's op. is booked in for next week. As she is a breed prone to glaucoma, we will check her remaining eye regularly for any sign of the condition, using a small instrument rather grandly known as a *Schiotz tonometer* which measures the pressure within the globe. If picked up early, glaucoma can be treated medically and the sight can be preserved. Animals are often very subtle in showing pain and checks like this are definitely worthwhile.

Another example of prevention being better than cure is our old cat dental from yesterday. She is doing well, but might not have been if her kidney malfunction had not been picked up on a pre-op. blood screen. Things are as they should be - happy animal, happy owner and happy vet.

Thursday 8th October

Our duck is doing well but his new owner's wife is much displeased - it takes almost half an hour to clean the bath after each of his physiotherapy sessions. Don appears for a bandage change - 'surfing' sock today. There has been an incredible improvement after his acupuncture a mere two days ago. The wound has dried up, there is fresh granulation tissue in the defect and more new pink skin. Needless to say, more acupuncture today.

Today's problem is Adolf, a young cat who has been missing for a week. His owners had been searching high and low with no luck, but this morning he tottered in through the door. He must have walked home but is not moving voluntarily now, lying miserably in a bath towel. I automatically go into examination mode, questioning the owners at the same time. Even before touching the cat, there is information to be gleaned - there are no obvious injuries and his breathing appears normal; he is alert if not exactly happy. Now the first hands-on pass, starting at the front end: checking eyes and mouth; looking at colour of membranes (slightly pale); exploring for damage and smelling breath for any clues. Neck glands normal size, chest sounds okay, feet and ear flaps normally warm. Reassured that there are no immediately life-threatening problems, I continue working towards the hind end. Several front and back toenails are broken, indicating probable trauma. All legs are working - he walked in to the house and can stand. Abdomen slightly tender and, the first major abnormal finding - his bladder is considerably larger than it should be. The diagnostic procedure is closing in. Adolf's tail is floppy and lifeless, even fierce pressure with artery forceps does not elicit any response from the cat. Gentle feeling around the pelvis is resented. Now the picture is becoming clearer. Adolf has been involved in some form of traumatic accident damaging his pelvis and sacral area. Nerves from this area of the spinal cord supply the tail and control normal bladder function. The normal scenario is as follows: when the bladder fills to a certain size in fit patients, stretch receptors in the bladder wall are activated. Nerve fibres relay messages via the spinal cord to the brain - *you need to go to the loo*. Once in a suitable spot, more nerve impulses instruct the valve holding the bladder shut to relax, the bladder muscles contract and the bladder empties. In cases of nerve damage, the bladder fills excessively until the sheer volume of fluid overcomes resistance and it empties. Apart from the hygiene implications of an animal who wets anywhere and everywhere, these patients are prone to bladder and kidney infections and in practice, do not 'do'. Our next step in managing Adolf's problems is to evaluate the damage radiographically - some cases will be obviously hopeless, others will show nothing at all. Even with no discernible bone damage, the nervous tissue may be damaged beyond repair - but could also be only temporarily out of action due to bruising. Once he is placed on a· drip, antibiotic, anti-inflammatory and painkilling drugs are given along with a mild sedative and Adolf's bladder is emptied manually. The contents are the colour of tomato soup - there has obviously been significant damage to the urinary tract. This is not unusual and will hopefully fade soon. If not, investigations would be required to trace the source of the bleeding. Since nothing shows on Adolf's X-rays, we insert a catheter into the bladder so it empties continually, secure it in place and fit him with an Elizabethan collar to prevent tampering. A big problem is not knowing *when* the damage ocurred. Most vets consider that if bladder function has not returned in a week, then it is unlikely to at all, but nothing is totally cut and dried in medicine. It is very hard to know how long to persist with treatment. Unlike a human, you cannot explain to an animal that they might get better, that the misery is not for ever. We have the means nowadays to do more than ever to resuscitate patients and keep them alive, but I am not sure that the end always justifies the means. Adolf's owner understands the situation and we agree to keep him as comfortable as possible and take things one day at a time.

Such open-ended cases always remind me of one of our more memorable patients - Fletch Goodall. Fletch's owner heard a noise from under the car bonnet while driving to work one evening. On opening the bonnet, the cat leapt out - straight into the path of an oncoming car (talk about out of the frying pan). Jim Goodall bundled the inert body in his coat and sprinted for the surgery, catching us on the verge of locking up. At first, we thought Fletch was dead, but his chest was moving shallowly and we heard a faint moan, so we quickly swung into action. Gillian fetched the oxygen trolley while I quickly examined him. Pale but not irretrievably so; pulse fast and thready (shock); pupils mis-sized (cranial damage); breathing shallow, chest harsh (lung damage); two-inch skin wound left shoulder; both front paws skinned to the bone; tail floppy (possible bladder nerve damage); possible pelvic fracture; broken left canine tooth. Plenty to be going on with, not completely hopeless but very serious. I felt he was worth a try and Jim gave his consent, so we set to work. The most urgent priority was to control the shock and improve his breathing. Hopefully his chest was only bruised but more serious injury was a possibility. Jim held the oxygen mask to Fletch's face while we positioned him in bubble wrap and inserted an intravenous catheter. I secured the catheter while Gillian connected the drip, then I injected a powerful anti-inflammatory drug into the line. Developed to be ultra-concentrated and easily portable by foot soldiers during the Falklands War, it is immensely useful in cases of suspect spinal injury if given soon after the trauma. Unfortunately, like all wonder drugs, it is not cheap.

After this initial flurry of activity, I injected more useful drugs, then discussed matters more fully with Jim. He needed to know that it will be a long and expensive path to fitness and a good outcome cannot be guaranteed. To use a racing analogy: there are many hurdles to go and he may fall at any fence. We seemed to have got over the first hurdle at least, Fletch seemed to be responding to the anti-shock treatment. Now he could be evaluated in finer detail and I gently probed and palpated every part of the little body. Gillian was monitoring breathing and heart rate, temperature, colour everything to let us know how he was doing.

Less urgent matters could be attended to now that he was stabilising. The front feet were badly damaged - splinters of bone and skin tatters flapped on the surface and the wounds were badly contaminated with grit from the road. First, a thorough soak in dilute antiseptic to clear the loose debris, then trimming away of dead tissue flaps and flushing with saline, the best we could do with a conscious patient. Each foot then had a *wet to dry* bandage applied. This is exactly what it says - a saline-soaked layer next to the wound then copious padding. This draws contaminated material from the wound and keeps the tissue moist. I estimated that Fletch would need three or four toes removed and possibly a skin graft. He would need to be anaesthetised before the situation could be fully assessed, but that would not be until he was stronger. Over the hour since he arrived, the more severe shock symptoms subsided; his membranes were pinker, his pulse slower and stronger and his extremities warmer. By late evening, his pupils were normal size and he was maintaining the correct oxygen levels in his bloodstream breathing room air only.

Day two. The next morning he was still lying flat out, but could lift his head. His bladder expressed easily. The drip continued and we passed a nasogastric tube directly into his stomach. He was to be fed through this four times daily using a semi-liquid, high-energy diet. Fresh wet to dry dressings were applied. By evening, he was lying on his chest and I thought I saw his tail twitch.

Day three. He had passed urine in the kennel, though it was hard to know whether this had been done consciously or not. He was sitting up, purring when stroked and his tail reacted when pinched.

This was encouraging. He could only stand when his hind legs were supported. Some food and drink were accepted. He complained more when the bandages were changed, but the wounds had cleaned up nicely.

Day four. Fletch was anaesthetised and his pelvis X-rayed. There was a fracture present, but it was nicely positioned and was expected to heal with rest alone. After suturing the shoulder wound and extracting the broken tooth, our attention turned to his feet. Two toes were amputated from one foot; one from the other. There was a shortage of skin on both feet and they needed to be kept dressed until the wounds healed over.

Fletch recovered well from his lengthy anaesthetic and on day five, could stand unaided for the first time. He was eating well, so the intravenous catheter and nasogastric tubes were removed. Since he was urinating in his litter tray, there was no doubt that his bladder was working properly.

Every two days for the next week, he was sedated while his feet were redressed. Fresh pink skin gradually crept across healthy granulation tissue and gradually filled the defect. Eleven days after the accident, Fletch went home with a cage in which he was to be confined for the following two weeks. Bandage changes occurred twice weekly. The last bandage was removed and Fletch finally discharged twenty nine days after his accident. He is a long-haired cat, his fluffy feet obscuring the missing toes. He walks without a limp and behaves exactly as before. The only evidence of his marathon recovery is in the area of his shoulder wound - the fur has regrown pure white. We will never forget Fletch, agonising over whether we were doing the right thing by attempting repair - putting him through so many procedures - and facing new challenges every day. It is a good feeling when he comes in the surgery now, knowing that if it was not for our dedicated team, he would not be alive today.

Monday 13th October

These last few days have been busy and not always particularly pleasant. Examining a pup for vaccination one day, I detected a heart defect. This could be important later, or not and I spent a long time explaining the ins and outs to the owner. As soon as she got home, she phoned the breeder who regards such a finding as a slur on her good name and somehow blames me. The breeder has persuaded the owner that there is nothing to worry about and the owner is displeased with me for having told her at all. Another unfortunate case centres round an emergency call at midnight on Saturday - a small dog had been attacked by the neighbour's German shepherd dog. Treatment involved extensive stitching that night plus follow-up treatment yesterday and today. The owner expects the neighbour to cough up for our work and is annoyed that we should ask *her* for money. In such disputes, it is surprisingly easy to become pig in the middle through no fault of your own. To cap it all, Adolf is not doing well. There is no evidence of any returning bladder function and the cat is apathetic and miserable. His owner has visited regularly over the weekend, but can stand it no longer and has asked for him to be put to sleep. So, after morning ops today, I escape up the hill with indecent haste, badly in need of relaxation and peace.

The trees are aflame at this time of year with vivid orange, lemon, gold and crimson standing out amongst the sombre green firs. The soft autumn sun suffuses the forest in a cosy glow, while the odours of burnt leaf and damp earth mingle with the resin tang of the evergreens. Fungi sprout everywhere and I release some frustration by childishly squashing puffballs, watching the green seed clouds burst out and disperse. It is nice to give in to the occasional destructive urge without doing any harm. Another outlet is to jump in frozen puddles in winter

Winding down, I sit on the stones surrounded by dying vegetation - the only flowers left are thistles and the occasional harebell - and ponder on what a strange job this can be. Sometimes you can be depressed at putting an old friend down; anxious about cases not going smoothly; frustrated at lack of finances (although seemingly working all hours); irritated by silly phone calls at unsocial hours; and just desperate for some light relief. Other times, you can be warmly satisfied after a successful treatment, basking in owners' gratitude and the pleasure of a recovered patient; intrigued by unusual cases and interesting clients; and laughing at humorous incidents. A friend aptly described these opposing states: 'Sometimes you are on top of the heap; other times, the heap is on top of you!'

Comforted by such philosophical thoughts, I set off homewards to face the rest of the day which is mercifully uneventful. Our duck comes into evening surgery, he is doing well and he has been offered a new home on a neighbour's millpond when his convalescence is over. At last - a happy ending.

Off to a meeting tonight. The subject concerns methods of fixing broken bones and concentrates on a technique known as *external fixation.* This involves fitting rather weird looking, cage-like contraptions to the *outside* of a broken limb. The technique is exremely versatile and is fast becoming a popular option for fixing all manner of orthopaedic complaints. Much early pioneer work was done by a Russian called Ilizarov, a human doctor working in the Soviet gulags. Apparently, his initial work involved transforming bicycle wheels and spokes into the first external fixators, which just goes to show that genius will shine through, no matter how basic the materials at hand. Many of the original principles which he worked out are still adhered to today.

Sunday 18th October

We are just back from a short holiday in Ireland - a family break: me, Jay and the dogs. Everyone has enjoyed it immensely and it was interesting to see how folks live on the other side of the Irish Sea. Our holiday base was a village similar in size to Clayfern and our first indication that things might be slightly different was evident on our arrival early one morning. Although well past 8 am., there was no sign of life, most shops not opening until 10 am. In Clayfern, the bakery, the newsagent and the general store would have been open before seven. The natives' driving is idiosyncratic - cars pull out *then* indicate, stop sharply outside the targeted shop - even if this entails double or triple parking and pull up opposite friends for a chat. Really not that much different to home. Irish pubs definitely have the edge over ours, with cheerful fires burning all day and creamy glasses of Guinness. It does take a while to wind down and get used to not being on call. Walking along the beach, we subconsciously strained to hear the pager against the background of Atlantic breakers and after a first Guinness, it took a few seconds to realise that I really could have another. And going to bed in a house with no phone is sheer bliss! My job is wonderful, but it is marvellous to behave 'normally' from time to time. We spent a magical few days taking happy dogs for long walks, eating, drinking and generally relaxing. Enthused by lively music sessions, we become proud owners of a tin whistle and a *bodhran* (a traditional drum). If we practise, we might realise a long-held ambition to be a musical ensemble rejoicing in the name - the Duo-Denum! Time passed quickly and we headed homewards bearing gifts: for Julie, a framed copy of Murphy's Law which she will appreciate, particularly - 'If everything is going well, you obviously don't know what is going on' 'Anything you try to fix will take longer and cost more than you thought' and 'The light at the end of the tunnel is the headlamp of an oncoming train.' For Alice, a local pottery duck to commemorate her first successful bird anaesthetic.

So now we are home. It was mild on the west of Ireland, but last night we had frost here. Today there is a biting wind. We collect the neglected Jonno and scale the hill to check out what has gone on in our territory since it was last seen. The track is covered with fallen leaves - sandy coloured larch needles and multicoloured beech, sycamore and ash. The larch needles make the scene look sunny even on the dullest of days. Like giant snowflakes, more leaves gently fall as we walk, fluttering and rustling downward in the bitter wind. Even from a distance, we hear the roaring of the rutting stag. This is the breeding season and he is geared up for action. As we near the fence, he stands proprietorally amongst his small herd of hinds, shaggy in their winter coats, daring us to come any closer. The pungent aroma of his copious urine-marking assaults the nostrils from many yards away. Clouds scud across the sky and we are caught in a brief hail storm - quite a shock after the mild rain of west Ireland. We can see snow on the distant hills and a skein of wild geese straggles overhead, their plaintive honking echoing through the valley. The seasons are turning once again and winter is not far away.

A little bit of business next - a trip to see Edith and Meeny. What an improvement. Meeny can now walk a few steps on all four legs before her weak hind end collapses. She is very tottery but has been walking well enough to allow the rubbed areas on the top of her hind paws to begin to heal. It is now over eight weeks since her surgery - a long haul but worth it in the end. Edith is thrilled. Some of her acquaintances had regarded Meeny as a lost cause and had suggested putting her to sleep, but luckily she has proved them wrong. To celebrate, we go for lunch at our local hostelry. The fire is blazing and cheery voices ask how the holiday was. It is nice to go away, but equally nice to come home. Only a week ago, we brought the locum here for lunch. Unable to get Alastair, we booked Jeff - a young Australian highly recommended by a friend for whom he has been working. With the surgery being single-handed, there is a lot of information to be passed on to a locum and Jeff was looking decidedly apprehensive at this time last week. However the week has gone exceptionally smoothly and Jeff has coped ably with everything. He has even kept the woodburner going - a first for any locum. Having a young handsome Aussie has also had unforseen benefits - Alice tells me that two or three young Clayfern ladies have been back to the surgery several times during the week. The first sight of Jeff has encouraged them to find other problems with their own pets or even those belonging to friends or relatives! We have done a roaring trade in overdue booster vaccinations, nail trims and health checks and the bank balance is looking surprisingly healthy. It might be worth our while to stay away for longer while Jeff's fame spreads to the outlying villages.

Thursday 22nd October

We are having wild weather this week, cloudbursts one minute then sunshine, all set against a backdrop of constant strong winds which cause fallen leaves to dance like dervishes across the roads and dislodge small branches from overhanging trees. The surgery has been quiet since our return from Ireland - a prime example of Murphy's Law - 'Surgeries are *always* quiet before a big drug bill is due, *especially* after a locum has been paid.'

Alice and I have exhausted the usual ruses to attract customers - opening a magazine, putting the kettle on, even going to the loo - but to no avail. Only a trickle of customers have darkened our doors, inevitably with the least lucrative of requirements. This morning, I have certified a hamster dead, trimmed a guinea pig's nails and reluctantly informed a client that she has come three months early for her dog's booster. In the veterinary field, this is not the stuff of which fortunes are made. Clayfern folk seem to have a mass consciousness - they either all come in or stay away *en masse*. It is reassuring to hear that the doctor's surgery is quiet as well and we suspect that it may be because this week is a school holiday - the old *Tattie Howking* week when kids made spare cash by picking potatoes. In these automated days, it is unlikely that many kids will even know what tattie howking means.

Back at Fern, I attend to a pitifully small ops list - one cat spay and one cat castration. The cattle are now in the back field and congregate by the window to watch the action. Sometimes they spectate for hours, but today their attention is diverted by the arrival of the tractor bringing a large round bale to supplement their grazing and off they trundle across the soggy stubble. For the last few weeks, we have been having mini power cuts - often only for several seconds - up to four times a day. Although not serious, they have been irritating, causing timers to fail, answering machines to reset and burglar alarms to go off. For days, the area has been flooded with power company workers, some in Landrovers, some on foot, others in low-flying helicopters, all desperately trying to locate the fault. Today, all the detective work has paid off; it is all the fault of our very own cattle in the back field. Apparently one of the porcelain insulators has a hairline crack and when a cow scratches itself against the pole carrying the supply, a short occurs (apologies to electricity workers if this explanation is not strictly accurate, but this is the gist of the problem) *another* quirk of country living.

At least when it is quiet, the paperwork gets brought bang up to date and there has even been time to practise the tin whistle. I wryly consider that, at this rate, I might need an alternative career by Christmas. However, if we do have to be quiet, then this is a lovely time of year for it. I set off up the hill with the dogs loaded into the back of the Tundra. The steep hill punishes old Kippen's legs, but with a lift to the top, he is like a pup. Once the door is opened, all three dogs dash headlong into a new lake created by the heavy rain, splash around happily, then divert fruitlessly to chase a hare along the track. Even Fintry gives up seconds into the chase, learning from the others that hares are incredibly fast and not worth the effort. Overhead a buzzard is being harried by a crow. The sun catches the upturned buzzard in all his glory - yellow feet and beak and brown and white patterned wings. He is bigger than the crow, but wheels and banks frantically to avoid the furious aggressor. Near the top of the stubble field to our left, a roe deer stands alert, watching our approach. Only when we move closer does he head for the woods, leaping in exaggerated bounds as if to taunt us with his speed and agility. It is the same beast that we have seen several times before - he has a distinctive white streak at his throat and seems braver than the other roe deer, often facing us down brazenly before retreating into cover. This area is certainly a prime habitat so he is likely to be a dominant buck. Unlike the red deer who live in herds, roe deer live in family groups and are territorial. The more dominant bucks claim the best territories while the poorer specimens have to make do with what is left. Some poor souls who are bottom of the pecking order are doomed to live in the thin strip of patchy woodland next to the river.

Further along the track, the red deer stag (who confusingly is white) extends his neck, opens his mouth wide and bellows mournfully, proclaiming his mastery of the surrounding herd of hinds and youngsters. Two of last year's youngsters are males and have sprouted spindly antlers. They are no match for Honky, but have been banished to a far corner of the paddock, out of view of the present 'Monarch of the Pen'. The scenery is utterly beautiful at this time of year; the warm sun casts a honeyed glow over the countryside - the forest a multicoloured flaming patchwork and the river sapphire blue with waves whipped into white horses by the wind. Down in the valley, the fields are greening already with next year's crops and the dusky pinks and faded terracotta of pantiled barns dot the landscape. Snow coats the faraway peaks like icing sugar. All looks peaceful.

On the way to evening surgery, the soon-to-be-setting sun shines directly through the windscreen - a reminder of the shortening days - and the hill behind Clayfern is ablaze with the russet of fading bracken, golden beech trees and crimson rowan leaves mingling with pillarbox red berries. There is an old saying that the heavier the rowan crop, the worse the winter. At this rate, we are in for a corker.

Evening surgery is largely taken up with Don who has had a major 'go' at his bandage and wound. What was lovely granulation tissue last time now looks as if it has been ploughed. Deep gouges cross the surface and strands of ripped tissue hang downwards like stalagtites. June is furious with Don and ignores his worried attempts to curry favour again, but relents somewhat when I suggest that the bandage might have tightened when wet and caused irritation. The wound doesn't look quite so bad after cleaning, but if it is not much improved in a few days, Don may require another anaesthetic to allow more tidying. As acupuncture has been shown to reduce local irritation and pain, it seems worth doing, so another ten minutes is spent twiddling needles inserted round the periphery of the defect before fitting a well padded bandage. Don and his wound will be frequently infiltrating my thoughts in quiet moments over the next few days before we see him again.

Luckily, there is no time to brood on lost ground tonight, as we have a night off to meet nephew Tom and his mum from the station in Stramar and enjoy a meal in the town. Not being used to unlit roads, young Tom is intrigued by the *cats' eyes* lighting the road home. I tease him gently - 'The reason that Sheila can afford to give so many cats a home is that they all donate an eye which the

217

council buy to put in the roads. They manage fine with their remaining one!' He doesn't believe me really, but is clearly intrigued at the notion. Over the few days of his stay, I must try to look for and point out the two one-eyed cats which actually do live with Sheila. The meal out is largely overshadowed by the show on the way home. First, a barn owl caught in the headlights on a fence post, frozen like a statue for several moments before spreading his wings and gliding gracefully across the field. Already travelling slowly to view the owl, we are ideally prepared to brake rapidly when a roe deer leaps from the woods into our path, pauses in confusion then clears the fence in one graceful bound. Often, more than one cross here and sure enough a second emerges from the undergrowth and follows the first into the stubble for a midnight feast. Tom and his mum are enthralled. Pausing on the doorstep at home, the wind is finally silent, allowing the night to envelop us. Frost lies on the ground and the sky is brilliant with stars. The geese are cackling by the water's edge, the stag roars on his hill and the shrill cries of calling owls filters from the wood. Only the biting cold persuades Tom to come indoors, where it takes hot chocolate and much talking down by the fire before he is even slightly drowsy. It is marvellous to see a city kid succumb to the magic of the countryside and Mother Nature has certainly put on a show for him tonight.

Saturday 24th October

A horrendous morning - high winds and merciless, lashing rain. Miserable weather for Tom's holiday. Jay is taking him to the cinema this morning so we part after breakfast.

'You're lucky to be going out while I'm slaving in the surgery,' I comment.

'Why! Is it hard work?' replies the lad in incredulous tones.

'Of course it is,' I reply.

'But you just call people in and tell them what's wrong with their pet,' he counters, quick as a flash

'But I have to think about the problem first,' I shoot back, rather stung by his dismissive attitude.

'But you've seen them all before' comes the final word. 'Who was it that said 'Never work with children or animals?

Driving to work in the reassuringly sure-footed Tundra, the countryside looks swamped. The potato lifting is two weeks behind schedule, tatties still lying in sodden ground. There has already been almost twice the usual rainfall this month. At Abbeygate, the ducklings and their mum are swimming up the flooded road and two swans are on the pond, probably blown off course on the way to the local wintering grounds. Under the circumstances, I expect surgery to be quiet but, the floodgates have opened and we are busy again. Don and June are waiting and I eye them apprehensively while calling in earlier appointments, looking for any advance warning as to how things have been. Both sit inscrutably in their corner giving no clues at all, so by the time it is their turn, both Alice and I are in a lather of anticipation. My hands even shake a little as I unwrap the bandage which seems pleasantly dry. There has been a terrific improvement in just two days: the tags of tissue have miraculously disappeared and once again we have a patch of healthy granulation tissue surrounded by pink new skin. 'This dog is going to be the death of me' I mutter, as we repeat the now familiar procedures. Relief all round is tempered by the realisation that anything could happen in the *next* few days. June tempts fate outrageously by mentioning that she has a bottle of champagne in the fridge for the final unveiling; Alice and I stare at each other in horror. For superstitious folk such as us, June has probably ruined Don's chances of healing this side of Christmas. Unperturbed, June smiles encouragingly, with touching faith in her dog's healing ability - if nothing else.

Jay and Tom are at home when I finish surgery and Tom proudly displays all his purchases. It is a revelation to see what wonders are taking the eight-year-old population by storm these days - finger skateboards and anything bearing the Southpark logo are all the rage; apparently we are also going to be 'growing an alien' over the next few days. This involves immersing a plastic 'egg' in a bucket of water; this 'hatches' and gradually grows into a repulsive looking 'alien'. *Why don't these children have nightmares?* Having been flavour of the month long enough to purchase the forementioned, Jay is ruthlessly cast aside while the afternoon's entertainment begins. This requires veterinary expertise - my turn. Walking the dogs yesterday, Tom and I came across some bones - the remains of a roe deer. The hunt for assorted body parts intrigued the lad to such an extent that we could not move on until we had virtually exhumed the entire skeleton. As foraging creatures had spread bones far and wide, this took quite some time, although Kippen and Fintry did their best to help. In fact, Tom had another willing accomplice, as I find forensic pathology fascinating. 'If you died here,Tom,' I explained, 'And weren't found for many years, scientists could tell from your bones that you were a human boy, about nine and roughly four foot ten inches high.' During the course of our search, he learnt other valuable things - to identify the musty, all-pervading smell of dead shrew and the pungent, astringent scent of fox-marked boundaries. How useful that will be in the city is debatable, but I'm sure it will come in handy sometime. At the end of our search for bones, there was still no sign of a head, but I dimly remember hanging a skull on a tree out of dog reach in the far woods and an expedition to investigate proved successful. It may not *exactly* match the other remains but it will do.

So, our project for today is to reassemble the deer. This is accomplished surprisingly well using a metal template (the inside of a roll of barbed wire) and assorted pieces of wire and Blu-tack. Some bits are missing but the finished article does give the impression of having once been an animal.

'I hope you've thought of a convincing excuse to persuade him *not* to take that home,' mutters Jay darkly as we go to bed. 'His mother will go berserk.'

Further debate is stifled by the sudden sound of crying from Tom's room. We rush through to find he is in fact laughing hysterically. 'It's so dark, he howls, ' I can't even see my hand in front of my face!'

Sunday 25th October

Unbelievably after yesterday's atrocious conditions, this morning is gloriously sunny - and, inevitably, windy. The clocks went back last night, a mixed blessing. Getting up in the morning will be easier in the light, but tearing away from the fire to drive to evening surgery in the dark will be a wrench. A bracing walk up Duncraig crag starts the day. The heather has faded and larch needles fly horizontally in the gale like flights of golden arrows. We pass the gamekeeper feeding his pheasants - building them up so that they can be flattened in the shooting season.

This is Tom's last walk as his parents come to collect him today. Their aim is to stop for lunch, but to leave early to drive home before dark. As it happens, they are lucky to get home at all. Rushing as always, they arrive here with a last gasp of petrol in the tank, expecting to fill up in Clayfern. Unfortunately, the garage in Clayfern does not open on Sundays and the nearest petrol station is over ten miles away. This is one of the quirks of country living which causes much incredulity amongst city dwellers. They also find it hard to appreciate that all the local shops shut for lunch between 1 pm and 2 pm, even the store which provides sandwiches and snacks for lunches! Even worse, the bank closes between 12.30 pm and 1.30 pm, extending the gap during the day when very little can be accomplished in the village. Luckily, we know that our friend Andy saves a full petrol can for emergencies and a quick trip to his cottage solves the problem. The excitement of looking round the farm distracts Tom to such an extent that he forgets to take his deer skeleton. We will save it for his next visit.

The remainder of the day is spent leisurely, catching up with accumulated washing and painting the outside of the surgery before the *real* bad weather sets in. Already, our cottage only catches the sun for a few brief hours during the day and soon we will move into unrelieved gloom when it fails to rise above the hill behind us. Collecting dog food from Clayfern surgery, I divert to drop off some medicine for Cagney Adams - nothing serious, only worming tablets. Since his radioactive iodine therapy earlier in the year, he has been very fit and well. The trips to Glasgow were definitely worthwhile. Mrs Adams is also doing her washing. Originally from the Western Isles, she admits to a frisson of guilt about working on a Sunday. At her island home, even the cockerel was segregated from the hens on the Sabbath.

The inclement weather and shortening days have evidently spurred our neighbours into action preparing for winter. I pass two of them towing trailers loaded with wood and the rasp of chainsaws echoes across the fields. There is no doubt that the sight of a well-stocked woodshed is immensely satisfying and we must attend to ours before long. At this time of year, a few extra tins and some candles begin to be added to the weekly shopping basket - just in case. A tell-tale rustling in the attic this evening shows that we are not the only ones preparing for winter. Yes, we have mice again. Last year, they caused major damage to electrical cables, otherwise they would be welcome to come in out of the cold. The cat is dispatched up the ladder on a mission to intimidate. She is too well fed to bother with hunting, but we optimistically hope that her mere presence will act as a deterrent. After a brief prowl, she appears at the top of the ladder, yowling to be rescued. This evening at least, there is no more scrabbling to be heard.

Friday 30th October

On Monday, an early morning request from Colin has had unfortunate consequences. While helping to move the cattle indoors for winter, the muddy bank on which I was standing collapsed into the path of the last of the stampeding herd. I have been left battered and bruised, with a damaged knee. Apart from pain, my main reaction is embarrassment, as if it smacks of incompetence to get into a position to be hurt by an animal. Rest and anti -inflammatories should have been the answer, but Murphy's Law has produced a very busy week so there has been no alternative but to hobble on. Luckily, my arms and hands were unhurt and driving has been just possible - if rather awkward and sore. The week has been spent learning to hobble effectively, without being able to flex the damaged knee. A walking stick seemed desirable before attempting any off-road walks with the dogs, but to our amusement, the department stocking them was housed on the top floor of the shop. Really practical. However, I am now the proud possessor of a customised (or sawn-off) oak stick. Friends tell me it will come in handy in old age for thrashing a path to the head of the pension queue in the Post Office!

Despite such distractions, work carries on as ever. Mickey the hyperthyroid cat is in today for a final check. He has been off all medication for a week and is looking good. He has gained two pounds in weight and is back to his normal staggery self. Another long-winded case also concludes today - Mac the terrier with the eye graft. He stands stock still while I instill local anaesthetic drops into his eye, then carefully cut the tissue bridge attached to the original corneal defect. The patch will gradually shrink until only a small area of opaque tissue is left. It took a long time but we got there in the end.

'You were like a ferret with a rabbit with his problem,' confides Mac's owner. I think I'll take that as a compliment. Final case of the morning is Lucky the cat. Although only a year old, he is already on to his second record card and has been unofficially rechristened Unlucky. He limped home last night after a week's absence with a swollen left stifle (knee) and a broken tooth. Today he is in for an anaesthetic so the tooth can be removed and the leg examined and X-rayed. The stifle is very loose on examination - the ligaments are certainly ruptured - but no other damage shows up on X-ray. Reporting to the owner, I catch myself saying '*Only* ligamentous damage.' After my own experience, I will not be so free with saying *only* ligamentous damage again. It does all doctors good occasionally to experience some of the symptoms from which patients suffer - it makes us much more sympathetic.

Since the clocks changed, I drive home from Clayfern in the dark each evening. Tonight the moon is bright through the window and the navigation buoys wink reassuringly on the river. From a mile away, the lights of home shine like welcoming beacons through the dark night. After a long day's hobbling, it is bliss to settle on the settee by the fire and be served a tasty meal by a solicitious Jay. Since the accident, I have been unable to bend my knee, so my feet have stayed miserably cold. Tonight however, there is movement enough to use my traditional foot-warming method - a flat stone from the beach is put on top of the woodburner for five minutes then placed on the floor by the settee.

Saturday 31st October

En route to morning surgery, a flock of fieldfares flit from bush to bush. These thrush-like birds join us in winter from Scandinavia and the Baltics. The two swans are still on the millpond being thoroughly spoilt by the local children bearing bags of bread and grain. They will move on eventually, but for now seem to be in no hurry. Time to drop in on Edith before surgery. And what a surprise! All three dachshunds are waiting at the gate - it takes a minute to distinguish Meeny from her sister since both are walking with the same ease. It has taken nine weeks but is certainly worth it. It will seem strange not dropping in every few days, but I'm sure Edith will find other problems requiring visits. She sympathises with my bad leg - crippled with arthritis herself, the difficulties of a hobbling lifestyle are all too familiar. She howls with laughter when I tell the saga of my first trip to the toilet post-accident. To understand the tale, it is necessary to know that our wooden toilet seat has a hairline crack at the very front - not normally a problem when one is aware of it and fully mobile. With a wounded knee, there comes a point in the descent to the seat when the knee must flex; this elicited my first yell of anguish and caused an undignified collapse onto the seat, only to be nipped by the crack - second agonised yell and involuntary rising giving rise to final screech of agony. Poor Jay dashed to the door not knowing *what* to expect, certainly not the sight of the invalid collapsed on the floor in peals of hysterical laughter.

After morning surgery, a trip up the hill in the Tundra, invaluable for me now as well as Kippen. All three dogs are shoehorned into the back, excited at the prospect of the first long walk in days. Out with the trusty stick and along the relative flat of the forest rides, more accessible now that the nettles are dying back. The track is carpeted with brittle leaves and wood pigeons erupt from the tree tops as we crunch along. More dried leaves and ash keys spiral to the ground as we wander along, approaching the stones gradually. I am glad for a breather and leisurely survey the ever changing scene. The woods are a multicoloured weave of green, russet and golden and a buzzard soars overhead. A roe deer grazes in the stubble - probably Whitethroat. We are too far away to pose a threat and he continues grazing. Although it is only mid-afternoon, the sun is well on its way westwards, its watery light illuminating streaks of wispy clouds layered parallel to the horizon. A freshening northwesterly wind brings chill from the snow capped mountains. You can't linger too long at this time of year.

Tonight is Halloween. In pagan times, it marked the beginning of the new year and was thought to be when spirits of the dead arise and visit homes. All the local children are out tonight - *guising*. Dressed as witches, ghoulies and ghosties, they patter excitedly through the streets in small groups, knocking on doors and delivering a party piece in exchange for some sweets or nuts. Perhaps they may even be invited in to dook for apples in a jeelypan full of water, or try to bite toffees hung on kitchen pulleys. Living four miles out of town, we often miss the fun, but tonight we are going with friends for a special Halloween meal at our local. The menu includes topical gems such as - *devilled ribs* and *the silence of the lamb*! Everyone has dressed up - Jay and I as Frankenstein and his monster - and a wonderful time is had by all, reviving happy childhood memories. It is great to let your hair down from time to time.

Monday 2nd November

A visit to the bank after morning surgery brings back memories of Halloween. They are having a 'Customer Appreciation Day' - a nice touch as trays of shortbread and fruitcake are on offer with a choice of whisky, sherry or fruit juice. Entering into the spirit of the time of year, the staff have dressed up for Halloween. The tellers sport red horns or witch's hats and, presiding over all, is our bank manager Fred. Short, stout Fred is in full regalia - horns, tail, red sweatshirt, cape and trident to boot. He is a sight to behold and, along with the whisky, is brightening everyone's day.

Suddenly, the door crashes open and my name is called: 'Help me Doctor, me dug's deeing', stops me mid-sip. Eck's friend Ralph stands frantically in the doorway, cradling a limp Alsation puppy in his arms. We repair swiftly to the surgery, Ralph gasping out details as we dash across the road.
'I think he's eaten some of my tablets overnight,' he grunts; 'I've just woken up and found him like this.'
Once safely on the table, it is evident that Rommel is out for the count. The tablets are a form of sedative and the pup is almost totally unconscious. He is breathing evenly but his temperature is subnormal and if not treated, he is in danger of slipping away entirely.

'I'll need to take him up to the farm surgery Ralph,' I say carefully - Ralph has a reputation for being slightly 'unbalanced' - 'We'll do all we can.' It is quite a coincidence to see Ralph today, so soon after last week's 'incident'. After an afternoon in the pub, Ralph and a fellow drinker had a spectacular falling out not far from the surgery. Rather than attack his (larger) opponent, Ralph relieved his pent-up frustration on a string of inanimate objects down the High Street. The surgery window copped for a karate-style kick which left the dusty imprint of Ralph's training shoe - otherwise no damage was done. Alice and I were secretly quite impressed that, even inebriated, Ralph could raise his foot to that height at all. I was consulting at the time and news of the debacle filtered through from Alice and customers in the waiting room. 'He's completely oot af his skull' was the unanimous opinion. Such is the nature of Clayfern, that by the end of surgery I had learnt from my clients, the perpetrator's name, his age and address, who his parents were and his other transgressions to date. The police were called and lifted Ralph to spend the night sobering up in the cells. This was a big event in Clayfern and was discussed exhaustively over the next few days. We are a village with a low crime rate - Jay's policeman brother goes into creases of amusement when reading the crime reports in the local paper: *Wing mirror damaged on car* and *Lawn mower stolen from garden shed* sound unbelievably quaint to someone more used to armed robberies and vice rings.

The drug which Rommel has eaten was popular in veterinary work years ago and I estimate that the dog has taken approximately ten times the usual dose. Karen the chemist fills in more details - 'For control of various psychoses,' she reads from the data sheet. That figures! We hope that Ralph is left with enough to prevent a re-run of last week's stushie. The drug is rapidly absorbed from the gut and is obviously well into the system now so there seems no point in stomach washes or trying to induce vomiting. There is no specific antidote - all we can do is provide supportive treatment. First job is to get the temperature up, so, as usual, Rommel is swathed in bubblewrap. The drug can cause heart irregularities so an ECG next. There is a variation in the wave form suggesting *myocardial hypoxia* (not enough oxygen getting to the heart muscle) and the pulse oximeter verifies this, showing only 88 per cent oxygen in the blood when it should be in the high nineties. We start a slow drip to help flush the drug from the circulation and administer oxygen through nasal clips. The pup is too flattened to object to any interference. Luckily, the day is otherwise quiet as Rommel needs near constant supervision. His temperature, oxygenation and responses gradually improve until 10.30 pm when he is almost back to normal. Having slept all day, he is bouncing with energy and desperate to play. After dealing with him all day, I am not in the mood for fun. He will come to Clayfern surgery tomorrow morning and be reunited with Ralph. Meanwhile, I am heading for bed, leaving the radio on in the surgery in a vain attempt to keep the puppy quiet. After his marathon snooze, he is once again behaving like a typical twelve-week-old pup. Thank goodness.

Thursday 5th November

Off up the hill with the dogs before breakfast. We have a busy ops list today, so it may be their only outing. It is a frosty morning; windscreens and puddles are frozen, crystallised leaves and clover dot the hard ground and cobwebs glisten like silver lace. There are always interesting smells on frosty mornings and the dogs whizz round with noses hoovering the ground. Smoke snakes lazily upwards from cottages in the valley. In the frosty stillness, flocks of chirping tits flit from tree top to tree top. A good way to start the day. In my pocket, I have a new innovation - a hand-warming stone. Five minutes on the woodburner and it stays warm for the whole walk. Later, Julie comments on the increasing number of stones by the fire and I joke that I am looking for long flat ones to heat my wellies. Taken to extremes, one could strap warm stones to all sensitive areas of the person.
'Better not go too near to the river - you'll sink!' she comments.

On the way to evening surgery, snow-covered cars pass from the north. There are two buzzards benefiting from road kills - perhaps the pickings on the hills are no longer so good. Today, I get the answer to a question which has been intriguing me - the leaves of ordinary beech trees go gradually browner before falling, but what happens to copper beech leaves? They go lighter. Today, they have a greeny tan hue.

During evening surgery there is the seasonal trickle of owners requiring tranquillisers for their pets. This week is miserable for many poor creatures terrified of fireworks. Next, a dog with indeterminate symptoms - off food, restless and vocal, yet he seems bright and examination comes up with no abnormalities. When symptoms are this vague, it is worth suspecting hormones. Such behaviour is common when a nearby bitch is in season and we know of two dogs similarly affected. To ease the poor lad's distress, I administer a drug known, rather chillingly, as a chemical castrator. It counteracts the body's male hormones and mimics to an extent the effects of surgical castration. In four to five days, he should feel less frustrated. His owner has two options for the future: either get him castrated, or find out when local bitches are due in season and have him injected beforehand. Another patient is in similar trouble. The whippet bitch is also unsettled and not eating. She is carrying a favourite toy everywhere and has developed milk in her mammary glands. Yes - a false pregnancy. Medication to counteract the effects of her hormone surge should put things right. It is not only in humans that hormones can cause havoc.

Our next patient comes in a cardboard box. A young hedgehog found by the roadside. She is staggering to one side, seems weak and does not curl up as usual. She is probably concussed from a knock from a car. She gets fluids, antibiotics and corticosteroids to counteract any bruising in her brain and her new minder goes off with some recovery diet. When sucked into a syringe, this is extruded in long 'wormy' strands which many hedgehogs find irresistible. Strangely, our last patient is also a hedgehog, found by our client when only nailbrush size (under two weeks old). He has been hand-reared and is in for a check up. Although at 400 grams he is massively larger than his original 60 grams, he is too light to be allowed to hibernate. He has insufficient body reserves to see him through the winter. Luckily, our client is enthusiastic about keeping him over winter. This involves not inconsiderable mess and the revolting smell of hedgehog faeces, but she is undeterred. Perhaps if our traffic accident hedgie survives, they can make a two-some. We chat about hedgehogs and I reminisce about radio-tracking one reared by a friend. The radio-tag for a hog is about the size of a penny and sports an aerial several inches long. The little transmitter is attached to the spines with *Superglue* (useful stuff to have around the surgery) and eventually falls off when the spines are shed. We spent many happy hours following our hedgehog's nightly ramblings and even witnessed his noisy mating ritual with his intended. Our client is enthralled and my enthusiasm is rekindled - perhaps we might track her hog in the spring. It would be interesting to find how a Scottish village hedgehog differs from an English city one.

On the way home, the moon is full and pearly white clouds scud briskly by. The fields lie pallid in the moonlight, the river a silver streak. Leaves and mud litter the roadside and stark branches loom overhead. I see the orange flashing light of an approaching gritting lorry and brace for the shower of sand hurled against my wheels. The balance has definitely tipped from autumn to winter.

Saturday 7th November

This morning's surgery has demonstrated some of the public's more unexplainable behaviours. An occasional client comes in for her dog's booster: 'He's been really licking his feet,' she says. 'At times they have been red raw and bleeding - but he's okay now.' WHY WAIT TILL NOW? Further questioning reveals that the peak of the dog's discomfort coincided with the berry bug season. Even a simple phone call at the time could have produced advice to ease the poor dog's distress. Surprisingly, this is not an uncommon occurrence: 'Well, his diarrhoea was dreadful two days ago, but its improving now'. SO WHY COME IN *NOW* ?? Alice is fooled by a new customer who telephones to say that her cat has *feline infectious peritonitis*, can she come in immediately? Knowing the poor outlook for this condition, Alice pre-warns me and fits the client in front of others in the waiting room. A remarkably bright cat exits from her box - certainly sporting the swollen abdomen sometimes seen with FIP - but there the similarity ends. The owner has not actually had the cat diagnosed - but she confides that she has seen one like it before. In fact, her cat is pregnant. If only veterinary work was so simple, why bother with five years of training. The 'It must be x because I've seen it before' syndrome can be positively harmful: dispensing ear drops will not help if a grass seed or tumour lurks in the ear canal; cough medicine will not cure a cough due to heart failure. There really is no substitute for examination and all the nurses are trained to suggest a visit to the surgery if any symptoms are present. If we have a practice motto, it is Be careful, never assume *anything*. I tell Alice about two barely credible cases from my city practice. Many years ago, puppy wormers were given out with the instruction to 'Administer tablets after a light meal; repeat in 10 days.' Our client brought in a miserable, weak pup, a total contrast from the lively youngster who was vaccinated five days previously. Wormers had been dispensed at the same time and it transpired that the client (who was not very bright to say the least)

231

assumed that no more food was to be given for the full ten days. Unbelievable, but true. Another memorable case concerned a constipated dog. The owner was advised to purchase some liquid paraffin to ease the problem: 'Is that like Esso Blue?' she asked. 'Never mind, we'll give you some,' was the rapid reply. Unfortunately, there is no intelligence test to be taken before owning a pet, so it pays for vets to leave nothing to chance.

Don is in for a bandage change this morning. He is looking very smart today having added a rather classy jacket to his attire. Both jacket and sock have matching reflective tape for safe evening walking. We have dubbed this *the council workman* look. Things have been going well since our last setback and the wound is gradually healing. It is about half the original size now, so we are not quite so anxious as before.

The dogs and I don't get out till nearly four pm. It is a dour day, intermittently raining with grey skies and a freshening wind. The weather dictates where we can walk. The fields and river paths are too muddy, so yet again, we head up the hill. Still stiff, I meander slowly through the woods. The ground cover is dying down revealing signs of much digging activity in the leaf mould. There are many potential culprits - deer, rabbits, foxes, squirrels, jays (who bury nuts) and even badgers. There are no resident badgers but they occasionally pass through and linger for a few days in an old fox hole. They mark territory by digging latrines at the edge of their territory, so a hole containing faeces is a sure sign that a badger has been around. Clearing the east woods, we progress along the grassy ridge towards the west woods. The red deer are lying in a hollow in the pen. There has been no roaring recently and the young stags are back with the herd. This means that most of the hinds are now pregnant. One young stag is filthy, covered in mud after wallowing in the boggy ground, typical behaviour during the rut. Several weeks ago, the whole herd had patchy dishevelled coats, but they now have their full luxuriant winter attire. In the west woods, the track is carpeted with golden larch needles and parchment-dry beech and sycamore leaves. The gaunt shapes of the nearly naked trees afford little shelter from the wind, so we venture amongst the fir trees. The dogs excitedly savour the less familiar territory. There are plenty fox faeces deposited on prominent tussocks or tree stumps. Foxes also use faeces to mark territory. Recently, we have heard loud squabbles between foxes, probably partly due to adolescents being forced to leave the family group. Under the firs, an oval, brick-red pod of rock catches my eye - the inside glistens through a small fissure in the shell. When cracked on a rock, the pod splits into segments of pinky white quartz - it is a *geode*, a rock cavity lined with crystals formed during volcanic activity. It is carted proudly home to add to our numerous other treasures. Dropping Jonno at the farm, much bellowing comes from the barn; Colin is feeding the cattle. I love the barn in winter; it is always warmer than outside and filled with pleasant aromas - the nutty smell of molasses in the feed, the fresh straw and the cattle's sweet breath. Not perhaps everyone's cup of tea, but definitely a bit special.

Monday 10th November

Like Alice says, typical baby weather - wet and windy! For the last few days, we have had driving rain and ferocious gales and the area seems under siege. The bridge over the estuary is closed as winds are gusting in excess of eighty miles per hour and various roads are blocked either by floods or fallen trees. High winds are not unusual for this locality and they might be exhilarating if not for the ghosts of six years ago. At the time, the newly-fledged surgery was housed in a humble wooden building beside the house. The building had started life as a holiday chalet and was bought after it had finished its career as a site office for a builder. Jay and I took much care kitting it out for its new role and all our customers seemed impressed with its deceptive spaciousness - one coined a nickname which stuck - the Tardis. As the practice grew, I spent many happy hours in the Tardis. Unfortunately, one January night with gales gusting more than one hundred miles an hour, it blew over in the middle of the night with an earth-shattering crash. Devastation - the surgery finished almost before it had begun. However, McKelvies are built of stern stuff and thanks to the help and ingenuity of friends and neighbours, the surgery was temporarily rehoused in our dining room. When the weather improved, the Tardis was repositioned with tractor and forklift and anchored in place with steel hawsers. Jay and friends mended the damage and once again we kitted out the interior. Like a phoenix, the new, improved Tardis rose from the ashes and was used for another year until the larger new surgery was built. All ended well, but we will never forget the feeling of utter desolation sifting through the jumble of equipment, record cards, drugs and syringes that once constituted our lovely surgery. So now, during wild weather, I still sleep uneasily with an ear cocked in case any dire fate befalls the present surgery.

Due to the weather, surgery is relatively quiet. Castration appears to be the topic of the day. Our 'restless' dog from last week has settled down a treat after his chemical castrator. He comes when he is called and has generally become a model citizen. His owner comments that the injection would be useful for her husband. Next, a regular client calls in to arrange castration for her two cats. She left a message on the answering machine last week and in turn, I left a reply on hers: 'Regarding getting your lads castrated, Friday suits me if it suits you.' I was a little surprised not to see her on Friday, but assumed that something had cropped up. All is explained today - she hasn't got an answering machine! Some innocent householder must really be wondering about that message.

There is a sad job to be done before returning to the farm surgery. In spring, an elderly dog - Lucy the Labrador - was rushed to the surgery in *status epilepticus* (continual fitting) and necessitated an all-night session in which she was anaesthetised to stop the fitting. Since then, she has been on fit suppressant medication and has only had an occasional fit until two weeks ago, when their frequency and severity increased dramatically. Her quality of life has plummeted and her owners have decided to call it a day. At least she has enjoyed the summer.

Only one operation today, the routine ones have been postponed until the roads are better. There is a wound to be stitched on a cat's leg. This is not just any cat, but a genuine Scottish wildcat. As a very tiny kitten, she was found beside her dead mother on a remote highland road. Her identity has been verified by genetic testing at Edinburgh Zoo and she certainly looks the part - light tabby in colour with a striped coat,and a distinctive bushy tail with dark rings. She has a lovely nature, not savage at all, the main feature distinguishing her from her domestic counterparts is that she has never miaowed. The stitching is uneventful and I settle in front of the fire to catch up on paperwork. Only minutes later, the phone shrills. A dog has rifled through his owner's handbag and eaten her anti-anxiety pills. I start on the familiar routine, first calming the owner (who could do with her tablets now) and asking for vital details: *what is the drug's name? How many could he have eaten? How long ago?* As the incident has only just happened, I advise the owner to give the dog salty water to induce vomiting. While she attempts this, I will gather more information and call her back. First stop is medical drug reference information, conveniently stored on CD-ROM. Then further details from Karen the chemist. 'He won't be anxious for a while anyway', she mutters drily while searching her records. Once all the information is to hand, we conclude that the dog is unlikely to come to much harm with the dose he will have swallowed. I ring the owner to report and give her more advice. A stodgy meal might help to delay absorption of the drug. She must watch him carefully over the next few hours, watching for doziness or any change in his demeanor. If the bottle had been full, we might have had the same situation as with Rommel the other day. With the blocked roads, even getting to the surgery might have been a problem. While we talk, I can hear the excitable collie bouncing around in the background. I think he will be fine. The surgery receives several such calls each year. The most common substances eaten are probably rat poison and birth control pills. The latter always cause much embarrassment for the owner - and much amusement for the veterinary staff and luckily, The Pill does not appear to do our patients any harm. Popular cat substance abuse includes bleach - which causes ulcerated tongues and mouths and car anti-freeze which is often fatal.

Half an hour late, the paperwork gets opened again. And almost immediately, the phone rings. Definitely an emergency - shrill agonised screeches from an injured puppy almost drown out the owner's voice. This is one of our puppy-party pupils who has injured her leg in the garden. Poppy is in such agony that a general anaesthetic is necessary before she can be properly examined and

X-rayed. She has badly fractured her elbow; this is a job for a specialist. I call our nearby orthopaedic referral practice to discuss the case, then pass on details to the owners. Heavily sedated and painkilled, Poppy will spend tonight at home before travelling to the specialist practice tomorrow. For a quiet day, it has been remarkably brisk.

Giving up all thoughts of paperwork, I take the dogs for a waterlogged walk on the back field. Not the best idea - the dogs sink up to their stomachs in mud before we climb the slope. The brilliant hues of autumn have given way to more muted, sepia tones and a hint of mist rises from the river. In the hedgerows, small flocks of birds feast on the remaining berries and gulls chatter from the flooded barleyfield. The sheep over the fence add a touch of colour with their bright blue and red rumps. At this time of year, the ewes are joined by the rams who wear harnesses which holds a colour block on their chests. The colour is changed every ten days or so. When they mate with a ewe, colour is deposited on her rear allowing the shepherd to know which ewes have been mated and when. This makes life easier in the spring when they have a rough idea when different coloured ewes are due to lamb.

On the way to evening surgery, I see the potato harvester moving slowly along our neighbour's field. The coloured machinery and halogen lamps light it up like a fairground ride. Not much amusement there, though I'm sure. A woeful client was telling of bogged-down machinery, potatoes embedded in large clods of earth and frozen fingers. Some farmers have given up altogether and have ploughed their ruined crop back into the waterlogged ground. In weather such as this, an indoor job sounds particularly attractive.

Monday 16th November

At last a bright frosty morning. What a relief after all the rain. The hard frost allows us to enjoy a morning walk across the frozen field to the river. Various ducks and geese are roosting on the sandbanks, their strident cries carrying over the water. The dogs enjoy their beachcombing session, but the frosty ground is proving hard for poor Kippen's old legs, so we return at a very leisurely pace. My knee is also slowing us down. It is almost three weeks since the accident, but it is far from right. It demonstrates just how long it can take for soft tissue injuries to heal. Colin the farmer has come to mend the fence between the field and our land and in a fit of generosity has made a stile allowing us direct access to the field. We have been hinting for ages, but guilt over my injury seems to have spurred him on. During our ops session, Julie and I ponder this. Police officers receive compensation in proportion to the injury received and we wonder whether flinging oneself in front of a cow again might be worth something. Perhaps a ski tow made from a tractor engine, or a nice swimming pond by the river?

Our old friend Jake Lafferty comes in during surgery. His diabetes has been well controlled for some time, but he is drinking excessively again and not eating well. I take blood samples before his morning and evening meals to check his blood glucose levels: too high. His owner has to increase the insulin dose and we'll check again in a few days. Tired of the usual sulking after collecting a mere drop of blood, I mention giving Jake's owner some EMLA cream (local anaesthetic) to apply before he comes in next.
'EMLA cream?' queries Colonel Lafferty, 'Is that a sherry?'
If only, Colonel, if only.

Calling in for a booster is Duff, another black Labrador. Clayfern is full of black Labs, it would be more sensible to have black flooring rather than our tan linoleum. Duff used to be scared of veterinary surgeries, but started coming here when the surgery was new and often quiet. He has learnt quickly where the doggy treats are stored and fixes the jar with an unwavering gaze for the entire consultation. I remember once hearing about a hypnotist who had a canine partner. The dog could also hypnotise people with its steady stare. I expect it was a Labrador. They have gannet-like appetites and are very susceptible to bribery.

After an uneventful day, I settle by the fire while supper cooks, but only manage to read one page of the newspaper before the telephone heralds an emergency. An eight-week-old kitten is carried into the surgery - soaking wet, limp and almost lifeless. His owner arrived home from work to find the kitten stuck down the toilet, barely conscious with only his head wedged clear of the water. He is not moving at all except for a gasping breath twice a minute. His heart rate at 40 is less than a quarter of what it should be and his temperature is below the lowest reading on the thermometer. This makes it less than 95°F when it should be 102°F. Pupils are semi-dilated and unresponsive to light. All in all, things look rather bleak, but we'll give treatment a try. We place him on a warm pad and Jay towels him and uses a hairdrier while I administer oxygen by mask and begin giving him warm fluids directly into his abdomen. There is no way that a vein can be found, his peripheral circulation has shut down completely. When he is drier, we wrap him in tin foil (from the kitchen cupboard) and continue with the oxygen. The heating is cranked up and we feel like greasy spots when the room temperature hits 90°F. After the initial activity, there is now little to do but monitor his progress. After half an hour, his heart rate has almost doubled and he is breathing five times per minute, but no temperature registers on the thermometer. By 8 pm (an hour after his admission), he begins to make small, lethargic struggling movements. He is transferred to a cage converted into an oxygen tent by placing it in a rubbish bag and feeding the oxygen hose into the interior. At 8.15 pm, his heart rate is 110 and he begins to shiver. This is an encouraging sign - shivering is the body's response to low temperatures, it generates heat. Jay stays with him while I bolt down some supper, then we both return to the house, Jay for supper and I to lie on the settee with the shivering kitten in a warm place - stuffed inside my jumper next to my skin - and thus we remain for the remainder of the evening. At 10 pm, the kitten's heart rate is 200, but his temperature is a mere 99°F. He is more responsive and can stand unaided. He accepts some recovery diet in a loaded syringe. By 11 pm, he can totter across the floor but his temperature remains at 99°F. We settle him for the night close to the fire in a cage full of bedding and a wrapped hot water bottle. At 5 am. we are wakened by strident yells and a normal-looking kitten leaps from the basket in search of food. A good meal settles him for an hour then the yells begin again - our kitten wants to explore and play. At 6 am, we don't. However, lack of sleep is compensated for by a great feeling of accomplishment. Showing no apparent ill effects from his misadventure, our kitten goes home during morning surgery. The owners have firm instructions to keep the toilet seat down. Nameless until now, the owners have been inspired to pick the perfect title - Harpic - because he is clean round the bend!

Thursday 19th November

An early morning walk up the hill to greet the rising sun for a daily 'fix'. The sun no longer reaches our cottage but only appears tantalisingly halfway down the field in front. We are now doomed to survive in shaded gloom until January. The winds have stripped most remaining leaves from the trees and gone are the bright colours of autumn. Instead the woods are a muted mix of ginger larches and sombre bluegreen pines. Up the hill it is magical; frost glistening in the sun and banks of mist filling the valleys. Wooded hilltops appear like islands in a white billowy sea. The river is totally obscured by a wide band of mist - this is confusing the geese who fly round in straggly skeins, honking wildly. The dogs run riot through the stubble; interesting smells linger from the antics of the creatures of the night. Returning through the woods, views which are obscured in summer appear through the stark branches and birds' nests and squirrels' dreys stand out devoid of their leafy camouflage.

Life slows down a little for the practice at this time of year. Time to revamp the surgery and attend to 'house-keeping' chores. Alice and I spend quiet moments in Clayfern reorganising the waiting room and planning our next educational topic. We try to keep the waiting room interesting and informative, but it tends to get neglected during busy periods. Our new display covers preventative dental care and Alice and her daughters have worked hard to make it eye-catching and interesting. It is so worthwhile for owners to invest in some animal toothpaste and a brush and spend five minutes a day attending to their pet's teeth. The animal feels more comfortable and fresh, no more infection causing pain and bad breath and no extensive (and expensive) dental work required in middle-age.

Home after morning surgery, I attend to some routine neutering work for Sheila, then settle to arrange servicing for surgery equipment. Regular services are now compulsory under a myriad of new Health and Safety regulations which have impacted on veterinary work over the last decade or so. They are undoubtedly for the best, but the work and expense involved has definitely made the job more stressful for practice owners. By mid-afternoon, I have arranged appointments for annual check-overs for our anaesthetic machine, X-ray unit and autoclave (steriliser).

Time for a break, but just as the excited dogs are being loaded into the Tundra, a car draws up and a distraught owner clambers out cradling an apparently unconscious dog. A disappointed Kippen and Fintry are swiftly ushered kitchenwards and the surgery is opened. Who would be a vet's dog. Believe it or not – it's another hypothermia case. Scamp had been missing for four days until finally located only moments ago, firmly stuck down a rabbit hole. Only his hind legs were visible and much frantic digging was necessary to dislodge him. At least I'm in practice for hypothermia cases - and his symptoms are much the same as Harpic's with the added problem of gritty earth obscuring his eyes and nostrils. It will be a worry if he has inhaled any grit into his lungs. Once the initial hectic phase of starting fluids and oxygen and swathing in insulated bedding is over, I can attend to his eyes. His nostrils and mouth clear easily but his eyes are badly contaminated. Although he is barely conscious, I instil local anaesthetic drops in each eye then flush repeatedly with warm saline. The grit is tenacious and it takes many flushes before the eyes look clear. Now some more local anaesthetic before *Fluorescein*, a special dye to show up damage to the cornea. Sure enough, the entire front surface of each eye takes up the green colour, but hopefully the damage is only superficial. Scamp will have eye drops for the next few days - if he survives of course. All cases are different, he may not respond as well as Harpic - *never assume*. Fortunately, Scamp does respond well over the next few hours - but wrapped up well in his kennel. He is definitely too big to be stuffed down my jumper.

Friday 20th November

Scamp has gone home, a little jaded, but otherwise none the worse for his ordeal. The weather has turned milder and is again wet and windy so the chances of seeing more hypothermia victims are slim in the immediate future. It is hard to know when to give up on these cases. Jay reminds me of an extreme case we had in the city practice: during lunchtime surgery, a five-year-old squirrel was brought in by clients we knew well. They had reared the squirrel as an orphan and although successfully living in the wild, he still returned to his old hutch for the occasional treats. They had just found him there, stiff and cold and requested a post-mortem to see what had befallen him. He was placed in a kennel until surgery finished two hours later, then, accompanied by two interested nurses, I prepared to begin the post-mortem. The operating lights were switched on as I loaded a blade on to the scalpel handle. We all leaned forward to watch while I tensed the animal's skin before the first incision. Suddenly the squirrel jerked and gasped. So did the three of us. Badly shaken, we leapt back and stood like statues, eyes glued to the 'corpse' which gasped again. This broke the spell and we went into action. Detecting a faint heartbeat, major resuscitation efforts followed. For a time, it seemed that our squirrel might make it (one nurse already dubbed him Lazarus) but he gradually slipped away - no heartbeat, apparently dead as a dodo. However we took no chances. He was placed in a kennel, the inert body outlined on paper with felt tip pen - untouched for twelve hours. Researching later, I found that there is some evidence that in extremely cold weather, squirrels can go into a state of 'adaptive hypothermia'. I have never seen the like - I would have bet a year's salary that that squirrel was dead. It was extremely lucky that afterwards there were not three veterinary personnel dead from heart attacks.

I am not pleased with myself tonight - I have almost had a row with a client during evening surgery. He owns a geriatric gundog with severe arthritis and bronchitis. We have been trying our best to alleviate his symptoms for weeks, only to find the reason behind today's relapse. He was out on a shoot *all day* yesterday - after all the advice about changing his lifestyle. Many gundogs love their work and are very disappointed if left at home, but there is a happy medium. A short outing before returning to the car, or being taken home early seems possible for other owners. This owner seems determined to carry on exactly as before. Whether anything said today will change his mind remains to be seen. Arguing with clients is usually unproductive and my more usual approach is to wear them down like a dripping tap, but he really got my goat tonight and I allowed anger to show through.

Luckily, there is no time tonight to brood on my lapse of restraint, Jay, I and our two friends from Strathdhu are visiting Mrs Cross for a social evening. It transpires that Bryn and Joe live on land where Mrs Cross grew up - although not in the original house. Although nearly ninety one, Mrs Cross is bright as a button and can remember her childhood in exceptional detail. The evening is fascinating. When Mrs Cross was a child, local produce was in demand and the raw materials were processed in the mills nearby. Though they are just placenames to us, she remembers a time when they were hives of activity, powered by water diverted from the loch. While renovating an outhouse, Bryn and Joe discovered old stone ovens sunk in the hillside and assumed that a baker lived nearby - but Mrs Cross remembers no baker. She can however recall the countryside blue with flax plants and suspects that the ovens were for drying flax. 'Aye, it was a great industry,' she reminisces, 'But I prefer my polyester!' Of our neighbourhood, she remembers the salmon fishing in its heyday, many of the fishing stations along the Clay being manned by Hebridean fishermen. The Highlanders had never seen trains before and would congregate on the hillside above her house to watch the local locomotives pass by. 'On Sundays,' she recalled with a faraway look in her eyes, 'they would sing hymns in Gaelic and the exquisite sound would rise hauntingly from the water's edge. I remember as if it were yesterday.' A marvellous evening is enjoyed by all and we finally depart into the night with a different perspective on our familiar landscape.

Monday 23rd November

Still mild, wet and windy. Everyone is well and truly fed up with trudging through endless mud and our kitchen floor defies description. Walking opportunities are severely limited, so we end up piling into the Tundra and heading up the hill as usual. The car itself is a uniform mud colour and needs the occasional dowsing with a bucket of water to allow the driver to see out. The Scots word *dreich* describes the conditions admirably - dull, dank, miserable - it encompasses them all. To avoid the worst of the mud, we amble through the woods. The floor is covered with a jumble of degenerating vegetation - leaves, broken ferns and brambles and moss-covered tree stumps. Many trees have toppled in the gales, some uprooted, others broken off clean through the trunk. At least there will be plenty of firewood. As always, there is something interesting to see. A woodcock flushes from nearby, a brown bird with a distinctive long beak and zigzag flight. This gives Fintry some sport but she is no match for the woodcock at weaving through the forest debris and soon reverts to investigating the numerous burrows dug into the hillside. Cobwebs continually caress my face as we wend our way to the top of the hill. The phantom plougher has been at work here too - even less grassland to walk in. The deer are filthy; all have been making enthusiastic use of the muddy wallows at the foot of the pen. From the top of the hill, I can see grain lorries down at the farm. They are hurriedly loading grain to catch container boats sailing from Dundee at high tide - off somewhere overseas. Hitching a lift sounds appealing. The outside world always sounds exotic and attractive when conditions here are so bleak.

In the kennels, there is an elderly cat recovering from a leg amputation earlier today. He was brought in last night after a traffic accident, in surprisingly good condition apart from a mangled leg. The operation went smoothly and already old Sam is demanding food. Aged creatures can be remarkably tough. The cat is looked after by a lodger as his businesswoman owner is overseas. We need to be back by 3 pm as she is ringing from Peking for a progress report. Such incidents add a touch of glamour to our life. The surgery locale does not abound with celebrities, so our opportunities for reflected glory are few and far between. So far, we have a dalmation patient who was a puppy in the film *101 Dalmations*, an Old English sheepdog who is distantly related to the Dulux dog and a lady whose son produces a well known television series. Otherwise the rich and famous have not beaten a track to our door.

Thursday 26th November

The first client of the day is the collie Robbie McRobbie. He is in for a check-up after surgery on a deep-seated lump situated on his neck just in front of his shoulder. He was operated on six months ago, when a large, orange-sized lump in the same spot suddenly became inflammed and painful. Surgery is always difficult in this area, crammed as it is with a frighteningly large number of major blood vessels, nerves and important organs. The entire operative site was very bruised with areas of fibrous tissue riddled with decaying nodules - rather like a Swiss cheese - and removal of all the abnormal material was far from easy. Histopathology reported no sign of tumour and we presumed that the abnormal tissue was possibly the result of a foreign body penetration from a stick injury. Robbie recovered well and had been fine until last week when a new lump appeared. It may be that a focus of infection was left from last time. We operated on Tuesday, through a new incision parallel to the original and removed an encouragingly concentrated mass - 'If this keeps happening, he'll be a sergeant in no time.' Julie joked, referring to the chevron-like pattern on his shoulder. As last time, we inserted a drain to allow excess fluid to escape. Robbie's owners have devised a neat idea to prevent tampering with the wound - he fits snuggly into a rather smart green body warmer which can be unzipped to allow inspection of the wound. He is rivalling Don in the best dressed dog stakes, but rather more country gentleman opposed to Don's council workman look.

The day becomes more dramatic when we make a start on today's operations. Our part-time nurse Cath has come to observe her first operating session. One patient is a middle-aged terrier with a pyometra. She is not seriously ill and I don't anticipate nasty surprises, but that just goes to show - *never assume*. During the op,

244

we have a drama. All appears well until the shrill screech of the pulse oximeter alarm splits the air. This alarm triggers when the oxygen concentration in the blood falls below 90 per cent. Julie is also monitoring the dog's anaesthesia and simultaneously reports a sudden drop in heart rate. The atmosphere becomes tense as we speak in terse bursts: 'Sats. down to 87 per cent,' - 'Right ...GA off, flush system ...Ventilate with oxygen' - 'Heart rate down' - '0.5 ml atropine.' Two pairs of eyes are glued to the pulse ox. display and we both continually monitor the patient. When at last our parameters improve, Julie reports status constantly while I recommence the surgery and we finish uneventfully. We hold a verbal post-mortem to try to pin down the reason for the problem, but nothing is obvious. It appears to have been 'just one of these things', rather unnerving, as there is nothing different that we would do another time round. Once she is back in her kennel, we observe our patient with paranoid detail. Normal recovery signs are scrutinised with extreme interest. Poor Cath has been an innocent bystander during all the action 'I am really impressed at how calm you both were,' she gasps, 'I was panicstricken.' Little does she know!! When she leaves the room for a minute, Julie and I turn to each other, eyes wide, hands outstretched and mouth a tension-relieving *'AARRRRGGGHH!!*

In such emergencies, experience and training take over automatically, but there is a terrible churning in your stomach and,when the danger is over, you feel as weak as water. It is an inescapable fact that *every* anaesthetic carries a slight risk and we are all constantly aware of this. One unnerving experience occurred nearly a year ago. We had a geriatric Jack Russell terrier booked in for dental work. She was very frail but had a horrendously filthy mouth which was obviously troubling her, so her owners bravely opted to go ahead. Dirty dental procedures are usually last on the operating list, so Kerry was lying peacefully in her kennel. Luckily, we were only preparing to begin another operation when Kerry let out a blood-curdling yell and keeled over, totally unconscious. Julie was nearest and quickly lifted her out on to the table, switching on the oxygen while I rapidly examined the limp body. No breathing, heart rate down to twenty per minute, horrible blue-white gums. We hurriedly inserted an endotracheal tube and Julie ventilated her with oxygen while I administered drugs which might be helpful.

Although her heart was still painfully slow, Kerry began to gag against the tube, so we carefully added just enough anaesthetic gas to over-ride the gag reflex. After what seemed like an age - but was only minutes - her heart rate and colour improved. With such a crisis, being under anaesthesia is quite a safe place to be - there is direct access to the lungs with the endotracheal tube and the animal is receiving 100 per cent oxygen instead of the fraction present in room air. In for a penny, we thought and, having got so far, decided to spend another five minutes doing the work she was here for - removing her disgusting teeth which were all painfully loose. She then made an uneventful recovery during which she had supplementary oxygen fed through nasal clips. Losing a patient under anaesthesia is bad enough, but losing one before you've done anything is quite another. If she had died, would her owners have believed us? When I carefully mentioned the day's events to Kerry's owner, she smiled; 'She has had several wee does like that,' she explained 'Each time we think she's gone, but she comes round again.' We will never know whether she would have recovered this time without our intervention, but she proceeded to have several more 'does' over the next few months until being found dead in her bed this April. Yet her heart and circulation checked out fine on examination. We can only presume that a damaged area of her heart caused an intermittent problem.

The remainder of our present day passes off peacefully with our final job - a lump removal for a portly spaniel. This dog belongs to Mr Keith, our local haulage contractor. As usual, he has all the time in the world for a chat when he collects his plump friend. Today, he has been carrying bananas from the Windward Islands and brings a bag for us. 'You can honestly say they came off the back of a lorry!' he jokes.

Our pyo case goes home with no apparent ill effects from the day's events. The day has taken its toll and as I set off for Clayfern, I fervently pray for a quiet surgery. There has been quite enough excitement for one day. Some light relief, thank goodness - Don is in for his bi-weekly bandage change. It is now twelve weeks after surgery and the wound has reduced to a two-by-two centimetre square. Things are getting exciting. We are beginning to take bets on how long it will take to close over entirely and we can get at that champagne bottle.

Tuesday 1st December

Not easy to get up this morning. Julie, her partner Bill, Jay and I ventured out to a St Andrew's night *ceilidh* yesterday. The injured knee stood up well to Gay Gordons, Dashing White Sargeants and Eightsome Reels but this morning, we are both stiff and tired. Getting a bit old for carousing late on a weekday night.

During morning surgery, we have an unexpected but welcome visitor. Our 'former student' Poppy has returned from the orthopaedic specialist sporting a very smart external fixator. She seems to be healing extremely well and is using the leg a mere eighteen days after the surgery. What a difference from the miserable, pain-wracked puppy she was when last seen. The metal framework is well 'lagged' with bandage to prevent damage to the furniture. Next, one of life's less pleasant tasks; I need to put to sleep my friend's beloved collie. He has had a long association with the surgery - had annual boosters, cut pads stitched, decayed teeth extracted and finally had bone cancer diagnosed a year ago. The cancerous limb was removed and he has had a happy year before fatal tumour metastases flared in his lungs. None of us expected him to live for so long after surgery, but even so, putting him to sleep is still a blow. As he is happy and confident in our company, the job is easily accomplished but his owner and I are both upset. He is the same age as Kippen and the two have been pals for years. Maybe I tempted fate by mentioning how well he was doing when the specialist and I were discussing Poppy. Perhaps a superstitious vet is not a good advert, but I hate when an owner mentions how well their pet is - I always glance around for some wood to touch. Any photos series that we have of interesting cases seldom show the original problem and the early days of treatment; I only feel confident enough to take them when things are going well.

It is still mild and soggy underfoot when the dogs and I escape in the late afternoon. We walk down the only stubble field left untouched by the plough. The heavy rain has gouged deep tracks in the earth exposing all manner of interesting stones. These are exceptional - blood red lumps of jasper, pinky white quartz and mustard-coloured agate mix with a selection of flecked, striped and spotty stones beyond my very rudimentary identification skills. A geology identification book would be a good idea for Christmas - I must drop some hints. The sky is spectacular this afternoon - in the west, the setting sun turns the clouds on the horizon luminous pink, giving way across the evening sky to darkening layers of pink, aquamarine and violet blue. All too soon, the sun disappears returning the sky to an all too familiar dull grey. Show over.

A bat flutters overhead when we return to the house. This is very late in the year for them - by now they have usually either moved south or hibernated. We do really need some colder weather to get into the mood for Christmas. With the beginning of December, brightly decorated Christmas windows have suddenly mushroomed like magic in Clayfern as if the inhabitants were just waiting for the first of the month before springing into action. At the surgery, we must dust off our decorations and think of a design for our window. Every year, there is a competition for the best-dressed Christmas window; we came third, two years ago but have not repeated this success - the competition is much too stiff. The seasonal theme continues when Mr Keith brings his spaniel for a post-op. check up; ' I'm sorry I can't bring you anything from the lorry today,' he says regretfully, 'but I've got a consignment of Christmas trees. The needles get everywhere but the van smells lovely.'

Friday 4th December

It seems exceptionally bright at 6.30 this morning. Moonlight floods through our north-facing windows projecting the criss-cross pattern of small window panes on to the floor. For almost the first time, it is frosty enough to venture over the new stile into the now firm back field. The ground is hard as iron and ice lies in the usually water-logged cow prints. Cars and shed roofs are shrouded in white and frozen cobwebs form lacey covers on the hedges. A yellowy full moon hangs over the river, illuminating a creamy path to the opposite banks. The dogs sniff far and wide as we traverse the field; unnoticed by them, a hare starts from nearby and lopes silently up the hill. The trees and deer are silhouetted against the south-eastern sky - inky blue against lighter violet. The cattle in the barn are shouting for their breakfast, the sound travelling undiminished over the frozen landscape. Seasonal weather at last. What a joy not having to dry mud-sodden dogs after every outing.

During a quiet morning surgery, Alice and I drag out the Christmas decorations. The window display usually consists of a tree bedecked with bones and other animal treats, stared at longingly by a circle of furry toys. In the background, a toy husky pulls a miniature sledge made by Jay in a fit of Christmas cheer. The sledge is loaded with dog and cat stockings and crackers. All nurses and vets must now put on their thinking caps and suggest some innovations. Trying to book an appointment for four weeks ahead makes me realise (a) Christmas *is* really rather close; and (b) we need new diaries for the new year.

Mrs Cassidy comes in with a request - would I pop across to visit her old cat? He is limping, but is evidently very frail and the visit to the surgery might finish him off. I should really have made more of an effort to persuade her to bring him in, but the spirit of Christmas *bonhomie* has triumphed so, off I go. It is a fallacy that animals are better behaved at home than in the surgery - usually quite the reverse is true. They are on home territory and have a plethora of inaccessible hidey holes in which to avoid detection. Tiddles is not the expected frail geriatric and seems remarkably hale and hearty. We spend an energetic ten minutes pursuing him under sideboards and on top of dressers before I finally corner him on top of a work surface in the kitchen. Triumph! Until the worksurface begins to vibrate. We are on top of a washing machine just going into its spin cycle. Reluctant to lose our advantage, I instruct Mrs Cassidy to restrain the cat for just two minutes while I examine something odd on his bad foot. The unfortunate cat is body-slammed on the machine in a mountain of wildly vibrating bosom. Worrying that Tiddles may suffocate, or Mrs Cassidy suffer a heart attack - her face has turned somewhat puce - I grab the paw. Our luck is in, the condition is easily cured. Tiddles has impaled his pad with a drawing pin. There is only time for a quick extraction before the washing machine accelerates to 1600 rpm, shaking Mrs Cassidy and

Tiddles slowly but inexorably sideways. Mrs Cassidy lands in the washing basket, Tiddles on her stomach and sprints for the safety of the sideboard leaving neat red footprints across Mrs Cassidy's blouse and the kitchen floor. Mission accomplished, but I think that next time, she'll bring him in.

Saturday 5th December

I am wakened by even brighter light than yesterday. Drawing back the curtains, a white world is revealed. Snow and moonlight, an irresistible combination. Clothes are flung on and dogs and I investigate outside. Four inches of dry, powdery snow sparkles in the moonlight. The valley is like a Christmas card, the white expanse broken only by the grey of two-tone trees. The back field is tussocky and there is probably not enough snow to cover all the bumps for sledging, so I grab the next best thing - the 'Norwegian shovel' - and set off through the stile. It is a lovely experience walking through the virgin snow. We can see from the prints who has been out and about: by the house are the small, neat prints of a cat; criss-crossing the field are the inevitable rabbit tracks, often converging and trampling an area where several have met. By the side of the field, the teardrop shapes of a fox's prints heading farmwards to see if any food is to be had - perhaps a nice plump duck. In the woods, roe deer tracks lead off into the distance. The field is obviously like Piccadilly Circus at night. The dogs are hysterical with excitement, snowploughing along with their noses, catching snowballs and rolling with abandon in the glistening white powder. Hurtling downhill on the red 'shovel', I am pursued by two wildly barking maniacs before we land in a heap at the bottom, totally covered in snow - the three abominable snowmen. A few more goes, then we collect the morning paper from our box and head home for breakfast. Sledging in moonlight is definitely an unforgettable experience. I realise with a shock that it is still early and hope that the neighbours will forgive the din. All is quiet otherwise, the road is still white and the usual gunshots from the wildfowlers are absent. The sky is yellow in the east and pink in the north where the first glow of dawn touches the hills. Jay is away on business and has missed the fun, but the message on the answering machine lets me know how predictable I am.

Being so early, there is time to digest the local paper at length. Since childhood days, this paper has held a great fascination for me, particularly the advertisements. In the sporting section are adverts for *rough terrain shoots* and *a fish tagging competition.* 'Under Timber' - *split hardwood logs for sale.* Someone in the 'Agricultural' section wants *a dung graip for a manitou forklift* (hope he gets it), while someone else can *remove earth and soft rots.* A *flipover saw* and *a planer thicknesser* are on offer in 'Machinery'. 'Articles for Sale' has the usual cornucopia of potentially essential items - *top soil, skis* and *a French woodburner* catch my eye today. A final glance at 'What's On', before getting on with the rest of the day.

Morning surgery is steady but pleasant, the bright winter attire of our clients making it rather cheerful and light-hearted. Groups of children pulling sledges pass the window, heading for the hills. Everyone laughs at the large puddles left under hairy dogs when they move into the consulting room. A dog with a cut paw to staple and last week's cut foot back for staple removal - both gundogs caught either by glass, wire or sharp reeds at the water's edge. Staple removal is a simple job - with the right equipment: a tiny tool shaped like miniature nail clippers. It corrupts the shape of the staple so the two ends pull clear of the tissue. Robbie is also in for his drain and stitches to be removed. He has healed well and we hope that he does *not* in time gain his sergeant's stripes.

More sledging in the afternoon, including an exciting run down the side of the deer pen. The two stags are sparring with one another - not seriously, but the dry clack of antler against antler raises visions of what damage they could cause. Poor Jonno does not understand sledging at all and nearly ends up on my lap near the bottom of the hill. Back home, Jay greets me with a mug of hot chocolate and chestnuts roasted on our fire. Peeled and served with salt, they smell and taste divine. The telephone never rings all evening so we watch a good film, relaxing with a bottle of wine. The perfect end to the perfect day.

Tuesday 8th December

The snow vanished yesterday, melted away by warmer weather so we are now back to a dreich, rainy day. The snow has left a legacy of sore paws (caused by the grit) and stiff muscles from over-exuberance. After all our sledging, my stomach muscles feel as if they have been kicked by a mule and my knee is complaining mightily so I feel a sympathetic bond with our hobbling patients. One such limping patient is Shuggie who belongs to Dod (rhymes with toad) Ross. Shuggie is a strange beast - the body of a Labrador fitted onto the legs of a corgi. He and Dod have been together for years. Dod is a little simple - he loves Shuggie dearly but cannot be relied upon to treat him as he should be treated. Luckily, his neighbour Beth keeps a watchful eye on the situation and alerts me if all is not right with the dog. We have occasionally killed two birds with one stone, curing Dod as well as Shug - last year the poor dog was tortured with flea bites and went nearly bald. Beth volunteered to apply spot-on flea treatment monthly and also treated Dod's cottage. Miraculously, the infected spots on Dod's legs disappeared. Angus, the local doctor was most impressed. When he in turn diagnosed ringworm on Dod, he tipped me off that Shuggie had suspicious bald patches. I arranged to meet Dod and Shuggie 'by chance', commented on his patches and suggested some treatment. When younger, Shuggie coped well with Dod's erratic behaviour - being locked out while Dod slept off a heavy session in the pub, or missing an occasional feed caused him no great hardship, but now he is getting older and could really do with some more TLC (tender loving care). Dod never dries him in miserable weather and lets him lie on the concrete floor with the result that he is terribly stiff and sore. I saw him limping along in Dod's wake this morning and a meeting with Beth in the Post Office confirms my suspicions that the old lad is having trouble. Diplomacy is called for here, as Dod reacts badly to any aspersions cast on his dog- handling capabilities. I arrange to visit Beth's cat on the way home and again manage to bump into Dod 'by chance'. In reality, 10.30am. on a Tuesday is a good bet as Dod has just been to collect his pension. We chat about the weather and I casually mention how it is producing many stiff dogs.

'Right enough,' he muses, 'the auld fella has been a bit stechy recently.'

'Well now Eck,' I say, as if an idea has just hit me, 'I've just had a drug company rep. in at the surgery with a new anti-inflammatory drug.' Pause for effect -'You wouldn't like to try them out on Shug, would you? It would be useful to know how good they are?'

'Aye, lass, I'll do that for you,' Dod replies magnanimously. 'Thanks Dod, that would be a great help,' I grovel, 'And if you really don't mind, I'll pop in a few days to see how you're getting on.' Beth then chips in with her lines

'I've been meaning to ask you, if you could spare him Dod, could I possibly borrow Shuggie some evenings when you're out. I'm getting a new kitten and I want to be sure that he gets used to dogs.'

'If that's what you *really* want, lass, then you're welcome,' comes the ready reply. Beth and I exchange winks as I drive off. With luck, Shuggie will now spend most evenings stretched out in front of Beth's blazing fire being well and truly spoilt. There is more than one way to skin a cat in this job.

The rest of the day, like yesterday, is hectic with work for both our local dog and cat charities. This is a busy time of year for them - the last thing some folk want for Christmas are dirty, noisy pups or kittens cluttering up the house. They ring the charity to take them away; give them to all and sundry; or just abandon them (often in boxes in doorways or lay-bys). One way or another, they all end up with the charities. Hard-working, overstretched and constantly strapped for cash, these worthy souls labour away, sorting out other people's responsibilities. In my experience, the buck always stops with the small local charities, as the larger, national organisations seem to have no trouble saying 'No.' Perhaps the little charities should, but it is hard when threatened with the alternative of the creatures being drowned or dumped. So, they get them treated for any ailments, rear them and get them neutered and re-homed. In between times, they-fund raise like crazy to pay for it all. We reduce our prices as much as possible, but the costs inevitably mount up - all because of stupid people not willing to take any responsibility or put any effort into pet ownership. Unbelievably, the charities have had animals returned after less then twenty four hours in a new home because 'She wet on the carpet', or 'He ripped up my shoe.' Perhaps some of today's consumers are not used to anything 'working' less than perfectly. They would be better off with an electronic pet or a furry toy.

On a happier note, one of the charities' pups has been rehomed with clients of ours. We treated their old dog for years until he was put to sleep in summer. Now they feel ready to start again. Having a new pup after an old pet is an unnerving experience - almost like having a different species. These clients are God's gift to vets - they actually listen intently to any advice given. We have talked ourselves silly about vaccination, worming, neutering and the importance of early socialisation and learning in the golden period before fourteen weeks of age. It is such a pleasure to preach to such receptive ears. They will no doubt be first through the door when puppy classes restart in the new year.

Friday 11th December

Today is one of those nightmarish days which occur every so often. Lucky we don't know in advance what to expect. We are geared up to a fairly busy day as Sheila has been trapping again. A colony of cats has built up round a large hotel and the management were on the verge of calling in a pest control company when Sheila's name was passed on to them. It makes more sense to neuter and return a manageable number to the site. If all the cats are removed, others will move in to fill the void and uncontrolled breeding will magnify the problem. Last night's trapping expedition has been extremely successful and ten feral cats now await neutering. Unfortunately, morning surgery has added not one but three emergencies which require swift attention. One is a cat having trouble breathing, then a dog with a cut foot and finally a shot gundog. The last sounds dramatic and is diverted to the farm surgery for immediate action. It could be worse - the dog manages to get into the surgery under her own steam. Not surprisingly she winces when lifted onto the table in time-honoured gundog owner's style - a handful of loose skin is gathered at the neck, another over the rump and the unfortunate beast is hoisted upwards, effectively slung in its own skin. At least the dogs don't struggle and the process is quick, but it always makes me cringe. Chasing pheasants too soon is this dog's downfall as she has caught the outer edge of the shot-gun blast. Luckily she was quite far away and the outer pellets travel more slowly than those in the centre, so the shot has only had enough power to penetrate the skin. Indeed some has fallen out on its own. Some painkiller, sedative and local anaesthetic allows removal of more pieces. She looks like a sieve, but should feel much better. Next, our snorting cat. This might take a while if we need X-rays, endoscopy and possibly surgery. As I open his mouth for a mere instant, I catch a glimpse of something abnormal. A short-acting general anaesthetic allows me to examine his throat with an endoscope and snare a blade of grass which has worked its way into the back of the nasal passages. Instant cure. The last of our emergencies is a suturing in yet another gundog. It is quite a straightforward wound, but progress is painfully slow as the wound is absolutely filthy. The damage obviously occurred during a shooting expedition and was not noticed until the end. A brief history of where the dog has been is contained in the underlying tissues. Grit, grass awns and pieces of fir branch need to be painstakingly removed before any stitches go in. The last are barbed and inveigle their way into the tissues, then break off when grasped with forceps. It takes over half an hour to clean the wound and five minutes to stitch it. Time is pressing on and the ten cats await. As they are feral, their sex is unknown. We hope for a preponderance of males - without going into full details, it does not take as long to remove two testes from a scrotum as it does to locate and tie off two ovaries and a uterus within the abdomen. Murphy's Law is in operation however as we pull out one anaesthetised female after another. The final count is nine females to one male. It is growing dark when we finish, only time for a rushed sandwich as a very late lunch before setting off for evening surgery. A large drug order has arrived this afternoon and I hope for a quietish surgery to allow time to put everything away. No such luck - three clients are already waiting and the evening continues in similar vein. The drug boxes are piled unceremoniously against the desk while Alice and I wade through a never-ending supply of clients. The first case is two kittens with flu. They were abandoned and have been taken on by our client. Small ulcers pepper their tongues and throats making them reluctant to eat and they are snotty and depressed, once pretty coats matted with discharge. Treatment is begun with fluids, antibiotics and vitamins but I warn their owner that dedicated nursing will also be necessary for success. She will have to tempt them to eat recovery diet from a syringe, wipe their noses and eyes, sponge their coats and generally keep their spirits up. Our aim is to keep the patients in as good condition as possible to allow their body defences to fight off the infection. These kittens are really poor, so we have a battle on our hands. This consultation has taken a while and I hope for something quick and uncomplicated to allow some catching up. Neither of us are prepared for our next patient. Last time we saw Don, his wound was the size of a postage stamp and we were anticipating opening the champagne next week. Instead, disaster. Don has again removed his bandage and launched a major attack on his leg. Once again, tags of tissue dangle from the raw surface of a much larger defect. Vet, nurse and client are all speechless. Even Don is not his cheery self. There is nothing for it but to keep going, but to borrow a phrase beloved of footballers, we are all absolutely gutted. To be so close then have this happen seems unbelievably cruel. The real worry is that there does not seem to be an obvious reason why the wound should be uncomfortable enough for the dog to do this. With the acupuncture, we had hoped to reduce any local irritation and only days ago the healing wound looked fine. When a case fails to go well, one gets a horrible 'flat' feeling and the day is suddenly tarnished. When a re-bandaged Don finally leaves, I feel more like heading home and losing myself in mindless activities than continuing with evening surgery but there isn't really a choice. On we plod for another two hours until the last one is gone and the door shut. The flat feeling returns and both vet and nurse trail dismally out of the surgery. Having been regaled with frequent bulletins on Don's progress over the last three months, Jay understands what a blow tonight has been and is touchingly solicitous, making supper and switching on my favourite TV programme. I try to concentrate on the programme but know with a feeling of doom that, like probing a sore tooth with one's tongue, my thoughts will frequently return to brood on Don's condition for some time to come.

Saturday 12th December

After yesterday's traumas, morning surgery is thankfully brisk but uneventful. Mairi's kittens - the ones with cat flu - are much the same and receive the same treatment. Fortunately they are eating recovery diet readily which is a good sign, but it is too soon to say whether they will 'do' or not. We just need need to soldier on. I share a welcome joke with a carpenter client sporting a large bandage. He cut himself while sharpening a chisel. I too am always getting pronged or slashed with needles or scalpels and show him my most recent wound. We are probably bad adverts for our jobs, but I know that his work is intricate and precise and my mistakes, I hope, are never made when operating on patients.

After surgery, I collect the dogs and head uphill, through the trees to avoid the worst of the mud. Russet larch needles carpet the forest floor, the lichen-covered trees standing in sombre grey rows. The undergrowth has died right down leaving naked nettle stalks and flattened bracken fronds amongst the fallen trees and rotting stumps. It is easier to see the resident birds when the foliage has gone and I watch a small wren flitting between two tree trunks. They have such a loud voice for such a small bird. The crack of flapping wood-pigeon wings occasionally explode from the canopy as we move along. Kippen seems unusually interested in an old rabbit hole. Now he is on his chest digging furiously. Intrigued, I stop to watch, he is not usually especially interested in the inhabitants of the numerous burrows in the wood. I am almost concerned when he disappears past his shoulders and am considering pulling him out, when he begins to reverse. Clutched in the jaws of the soil covered dog is an old squeaky toy which he lost a year ago. For a time, he was addicted to these toys and would carry one on all our walks. Young Fintry continually tried to pinch them, then lost interest and dropped them and his attachment gradually wore off. Now he is very proud and will bear his trophy home in triumph. His *piece de resistance* in the lost-toy stakes was a toy dropped in the river one day and retrieved two weeks later from the river's edge a mile downstream. Today Fintry is running around with some animal's shin bone so is unlikely to kidnap the squeaky. Along the way, I stop below a tall pine tree, a favourite owl perch. There are owl pellets on the ground - regurgitated remains of a good meal. Identifying the small bones mixed with fur or feather gives an accurate idea of what (or who!) the owl has eaten - another exciting pastime to share with young Tom. Life slows down on walks and undoubtedly helps to preserve my sanity.

Nicely relaxed, I meet up with Jay and we go to choose a Christmas tree. We usually end up with the runt out of pity as no one wants it, but this year we fare better. We are both working hard and it is difficult to find time for Christmas preparations, but we always make time to decorate the tree. Before we settle to admire our handiwork, one last task remains. Our mice have been active these last few days, the cat is obviously not deterrent enough and tougher measures are called for - the dreaded lemonade bottle. A plastic lemonade bottle is baited with cheese and laid where the mice are active. They venture inwards after the cheese and are unable to escape. It then only remains for one of us to trek a few hundred yards from home and release them. We try not to think of splitting up little mouse families as we do the deed. If they didn't chew through wiring and plumbing, they would be welcome to stay.

Sunday 13th December

A real rude awakening this morning with an early call from clients Isobel and Jeff Smeaton. Their border collie Fly was a little quiet and off-colour yesterday, but this morning she can hardly even stand. A worried Jeff carries Fly into the surgery with Isobel bringing up the rear. The dog is obviously very weak and lies flat out on the table breathing heavily. Lifting her lip reveals lemony-white coloured gums. This dog is jaundiced and badly anaemic. After a full examination, one diagnosis seems most likely, a condition called *auto-immune haemolytic anaemia.* This is a disorder of the immune system where the body turns on its own red blood cells, destroying them. This reduces dramatically the amount of oxygen which the blood can carry to the tissues, causing the dog to appear short of breath. Normally, old red blood cells are broken down in the liver and the waste pigments passed out along the bile duct into the intestine. The massive breakdown of red cells in this disease has overwhelmed the liver and it is the damming back of waste pigment into the circulation which causes the distinctive yellow tinge to the skin and mucous membranes. If the condition comes on more gradually, high doses of corticosteroids will usually stop the red cell destruction, but this has hit Fly like a ton of bricks. Her blood is now very thin and her circulation is in danger of collapsing. Unless we do something dramatic, her outlook is bleak. Jeff and Isobel leave despondently, still trying to come to terms with their usually fit dog being suddenly at death's door. While Jay gently holds an oxygen mask to Fly's face, I take a small blood sample for testing. The test I am about to do measures the percentage of red cells in the blood. A narrow capillary tube is filled with blood then placed in a centrifuge and spun. This causes the heavier red cells to sink to the bottom of the tube. After spinning, the capillary tube is placed in a special scale which calculates the percentage of red cells. This result is known as the dog's *haematocrit*. A normal dog's haematocrit is around 40 per cent. Fly's is 12 per cent, confirmation that things are extremely critical. We set up a drip then consider the options. From the way Fly looks and with a *haematocrit* like that, it is very unlikely that she will survive without aggressive intervention. A blood transfusion is her only hope. Ideally, blood typing should be done before giving blood but we do not have the facilities, usually sending any likely cases to the Veterinary School in Edinburgh. However, an initial transfusion is unlikely to cause a problem and the situation is dire. Fintry is volunteered as a donor. She comes willingly into the surgery to be given a mild sedative injection, then her vein is trimmed up and local anaesthetic cream applied. While the drugs take effect, I check her *haematocrit* – 42 per cent and calculate how much blood she can safely donate. Once she is pleasantly relaxed, Jay hoists her onto the table and croons gently in her ear while I insert the wide gauge collection needle into her vein. Blood drains steadily into the special collection bag which I gently turn to mix blood and anticoagulant. Once enough is collected, Jay takes our brave 'volunteer' into the house, no doubt for the mandatory tea and biscuits. I attach a special blood giving set to the bag of blood and connect it to Fly's intravenous canula. Drip by drip, the blood passes through a filter into Fly's circulation. Slow infusion is necessary in case the dog's body reacts adversely to the foreign blood - a transfusion reaction. In that case, the transfusion must be stopped. I sit by Fly's head, gently stroking the silky muzzle and ears. She is not in pain but is very weak and tired - she can barely lift her head from the bed. How marvellous it would be if our brave dog helped to save her life. A lovely thought, but looking at Fly, perhaps not too likely. One of the worst feelings in the world is watching a patient fading before your eyes and not having any aces up your sleeve. The day is spent monitoring Fly closely. Her haematocrit in the afternoon has gone up to 14 per cent and the dog seems a little brighter, could we be getting somewhere? She even takes a little recovery diet at 6 pm and I tell her owners that she is holding her own. Unfortunately, this has been her swansong. She gradually deteriorates during the evening and by 11.30 pm, it is painfully apparent that she will not recover. We summon the owners and they are with her as I put her to sleep. What a sad, sad day. If only she hadn't shown signs of improvement and raised everyone's hopes. Once the empty kennel is cleaned out and the surgery tidied, I wearily head into the house. Fintry greets me as I enter the living room, obviously bearing no grudges. I am very proud of her, she was so well behaved when we took her blood and yet it was all for naught. Once again that flat feeling encircles us both like a dense fog. 'You can't win them all', I think wryly as we head wearily to bed.

Tuesday 14th December

This seems a very strange time of year in a veterinary surgery. Christmas cheer and light-heartedness rub shoulders with upset and misery. Some days during the festive season, I feel like the Grim Reaper - many old pets seem to reach the end of their tether at this time of year and the time comes to call it a day. I have already put two old cats and a dog to sleep this morning. At least this week is better than next when all vets dread a serious problem developing in the beloved pet belonging to someone (usually elderly) living on their own. If fate is really unkind, this culminates in a putting to sleep on either Christmas Eve or the day itself. Sad events appear sadder anyway at Christmas and not much imagination is required to visualise what sort of a Christmas these poor souls will have. In this area, most old animals that are put to sleep now are much loved and mourned, but, especially in city areas, there is a barely credible feature of the festive season which hits the charities hard. Not only are they full of unwanted pups and kittens, but some despicable individuals choose now to abandon their old dog or cat - no doubt ensuring a clean house over the holiday. It is up to the charities to do their best for these upset and confused old creatures. Sometimes a peaceful end is the most humane solution. It is impossible to fathom the mentality of such owners - to have a pet in their family for eleven or twelve years, yet be able to cast it off without a qualm when it becomes inconvenient. Some do not even have the decency to deliver their old friend to a vet or rescue centre, but abandon them to roam. Doesn't bear dwelling on really.

Mairi's kittens are still being treated daily. The tiny ulcers in their mouths have enlarged and coalesced causing horrible lesions and their temperatures are sky high, yet they are readily hand-fed and are cheerier than they were. It is a hard decision whether to press on or call it a day. Cases like these can sometimes hang in the balance for days before either picking up or going downhill. We decide to press on and review the situation daily. Poor Mairi is looking frightful, she is staying up all hours to nurse the kittens and it is wearing her out. Nursing is vitally important however so there is 'No rest for the wicked' yet. More and more sick cats have appeared during this week's surgeries and suddenly we appear to be in the middle of a flu epidemic.

We have now started our novel Christmas window display - an Advent calendar featuring the 'Twelve days of Christmas' with a veterinary slant. Thus on the first day of Christmas, my true love sent to me not *a partridge in a pear tree* but *a puppy with a few fleas*. A new cartoon (drawn by Cath) is to be put in the window each day in the run up to Christmas. This is a compromise between the spreading of Christmas cheer and blatant commercialism. Below each headed cartoon is an additional slogan - *Ask us about flea treatments* decorates the first. Other gems to be utilised over the festive period include *two soggy dugs* - promoting hygiene and grooming; *five big bills* - pet insurance; *nine puppies prancing* - puppy classes; and *twelve kittens sneezing* - vaccination. The last has proved to be rather prophetic.

Tonight is the surgery Christmas dinner in our local restaurant. A time for us all to get in the Christmas spirit and hope the pager stays quiet. As always when vets and nurses get together, work dominates the conversation and we roar with laughter at tales laced with the black humour so prevalent in our profession: our unfortunate colleague accused of strangling a budgie with his stethoscope (!) and Cath's misplaced sensitivity with a young owner whose gerbil was deceased: 'You can bury him in a nice box in the garden and he'll go to heaven,' yielding the disgruntled reply 'Aw, No! I want to take him home and watch him rot!' Luckily, or perhaps with forethought on the part of our friends, mine hosts, we have the restaurant to ourselves. A strategic tape recorder could keep them in clover for quite some time.

Thursday 16th December

Mairi's kittens are still on the go. Unfortunately, Mairi's own kitten has also developed symptoms and is really quite ill. Although older than the fostered kittens, he has not yet completed his vaccination course so is not fully protected. During this epidemic, we have also seen symptoms in older, vaccinated cats. As with human flu, the vaccination does not give a 100 per cent protection against the disease. The viruses responsible change so frequently that this is not possible. What we hope for with vaccination is that any disease symptoms are less virulent and the animal recovers quicker. Today, we have seen twelve cases of cat flu. The process of examination followed by the administration of drugs and fluids, then advising on nursing care is time-consuming and dealing with patients of the flu outbreak is taking almost ninety minutes per day.

Don comes into evening surgery for yet another bandage change. The wound is looking healthy and is healing well, but we all experience an uncanny feeling of deja vu while strapping up the leg. The effect of Don's attack on the defect has put us back about three weeks. Don has definitely won the *Most drawn out case of the year* award and it is unlikely that he will be fully healed by the end of the year. June is resolving to keep a sock on his leg for several months after the area is fully skinned and I am inclined to agree. He could have a whole new wardrobe for the New Year.

On the way home after evening surgery, I spy Dod and Shuggie heading towards the chip shop and stop for a chat. Shuggie is moving more enthusiastically than he was last time and Dod reports that the pills seem to be doing him good, 'I've tried one or two myself,' he confides, 'Good stuff, good stuff.' I suggest that Dr. Angus might have something more suitable for humans (i.e. free on prescription) and pass on more tablets for Shuggie's use alone. Beth told me recently that she has made Shuggie a bright new bed for Christmas - a good time to present Dod with dog-friendly products without the risk of offending him. One of the pleasures of this job is the rich variety of characters which cross our path.

<u>Saturday 19th December</u>

I wake with the feeling of nervous anticipation which has dogged my unconscious thoughts for the last few days when I have gained the distinct impression that we have patients virtually queuing for the privilege of being this year's 'Christmas Problem'.

Will we spend half of Christmas day baling fluids into fluey cats, or will we be removing tin foil from the stomach of the dog who has just eaten an entire packaged steak pie? Perhaps one of the two bitches due to whelp might require a caesarian section, or the dog with the grumbling slipped disc might suddenly worsen. We have so many potential cases pending that I feel more that a bed of nails hangs over me than merely a sword of Damocles. As I am hoping to do some shopping in Stramar after morning surgery, an early walk with the dogs is in order. The wind is howling plaintively through the telegraph wires as we head up the hill. By the time we get to the area known as the 'dinosaurs' graveyard', the roar is all pervading. Casualties of earlier gales have produced the 'graveyard'. Two head-like stumps are attached to long spines - fallen pine trunks with vertebrae and rib-like protrusions along their length. In today's storm, the place is truly atmospheric. Wildly swaying trees clonk and screech against each other when they touch, producing agonising wails and piteous squeaks. I try not to think of the tiny mouse released yesterday from our lemonade-bottle trap.

Back at work, Mairi's kittens are picking up AT LAST. They are eating on their own and have even been playing. They have been seen daily for the last nine days, perhaps now they might be able to 'fly' on their own. Her kitten also seems improved, but will be seen again tomorrow to press home our advantage. With even more flu cases appearing, surgery runs an hour late and I need to rush to meet Jay in town. Lunch is followed by some hurried shopping before the pager shrills and I am summoned back to Clayfern. One of life's sad cases - a cat run over by its owner, too badly injured to save. I try to comfort the distraught owners as much as possible, but they will doubtless feel terrible whatever anyone says. This type of accident is surprisingly common, animals seem impervious to the dangers of cars in their own gardens and even normally traffic shy creatures will cheerfully linger round the wheels of their own family's car with tragic consequences. With Christmas spirit dimmed, I abandon shopping for the final task of the day, a trip to deliver Edith McNaughton's dog food - and a small Christmas remembrance. I am pleased with this year's find - a crocus planter in the shape of a dachshund.

'You're visiting a house of invalids,' she exclaims as I cross the threshold. This is hard to believe as three excited dogs jostle and leap for attention. Edith does worry about her girls. Ten minutes later, their very minor problems are sorted and Edith's fears allayed. We chat for a while before she presents me with a basket of beautifully arranged homegrown flowers. What a lovely centre-piece for our Christmas table.

As I drop into the surgery before heading home, the Christmas lights cast a warm glow over our Christmas window and the now quiet waiting room, decorated with tinsel and our crop of Christmas cards. It looks wonderfully peaceful and I desperately wish that no bad things happen to patients and owners for the next few days. What a good Christmas present that would be.

For the last time before Christmas, Linda is on call tonight while Jay and I go to yet another *ceilidh*. It is said that dancing is a prime method of relaxing and cheering up and it certainly works for us. We meet Julie and Bill there, along with a friend who is an avid Scottish Country dancer. *Ceilidhs* are a bit beneath her dignity but definitely our favourite. Neat measured steps are not for tonight's participants. Total confusion reigns most of the time and there is much charging about to regain lost positions. No one minds and happy smiling faces shine out amid the birling and hooching. A wonderful way to unwind after a long, anxious week.

Owls are calling in the woods and woodsmoke hangs in the still air as we walk to the door. Stars glitter in a vast clear sky and frost glistens on the hard ground. Totally relaxed we wend our way to bed.

Monday 21st December

The shortest day of the year. For weeks now, the trips to Clayfern surgery have been in the half light and the dogs' early walk has been virtually in darkness. Not so easy in an area with no street lights. At least from now on, we are past the worst. Morning surgery is brisk with a surprising number of booster vaccinations. This has caught us out in previous years, but we now know to order enough vaccine to cope with the rush. Either all these pets were presents at previous Christmases, or their lucky owners are off on holiday and the pets are due in kennels. Dod's ruddy face appears unexpectedly in the waiting room. It is unusual for him to come to the surgery at all, his preferred *modus operandi* is to accost me or Alice in the local shops, but today he has brought a friend Doug (pronounced Doog) with his two new puppies entrancingly called Stour and Glaur - roughly translated, Dirt and Muck. As they have been playing in the farm muck heap, the names are strikingly apt. Doug had not intended to come to the surgery until he had the money to pay for vaccinations, but Dod had assured him that I wouldn't mind. 'Honest, vitnary,' he confides, 'Doug'll see ye richt. He's as honest as the day is long.' Perhaps not the best recommendation given today's date - but I'm sure that Doug - like Dod, Hector and many more - will eventually *see me richt!*

We wade through the inevitable fluey cats before I head to Fern for the day's ops. Again, a surprising number of routine procedures for the time of year. Quite a few people seem to be on holiday now and prepared to have the cat spayed or the dog castrated before Christmas. They have no doubt had plenty time to do the shopping and get the house in order for The Day. 'Lucky them,' I mutter, heading for the car. Alice is also muttering and fiddling with the rear of her car. Yes, she has locked herself out again. This is not normally a problem: she just opens the tailgate and clambers through; but today the tailgate catch is jammed. After some careful manipulation with an old pair of artery forceps, the problem is solved and she climbs into the front seat over assorted horse and dog paraphenalia. Artery forceps are such versatile tools, handy for a multitude of purposes. I often wonder how the average person manages without access to such useful instruments.

In the afternoon, farmer Colin asks me to look at one of his cows. She banged into a gate recently and is now sporting a large, fluid-filled swelling on her flank. *There really isn't much finesse in farm work,* I think as I stab a scalpel into an area of skin deadened with local anaesthetic. Warm, clear fluid gushes out, steaming in the frigid air and three gallons later, the cow has visibly deflated.

'That's her career as a water bed over,' I joke as we finish with some antibiotic. Some ribald comment is passed in return. The easy cameraderie and banter with farm workers always was a pleasant part of large animal work, but I'm not sorry that I don't do any now. Quite apart from anything else, it is bitterly cold, cold, cold on farms at this time of year. Give me a centrally heated surgery any day.

Thursday 24th December

What a week this has been. One of our periodic busy spells coinciding with the run up to Christmas. The flu epidemic has claimed at least one hour per day - at night we don't count sheep but fluey kittens. No one realised that the *twelve kittens sneezing* on the advent calendar would be quite so apt.

Morning surgery culminates in the putting to sleep of Chloe, one of my longest serving patients. The insurance company will be celebrating; that dog has had more long, involved, life-threatening conditions than any other animal and has cost thousands of pounds. Every illness has been a challenge, partly as Chloe produced different symptoms from anyone else and partly because she was so awkward. Usually sweet natured, whenever anything had to be done which was not to her liking (which included most veterinary involvement), she transformed into a writhing, teeth-gnashing fiend. It required great ingenuity to muzzle her before proceeding, but once the deed was done, she gave up gracefully and allowed further interference without complaint. 'It's a fair cop, Guv,' she seemed to say from the depths of the nylon muzzle. She never bore grudges and once released from the nylon banding, she reverted immediately to her usual sunny self. We will all miss her.

One stitching this afternoon, another gundog - a flighty Labrador. 'He's worse than a spaniel,' grunts his owner while swinging the creature on to the table; the ultimate insult. 'Let's see if you have more luck with this one than with the last two.' This seems a little uncalled for, as one dog was put to sleep with terminal cancer and the other was never seen in the surgery but died at home in his sleep. Jay, who is helping, is quite aggrieved on my behalf, but I find it rather funny. I get on well with this client and can give as good as I get. 'By the way,' I comment, finishing the last stitch, 'I hear that the vets in Stramar are specialising in gundog injuries - especially over the Christmas period.' Chance would be a fine thing!

Just time before evening surgery for a walk through the woods to collect fir branches and holly for last minute decorations. We seem to have suddenly run out of time to prepare for the holiday. All the presents need to be wrapped tonight and food made ready for the morning. Enjoying the brief interlude in the woods, I emerge by a field with arms full of fragrant branches only to spot a sheep collapsed by the fence. 'No rest for the wicked,' I mutter and grumble, dropping the foliage and clambering into the field. Luckily, the sheep is only tangled in some loose wire and has ended up on its back - a difficult position for sheep to recover from. She lies quietly while I unravel the wire from her fleece then hoist her to her feet. The minute her feet touch the ground she is off down the slope like lightning to join her pals. Thank goodness, no veterinary input is necessary and my hands have benefited from handling her lanolin rich wool - the best moisturiser there is.

Evening surgery tonight is, at last, quiet. Just a few of our 'pending' cases which seem thankfully to be holding their own. Three will need to be seen tomorrow for ongoing treatment, but shouldn't take too long. If I play my cards right, I can be seeing them while Jay is making the festive lunch.

So, this long week is finally over and all is quiet. Christmas day can normally be relied upon to be quiet apart from dire emergencies (not much consolation after doing a two-hour caesarian however). We are all feeling exhausted and I privately decide that at this stage, a long lie and no problems for twenty four hours is the only Christmas present I really want.

Saturday 26th December

Yesterday was wonderful and peaceful apart from the three ongoing cases. Back to reality this morning with an 8.00 am. phone call. 'When is the surgery open today?' is the brisk query.

'We're open for emergencies only', states a sleepy Jay,'What's the problem?'

'Well, I don't suppose its *really* an emergency', comes the grudging reply, 'but my cat needs leukaemia testing before she breeds.'

Sorry Madam, but you've got *no* chance today. Otherwise, the day has not been bad, a few phone calls - advice required for an assortment of Christmas-related ailments, including the inevitable eaten Christmas toy and turkey tummy. At teatime, a knock on the door heralds two clients carrying 'A duck with a broken wing' found on the road which turns out to be a goose, badly wounded in today's orgy of shooting parties. Nothing for it but to put it to sleep. After the same three ongoing cases as yesterday, the day's work is done. The weather outside is getting nasty, rain pours and wind howls, rattling doors and rustling through the slates like castanets. The trees are swaying alarmingly up in the woods producing a fearsome roar which fills the air and the poor deer are huddling in the lee of the hill, sheltered from the building gale. Definitely a night for battening down the hatches and settling in front of a blazing fire.

Thursday 31st December

Hogmanay! New Year's Eve - or Old Year's Night as it is called here, a title which sounds rather dignified and atmospheric. We have worked as usual this week, still clearing up potential problem cases. We have had our two bitches whelping - resulting in several middle-of-the-night phone calls but fortunately no need for veterinary interference. Many folk are off work for the whole festive period, giving them time to visit the surgery with routine matters. Driving to Clayfern is quieter than normal and the first half of surgery is dead, getting busier as 10 am. draws closer - obviously long lies are the order of the day, preparing for a long night. There is an air of expectation in the High Street, tonight is a Big Night in the Scottish calendar. Everyone is out and about, buying in supplies for the next few days, including the inevitable steak pies to line the stomach tonight. Once morning surgery is over, there are no ops, but a small dog with kidney failure requires a drip and comes with me back to Fern. She may improve after a day on fluids, or she may not - a miserable thing to hang over her owners on what should be a cheerful occasion. Unfortunately, illness never takes a holiday. Jay and I spend the day peacefully, walking the dogs and watching old films on the television with occasional trips to the surgery to check the patient. She is no doubt experiencing now what many people will suffer tomorrow - a cracker of a hangover. Unfortunately, her symptoms are not self-inflicted. By early evening, she is a little brighter and accepts a small portion of chicken - one advantage of being ill over a holiday period is that the food around here is superior to the usual.

Leaving her settled in a kennel with the radio on low for company, Jay and I sally forth for the annual Clayfern procession. Everyone turns out to watch and to follow a band of locals carrying flaming torches from one end of the village to the other, accompanied by a band - and the inevitable piper. This tradition has ancient roots involving the driving of evil from the burgh, but tonight it is an excuse for a get-together and fund-raising for local charities. Masked men accost us with buckets into which we throw our donations. We have come prepared with pockets bulging with change. It is a little unsettling to be chivvied for cash by unidentified strangers who clearly know us well - there are comments that it is about time that the tables were turned. Luckily the night is fair and cold and the whole town turns out, either marching behind the band or watching from windows and doorways. Clayfern has a great community spirit and tonight almost feels part of a single big family. It is also tradition that the torch bearers and band stop at each local hostelry for a drink, so the procession becomes increasingly strung out and disorganised as the evening progresses. Once the evil spirits are duly banished (by the discordant wail of the drunken piper if not by the torches), everyone returns either to friends' homes or to the hostelries to celebrate the passing of another year. After a restrained drink with our friends, we all head back to Fern to see in the New

Year quietly. The first half an hour of the New Year is spent in the surgery with our patient. Holidays come and go, but it seems, work goes on forever. Annoying sometimes, but in truth, I would not have it any other way.

About The Author

Kate was born in Perth and brought up in Crieff. After qualifying as a Vet from Glasgow University she practised in Manchester for sixteen years before returning to Scotland where she now continues her work as a Veterinary Surgeon in Fife. As well as a Veterinary degree Kate has also obtained an Msc. in behavioural ecology for her work with badgers and was heavily involved in the treatment and rehabilitation of other wildlife including dealing with lead poisoned swans. She has always been a supporter of animal welfare and has close links with many animal charities.